ENVIRONMENTAL SCIENCE, ENGINEERING AND TECHNOLOGY

RESEARCH AND APPLICATIONS FOR ENERGY, THE ENVIRONMENT, AND ECONOMICS

ENVIRONMENTAL SCIENCE, ENGINEERING AND TECHNOLOGY

Additional books in this series can be found on Nova's website
under the Series tab.

Additional e-books in this series can be found on Nova's website
under the e-book tab.

ENVIRONMENTAL SCIENCE, ENGINEERING AND TECHNOLOGY

RESEARCH AND APPLICATIONS FOR ENERGY, THE ENVIRONMENT, AND ECONOMICS

RIAD BENELMIR
EDITOR

nova publishers
New York

Library of Congress Cataloging-in-Publication Data

ISBN: 978-1-62948-892-9

Published by Nova Science Publishers, Inc. † New York

CONTENTS

PREFACE

This book sheds light on the interaction between the utilization of energy and the environment, as well as the economic aspects involved with this utilization. It is a vehicle for an international exchange and dissemination of ideas in the multidisciplinary field of energy-environment-economics between research scientists, engineers, economists, policy makers, and others concerned about these issues.

Chapter 1 - Despite the introduction of reforms since 1991, the Electricity sector in India continues to be plagued with chronic shortages. The primary reason for the widening demand-supply gap lies with a financially crippled distribution sector. In India the power distribution has been the responsibility of the State Electricity Boards (SEBs), the state-owned electric utilities that were constituted in the era of nationalization under India's Electricity Supply Act of 1948. Except for a few private players who mainly operate in a few metropolitan cities and catering to the needs of urban consumers, these SEBs have retained the monopoly in power distribution in the country. Over time, these SEBs have accumulated gross financial losses. Apparently, the financial losses have reached $ 5.2 thousand millions per year and no SEB currently recovers the full cost of power supplied. These financial losses cannot be made good from State budgets, as the states are themselves under severe financial strain; the result is that the SEBs are starved of resources to fund required expansion and typically end up neglecting even the essential maintenance. This has led to an undermined infrastructure base that constitutes a major roadblock in attracting much needed investment from the private parties.

Chapter 2 - An analytical evaluation of energy from some fuelwood with potential for charcoal production is presented. Specifically, the major parameters: ash, fixed carbon, volatile matter and moisture content, which determine the magnitude of specific heat of charcoal derived from the fuelwood, are evaluated. The paper also presents analysis of how each parameter contributes to the specific heat of charcoal from a given fuelwood. A scientific method which can be used by decision-makers/ authorities, organizations or individuals in proper land-use for the enhancement of the environment by way of afforestation/agroforestry, while at the same time satisfying the energy needs of the rural and urban population, especially in the developing countries is thus presented.

Chapter 3 - This paper presents a matrix method approach to modeling of energy usage and financial planning for households, industries, institutions and communities. A discussion is then presented on how the model can be modified and implemented for national or global use.

Chapter 4 - According to EU competition law, mergers that significantly impedes effective competition, particularly by creating or strengthening a dominant position are prohibited. To identify these cases, authorities need a quantifiable model of the relationship between the variables that are affected by the merger and some measure of competition. Furthermore, the authorities must make their decision quickly, rendering deliberate data collection and econometric analyses infeasible in practice. The decision must be based on easily accessible data. In this paper, a simple model of the interaction between the retail and wholesale markets is constructed, calibrated and simulated based on a concrete case (the acquisition and merger of 250 shops previously organized in a voluntary chain of shops comprising roughly half of the market for high-end cosmetics in Denmark). Model simulations predicts that the merger would most likely significantly affect retail prices. The harmful effects are markedly intensified through the possible abuse of buyer power to raise barriers to the market and curb the competitiveness of minor rivals. However, the dominant position is vulnerable if increased profits induce the entrance to the sector of more independent competitors. The competition authorities were justified in conditioning its approval on the removal of contract-based barriers to entry. Analytically, the main results of this work are the following: (1) In a linear model characterized by heterogeneous products and constant marginal costs, the optimal (Nash equilibrium) wholesale price is unaffected by the structure in the retail sector. (2) The effect of buyer power- induced quantity discounts depends crucially on the specific design of the rebate scheme: A relative discount on the list price that the independent shops are charged *increases* the average retail price, whereas a fixed reduction relative to the pre-merger price *reduces* the average retail price. (3) Buyer power-induced retail price maintenance (RPM) increases the average retail price. RPM increases the competitiveness and profits of the merged shops only if the producers keep the wholesale prices unchanged. If the producers adjust their wholesale prices, then RPM hurts both the merged and the independent shops and benefits only the producers. The harmful effects on consumer welfare and efficiency are intensified.

Chapter 5 - Alkaline hydroxides, especially sodium and potassium hydroxides, are multi-million-ton per annum commodities and strong chemical bases that have large scale applications. Some of them are related with their consequent ability to degrade most materials, depending on the temperature used. As an example, these chemicals are involved in the manufacture of pulp and paper, textiles, biodiesels, soaps and detergents, acid gases removal (e.g., SO_2) and others, as well as in many organic synthesis processes. Sodium and potassium hydroxides are strong and corrosive bases, but they are also very stable chemicals that can melt without decomposition, NaOH at 318°C, and KOH at 360°C. Hence, they can react with most materials, even with relatively inert ones such as carbon materials. Thus, at temperatures higher than 360°C these melted hydroxides easily react with most types of carbon-containing raw materials (coals, lignocellulosic materials, pitches, etc.), as well as with most pure carbon materials (carbon fibers, carbon nanofibers and carbon nanotubes). This reaction occurs via a solid-liquid redox reaction in which both hydroxides (NaOH or KOH) are converted to the following main products: hydrogen, alkaline metals and alkaline carbonates, as a result of the carbon precursor oxidation. By controlling this reaction, and after a suitable washing process, good quality activated carbons (ACs), a classical type of porous materials, can be prepared. Such carbon activation by hydroxides, known since long time ago, continues to be under research due to the unique properties of the resulting activated carbons. They have promising high porosity developments and interesting pore size distributions. These two properties are important for new applications such as gas storage (e.g., natural gas or hydrogen), capture, storage and transport of carbon dioxide, electricity storage demands (EDLC-supercapacitors-) or pollution control. Because these applications require new and superior quality activated carbons, there is no doubt that among the different existing activating processes, the one based on the chemical reaction between the carbon precursor and the alkaline hydroxide (NaOH or KOH) gives the best activation results.

The present article covers different aspects of the activation by hydroxides, including the characteristics of the resulting activated carbons and their performance in some environment-related applications. The following topics are discussed: i) variables of the preparation method, such as the nature of the hydroxide, the type of carbon precursor, the hydroxide/carbon precursor ratio, the mixing procedure of carbon precursor and hydroxide (impregnation of the precursor with a hydroxide solution or mixing both, hydroxide and carbon precursor, as solids), or the temperature and time of the reaction are discussed, analyzing their effect on the resulting porosity; ii) analysis of the main reactions occurring during the activation process, iii) comparative analysis of the porosity development obtained from different activation processes (e.g., CO_2, steam, phosphoric acid and hydroxides activation); and iv) performance of the prepared activated carbon materials on a few applications, such as VOC removal, electricity and gas storages.

Chapter 6 - Several European countries are at high risk relating to government debt, thus economic consequences of soaring public debt have developed into a crucial topic not only across Europe but also worldwide. This paper is the first to investigate the way in which energy consumption is correlated to inflation, investment and particularly government debt, for a panel of 15 European countries from 1995 through to 2011. Given the relatively short span of time series data, a GMM model was employed to evaluate the correlation. The study forms the conclusion that energy consumption has a positive correlation with these three variables, whereas only the degree of effect differs. Investment has the most intense influence of these independent variables on energy consumption. According to the results as well, fiscal tightening would moderately decrease energy consumption.

Chapter 7 - District energy systems are a technology for using energy effectively and efficiently, at local or municipal scales, especially for thermal energy. Combining other beneficial energy technologies with a district energy system can significantly improve the efficiency of the combined system. The use is invesgtigated here of thermal energy storage (TES) in the Friedrichshafen district energy (DE) system, which uses solar energy and natural gas. The use of TES is observed to enhance the performance of the DE component of the Friedrichshafen system. In particular, TES improves the performance of the solar energy system, reducing annual natural gas consumption and annual fuel cost by 30% and harmful environmental emissions by 46%.

Chapter 8 - It is certain that energy production and, particularly, the generation and sustained growth of electricity, constitute indispensable elements for the economic and social progress of any country. Energy, undoubtedly, constitutes the motive force of civilization and it determines, to a high degree, the level of the future economic and social development of a country. To ensure adequate economic and social growth of a country it is vital that all available energy sources are used in the most efficient and economical manner for the generation of electricity. In the Latin American and the Caribbean region, all types of renewable energy sources can be found, most of them already used for the generation of electricity. In some countries, some renewable energy sources can be used more effectively for the production of electricity than in others. For example, in some countries, the use of specific renewable energy sources such as geothermal energy cannot be used for the electricity generation due to the nonexistence of volcanic zones. In some others, the use of hydro power for the generation of electricity is very limited, due to the lack of big rivers or due to large period of dry seasons or because the possible new sites to be exploited are located very far from populated areas. The generation of electricity using fossil fuels is a major and growing contributor to the emission of carbon dioxide, a greenhouse gas that contributes significantly to global warming that is producing a significant change in the Latin American and the Caribbean climate. These changes are affecting, in one way or another, almost all countries of the region. One of the main problems that the region is now facing is how to satisfy the foreseen increase in electricity demand using all available energy sources in the most efficient manner, and without increasing the emission of CO_2. The paper will talk about the possible future role of the different renewable energy sources available in the region for the generation of electricity.

Chapter 9 - This paper reviews the main characteristics of climate policy, emission trading and the European Union Emission Trading Scheme (EU ETS). First, we present the origins of emission trading and climate policy. We also discuss the last negotiations on how to prolong the Kyoto Protocol and the international climate policies beyond 2012. Second, we review previous experiences of emission trading prior to the launch of the EU ETS. Finally, we give a wide overview of the EU ETS. The main factors that affect the functioning of the EU ETS are then discussed, as well as the changes that will be effective for Phase 3 (2013-2020).

Chapter 10 - Extraction of the light weight radioisotopes (LWR) ^{89}Sr/^{90}Sr, from the expended nuclear bars in the Fukushima reactor, should have decreased the extent of contamination. Known technologies could be used to relate into innovative ways LWR, to obtain nuclear energy at scales smaller than those of nuclear reactors. This would lead to devices without moving parts, because LWR interact by contact with scintillators. Their applications could pay for the extraction treatment of ^{89}Sr/^{90}Sr, by the added value of obtaining an additional source of energy, through conversion of β-radiation into light-energy.

Chapter 11 - Electricity demand forecasting is an imperative tool for the planning and operation of electric utilities. With today's uncertainty and turbulent economies, the development of long term forecasting models requires careful consideration. The mixed forecasting model proposed in this paper was developed for the long term electricity demand forecasting for the countries of south Europe andis capable of determining the per person annual electricity demand by using economic variables alone. The forecasting model displays excellent fit to historic data for all four of the countries under study, namely Greece, Spain, Portugal and Italy, the four of which were hit the hardest by the latest economic recession. Furthermore, the economic variable's coefficients need not to be recalculated for each country as the proposed model was developed in order to fit the electricity consumption profiles of all 4 countries. Finally, additional investigations revealed that the proposed model also fits the historic data of countries in central Europe, with the variable coefficients still unchanged.

Chapter 12 - An equilibrium economic model for policy evaluation related to electricity generation was developed; the model takes into account non-renewable and renewable energy sources, demand and supply factors and environmental constraints. Non-renewable energy sources include three types of fossil fuels: coal, natural gas and petroleum, and renewable energy sources include nuclear, hydraulic, wind, etc. Energy demand sectors include households, industrial manufacturing and commercial enterprises. Energy supply takes into account the electricity delivered to the consumer by the utility companies at a certain price which maybe different for retail and wholesale customers. Environmental risks primarily take into account the CO_2 generation from fossil fuels. The model takes into account the employment in various sectors and labor supply and demand. Detailed data of electricity supply and demand, electricity cost, employment in various sectors and CO_2 generation were collected for a period from 1990 to 2006 in U.S for model calibration. The calibrated model was employed for policy analysis experiments if a switch was made in sources of electricity generation, namely from fossil fuels to renewable energy sources. The consequences of this switch on supply and demand, employment, wages, and emissions were obtained from the economic model under three scenarios: (1) energy prices were fully regulated, (2) energy prices were fully adjusted with electricity supply fixed, and (3) energy prices and electricity supply both were fully adjusted. The model output suggested possible increase in employment with such switch, while government regulation was necessary to achieve any sort of carbon reduction through such switch.

Chapter 13 - On the purpose to reduce the amount of energy used and to create environmental friendly indoor climate, heating and cooling systems can be substituted by passive climate control methods. Despite the fact that building thermal inertia is being analyzed in depth, there are other kinds of hygroscopic inertia that is reaching a special interest. Wall materials can serve as passive climate control methods. In particular, internal wall coverings materials have showed as the main barrier between indoor air and the construction walls which can act as reservoirs of humidity releasing it when the relative humidity level in the indoor ambience is reduced. In present paper main results obtained by the University of Coruña in different research works about this topic were summarized. These papers are based on real sampled data in 25 office buildings located in the northwest of Spain that showed the same construction characteristics except its internal wall coverings. By a statistical study it was concluded that real internal coverings can be classified in three different levels of permeability. Furthermore, these internal covering exert as control system of the indoor air condition defined by means of physical parameters, such as enthalpy, partial vapor pressure, temperature and etc. Finally, possible methods which contribute to providing comfortable indoor climate and, in consequence, to saving the amount of energy used inside the building were discussed and proposed.

Chapter 14 - Heat pumps are primary candidates for providing space heating with reduced emissions and economic benefits. Geothermal heat pump (GHP) systems use the earth just below the surface to supply a heat pump cycle with the thermal energy it requires for heating a space. Assessments of new GHP systems with alternative designs are reported to improve designs and facilitate more extensive applications as well as to provide information on how various operating conditions for varying heat pump arrangements affect performance and ground loop requirements. Three heat pump arrangements including the traditional heat pump cycle and two advanced cycles are considered within parametric investigations. The analyses, comparisons and parametric investigations reported of advanced GHP arrangements and systems improve understanding and design. These assessments reveal the sensitivity of the performance of the overall system to variations in numerous operating conditions and component efficiencies.

Chapter 15 - This paper presents Transient Stability Analysis of Synchronous Generator.

In: Research and Applications for Energy …
Editor: Riad Benelmir

ISBN: 978-1-62948-892-9
© 2014 Nova Science Publishers, Inc.

Chapter 1

DISTRIBUTION SECTOR REFORMS IN INDIA

S. C. Tripathy* and Tripta Thakur

Ghanashyam Hemalata Institute of Technology and Management,
At: Bhuan, Po-Chhaitana, Puri, Orissa, India

INTRODUCTION

Despite the introduction of reforms since 1991, the Electricity sector in India continues to be plagued with chronic shortages. The primary reason for the widening demand-supply gap lies with a financially crippled distribution sector. In India the power distribution has been the responsibility of the State Electricity Boards (SEBs), the state-owned electric utilities that were constituted in the era of nationalization under India's Electricity Supply Act of 1948. Except for a few private players who mainly operate in a few metropolitan cities and catering to the needs of urban consumers (Table A.3), these SEBs have retained the monopoly in power distribution in the country. Over time, these SEBs have accumulated gross financial losses. Apparently, the financial losses have reached an $ 5.2 thousand millions per year (IT Task Force, 2003) and no SEB currently recovers the full cost of power supplied. These financial losses cannot be made good from State budgets, as the states are themselves under severe financial strain; the result is that the SEBs are starved of resources to fund required expansion and typically end up neglecting even the essential maintenance. This has led to an undermined infrastructure base that constitutes a major roadblock in attracting much needed investment from the private parties.

The implications of a financially crippled distribution sector go far beyond. Because the SEBs have been loss-makers, the generation companies do not recover their dues from their biggest buyers, the SEBs. This has eroded the financial capacities of the generating companies to expand and upgrade services and face the challenge of deficits in the generation capacities.

In view of the above facts, the focus of the power sector reforms in India has now shifted from deficit mitigation through purchases of power from independent power producers (IPPs) to privatization of distribution sector. This shift reflects the recognition that the foundation for

---

* E-mail address: sarattripathy1@gmail.com.

sustainable power sector reforms must be financially and operationally viable (or efficient) distribution entities (Agarwal et aI, 2004). Hence, restoring the health of distribution sector assumes top priority in the reform process (MoP, 2002(b); Banks et aI, 1998) and restructuring and privatization of distribution sector are receiving paramount attention. With the inception of the new Electricity Act, 2003, a new liberal and competitive framework has been created for development of the Indian distribution sector.

This paper attempts to present an assessment of the Indian electricity distribution sector: the problems specific to the distribution sector, the reform strategies and measures initiated by the government for restructuring of the sector, reorganization of the distribution sector in recent times, followed by a discussion on the tasks that lie ahead for the distribution reforms to succeed. The paper also attempts to spell out and suggest steps for reframing the future course of reforms with an objective that the outcome may help policy makers to initiate step for the improvement of the sector.

NEED FOR DISTRIBUTION SECTOR REFORMS

The Indian Electricity sector constitutes a contrast - a highly sophisticated modern generation and transmission system, but a very poor distribution system in several utilities. This situation may have arisen due to a lack of focus on the distribution aspect reflected by a lack of investment in distribution. An example that illustrates this fact is exhibited in the growth of T &D network. The network length increased from about 5.1 million circuit Kms in 1995-96 to about 5.9 million circuit Kms in 2000-01 (Figure 1) at a compounded annual growth rate (CAGR) of only 2.8% and was not commensurate with the increase in installed capacity which had increased at a CAGR of 4.1 % over the same period (CEA, 2002). This shortcoming was identified when the reform initiatives launched in the form of opening the market for IPPs in 1991 were critically examined and it was realized that the mere opening up of generation to private investment in the absence of meaningful all round reforms proved ineffective and inadequate. The IPPs were expected to sell power to SEBs, but the latter were not in a position to pay for the power purchased. The result was that the inflow of private investment remained much below the targeted level as evident in the Ninth plan (1997-2002) report of the Planning Commission which revealed that out of an additional target of 17,588 MW of power, the actual achievement was only 5,061 MW (Table 1), i.e., a fulfillment of just 28.7% of the target value. The distribution sector has therefore been identified as the key focus area in the power sector reforms process as maximum revenue loss had been occurring in this part of the sector.

The performance of power distribution entities in India, as in several developing countries has been characterized by inefficiency, low productivity, frequent interruptions in supply and poor voltages, all of which have resulted in poor quality of service for consumers and huge financial losses for SEBs (Alberto, 2004). As a consequence, the performance of the SEBs has been deteriorating over the past few years. Commercial losses were estimated at about $ 5200 Million during 2000-01 Gross subsidy which was $ 1490 Million in 1991-92, was estimated at about $ 7600 Million in 2000-2001 (Planning Commission, 2002). The pricing mechanism led to a situation where, on an average for the entire country, the tariff provided for only about 69% of the cost of supply of power (year 2000-01 (Planning Commission, 2002).

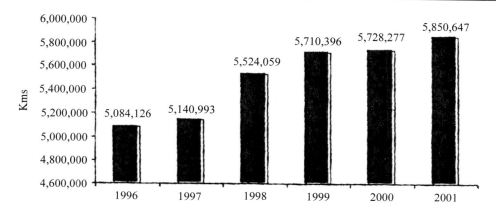

Figure 1. T& D Line Lengths in India (Source: CEA (2002).

This has led the SEBs to demonstrate an average rate of return (without subsidy) of -33.8% in 1999-2000 indicating further deterioration from -12.7% at 1992-93 levels (Planning Commission, 2002). As on March 31, 2001, the total outstanding payable amount by SEBs. to the central power sector and related entities stood at about $ 5552 Millions (MoP, 2002 (a)). The unsatisfactory financial health of SEB's has been a major constraint in way of attracting adequate investments for improved utilization of existing capacities, and for new capacity creation, leaving no options but to reform and restructure power distribution industry in order to make it viable.

Another issue that hampers the viability of the Indian Power Sector concerns the mounting T &D losses due to rampant theft and pilferage of electricity, meter tampering, unauthorized connections and un-metered supply. As compared to other developing countries such as China and Thailand where the T &D losses are at a much lower level of 8-12% (IT Task Force, 2003), in India these losses officially amount to 32% (MoP, 2002(b)). However, the unofficial calculations put these losses to be in a much higher range of 40-50% (Distribution Policy Committee Report, 2002). The figures vary because of large and unknown pilferage of electricity, hidden by claiming a large consumption of electricity in the agriculture sector. The fact that the agriculture sector remains mostly unmetered enabled the SEBs to claim less than the actual losses. However, the restructuring of SEBs and take-up of distribution in some of the states by private players has revealed that when losses are calculated more precisely, the actual T &D losses amount to a much higher range of 45-50% (Distribution policy committees report, 2002). This situation clearly warrants fundamental changes to be incorporated in the working of the power sector utilities to realize the vision of "reliable, affordable and quality power for all by 2012" (MoP, 2001).

The key areas of concern in the distribution sector can be divided into financial and technical categories. Factors that affect the financial viability include:

- Inappropriate tariff policies and power pricing
- Poor Metering and billing practices
- Inadequate investments in T & D network.
- Structural framework of Institutions- The sizes and monolithic structures of SEBs
- Commercial losses reflected in increasing gaps between revenue receivables and Expenditure

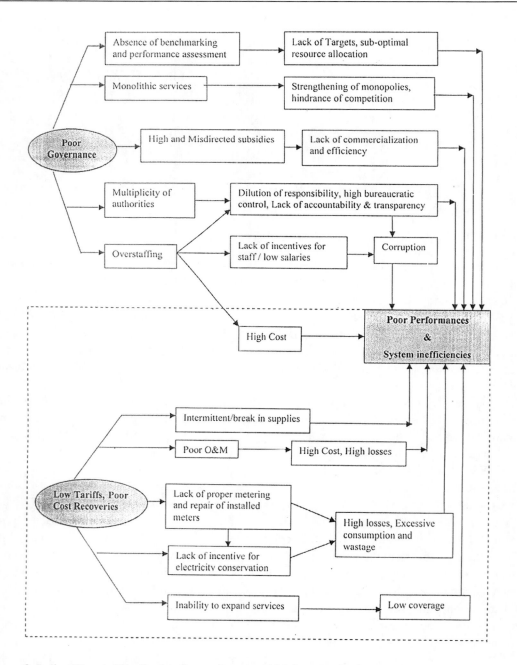

Figure 2. Indian Electric Distribution Sector: Issues and Linkages to Performance.

The Technical factors that affect the viability of the sector include:

- Operational inefficiencies- Poor performance of the state owned entities coupled with a complete ignorance of the concept of efficiency and its measurement
- Renovation & modernization- often inadequate due to under-provision of adequate investments.

- T &D losses- High level of actual losses (aggregate technical and commercial losses) estimated at about 40%-50%.
- Poor Management and poor governance - lack of commercial orientation of
- Distribution entities and poor work culture amongst the employees.

Some of these issues and their probable linkages to sector performances have been summed up in- Figure 2. An in-depth analysis of the Indian distribution sector confirms that the power distribution problem in the country is a multi-dimensional one. There are clear technical problems indigenous to the distribution system. Likewise, there are also economic, social, and political dimensions to the problem that need to be addressed.

From a strategic standpoint, therefore, any solution must necessarily target the issue of high T &D losses and tie it with technical, economic, social, and political remedies in concert. Some of these impacts are quantifiable and can form the basis of measurement of performances in the sector.

DISTRIBUTION REFORMS IN INDIA

Reforms Initiatives in the Distribution Sector

The Government of India has in the recent times indicated a genuine predilection for introducing reforms in the distribution sector. As a first step, to generate political consensus for the reforms and to enhance the understanding between the center and the states, the state chief minister's conferences were convened in the year 1996, 1998, 1999, 2000 and 2001[1]. These conferences led to an agreement that there was an urgent need to depoliticize power sector reforms and speed up their implementation.

The other initiative that the government of India took was to constitute a number of committees to design and recommend reform measures. These committees comprised the Coelho Committee (March 1998), Mantek Singh Ahluwalia Committee (May 200 I), Godbole Committee (July 2001), Ashok Basu Committee (March 2002), Deepak Parekh Committee (September 2002); details of which are available online at the Ministry of Power website.

In order to provide financial support to the SEBs for pursuing reforms programme, the Accelerated Power Development Reform Programme (APDRP)[2] was introduced in February, 2000 and spelled measures to provide easy loans, grants and incentives on the basis of utility performances. The main purpose of this programme was to address the issues at the micro-level (consumer, feeder, and sub-station) and at the macro-level (circle, state, and national), covering interventions at these six stages. The APDRP was formulated to finance specific projects relating to:

---

[1] Under the federal structure in India, the major share of distribution business lies with the states and the responsibility for the development of the sector lies jointly with the center and the states.

[2] Three key components in the APDRP are (i) inclusion of specific''' distribution reform measures through Memorandum of Association (MoAs) negotiated with individual States, (ii) expansion of the program coverage beyond the initially selected 63 distribution circles to include all 454 distribution circles throughout the country; and (iii) extensive capacity building of the State Electricity Boards (SEBs) and the distribution companies (Discoms) through provision of training and technical assistance by the various Advisor-cum-Consultants (AcCs).

- Renovation and modernization, life extension, upgrading of old thermal/hydel plants.
- Upgrading and strengthening of sub-transmission and distribution network (below 33kv or 66kv) including energy accounting and metering in the distribution circles.
- Development of state-wise centers of excellence for upgrading sub-transmission and distribution networks.

The APDRP provides much needed investment to the distribution sector, and incentive to the utilities to motivate them to bring down their cash loss[3]. Under the restructured APDRP (MoP, 2007), the states will be required to adopt reforms in order to become eligible for the scheme.

MoP has also undertaken initiatives with international agencies For example, United States Agency for. International Development (USAID)-India. has designed the Distribution Reform Upgrades and Management (DRUM) project with the purpose "to demonstrate best commercial and technological practices thm improve the quality and reliability of 'last mile' power distribution in selected urban and rual distribution circles in the country. The project is in synch with the GoI policy on power sector reforms, the Electricity Act 2003, and the restructured APDRP scheme. DRUM is a 5-year bilateral project with a planned Life-of-Project funding of US $30 million[4]4.

For rural India, Rural Electrification Supply Technology (REST) Mission was initiated in August 2002. The mission targeted electrification of 10 million households through decentralized distributed generation systems with focus on rural electrification through technology options, innovative financing and grass-root level institutional arrangements.

Other reform measures comprised the Act that were initiated at the policy level to roll out the reforms. These are briefly described below:

The Energy. Conservation Act: This Act came into effect on March 1, 2002, spelling various measures to ensure efficient use of energy and its conservation. A Bureau of Energy Efficiency (BEE) has been set up to formulate regulations to further the objectives of the Energy Conservation Act. Further, the central and state governments have been empowered to facilitate and enforce efficient use of energy and its conservation.

The Electricity Act 2003: This Act is likely to completely transform the Indian power sector. The Act has laid down a decisive direction for introducing liberalization and competition in the power sector that has been lacking so far. As more players enter the sector, some in niche areas, competitive forces will force a change of mindset to foster and recognize

---

[3] The Government had approved the programme with a budget provision of $800 Crore during Xth Plan, out of which Rs. 20,000 Crore was allocation under Investment component and $400 Crore under Incentive component. However, the Government actually allocated only $ 246.50 Crore. Under the investment component, Ministry so far sanctioned 583 projects with overall estimated outlay of $382.60 Crore. However, the Utilities were able to complete only about 50% work amounting to $194.6 Crore. Under incentive component of APDRP, 19 states submitted their incentive claims to the Ministry amounting to $382.60 Crore, since launch of the programme. However, on scrutiny by independent evaluators, only 8 states were found eligible for incentive. Total incentive amounting to $30.7 Crore was released among these states (MoP, 2006).

[4] The objectives of the DRUM program are (a) to establish the framework, institutional capacity and project development functions at the central and state levels and, (b) to enable implementation of several full-scale commercially replicable distribution initiatives in key reform states in India. It is expected that a number of pilot projects would be implemented over the Life of Project. Initially the work would be initiated in two states where distribution circles would be selected for implementation of projects. Based on review and experience and subject to availability of funds, additional states can subsequently be added.

the electricity supply service as a 'business' to which principles of sound business management will have to be applied. The probable impacts and implications of the Act are likely to have far reaching consequences on the Indian Power Scenario, including the ways in which distribution utilities operate and function (Thakur et aI, 2005).

Table 1. Lessons Learnt in Orissa and Delhi State Privatizations

Issue	Orissa State	Delhi State
Government Commitment	Government distanced itself as soon as the privatization took place.	Government has shown good commitment to the success of the Reform Process. • Clear cut policy directions for 5 years • Committed support- about $ 52cr. • Antitheft legislation to be enacted
Loss Levels	• Base-line date mismatch • Difficulty segregating losses in	Concept of Aggregate Technical and Commercial (AT & C) losses to • Reduce scope for baseline date errors • Provide more realistic loss levels • Provide greater comfort & since approved by commission
Receivables	Unrealistically high	• Limited to last month's receivables • Past receivales to the account of Holding Company- No obligation to collect (20% incentive on amount collected) • Level of Receivables in line with the average monthly billing of the last 6 months.
Regulatory Involvement	No prior involvement	• Full involvement from the beginning • Indicated amenability to the reforms process • Policy Directives accepted in Bulk Supply Tariff (BST order • Recognition of Discom in BST order
Asset Valuation	Assets revalued at higher value prior to bidding process.	Assets valued through Business Valuation based on revenue earning potential.

Source: IIM Bangalore, 2003.

Status of Distribution Reforms in India

The restructuring programme in. the form of complete privatization of SEBs started with the state of Orissa in 1993. Orissa then became the first state not only in India, but also in the entire South Asia, to implement a comprehensive power sector reforms programme. This restructuring programme had the active involvement of multilateral lending agencies like the World Bank, Department for International Development, Government of UK (DFID) and the

Asian Development Bank, and several leading management consultants (Thillai and Anand, 2000). The experience of Orissa has been important to other states in India, which are restructuring their SEBs more or less on the lines of the Orissa experiment. In July 2002, Delhi became yet another state that opted for privatization of the Delhi Vidyut Board, the state owned utility that served the 14 million people of metropolitan Delhi. The Government in the state of Delhi was able to sell majority stakes in three distribution utilities covering the entire metropolitan area even though the total operational and commercial losses were close to 50%. The experiment in Delhi has been successful so far[5], although it would be a bit premature to declare complete success for the Delhi privatization in a time of just 2 years. Table 1 compares the issues in privatization for the Orissa and Delhi states.

27 States in India have so far initiated restructuring process of their SEBs and these are at various stages of implementation. These states have already signed memorandum of understanding with the Ministry of Power of Government of India to implement reforms at distribution sector in a time bound manner. Orissa, Haryana, Uttar Pradesh, Andhra Pradesh, Karnataka, Rajastan, Madhya Pradesh and West Bengal were the first Indian States that had unbundled their activities and have separate generation, distribution and transmission companies. These states have commercialized their activities but they are still in the government control effective privatization has been introduced only in Orissa and Delhi states. A close look at the internet sites of reforming states like Orissa, Andhra Pradesh, Haryana and Delhi reveals that financial performance of unbundled utilities has improved to a certain extent. These states have invariably taken up the installation of meters in a big way with the financial assistance from World Bank and Power Finance Corporation (PFC), and these measures led to an improved revenue collection.

The six main private distribution utilities in India, namely, BSES and TEC in Mumbai, CESE in Kolkata, AEC in Ahmedabad, SEC in Surat and NPCL in Greater-Noida have also performed satisfactorily. The company financial performances available in the public domain on the Internet indicate that these entities have earned profits, thereby making the operations commercially viable. However, it is important to note that all these utilities are primarily catering to urban areas, which have a large number of industrial consumers, but hardly a few agricultural or rural consumers, if any. This assures the utilities that they are paid higher and assured tariffs (Industrial and commercial tariffs are greater), have defined demands, and receive regular revenues for reinvestments.

With the Electricity Act 2003 introduced in June 2003, it is now mandatory for all states to unbundle their services in order to bring about increasing accountability in operations so that their efficiencies can improve. So far, however, only ten states have complied, and completed the process of unbundling, indicating that substantial work still needs to be carried out on the reforms front.

Reform Initiatives in Rural Electrification

According to the 2001 Census, 6.02 crore households use electricity as the primary source of lighting out of a total of 13.8 crore households in the country (Modi, 2005). According to Ministry of Non-Conventional Energy Sources (MNES), 5000 villages would be electrified in the 10th Five-year Plan (2002-2007) and by the year 2012 all the 18,000 villages would be covered. It is estimated that on an average, an investment of $ 0.04 million would be required to electrify a remote village (four hours of power supply per, day) (Infraline.com, 2003). Thus implications in terms of the massive investment required are significant with minimal possibilities of returns in terms of revenues. It is not very likely that the private sector will find the task attractive and the only hope would be the international aid in the form of loans etc. The government of India has initiated measures to ensure rural electrification by including the programme as a component of the Pradhan Mantri Gramodaya Yojana (PMGY)[5] and the states are being encouraged to pool resources from other schemes under the Minimum Need Programme (MNP) and Rural Infrastructure Development Fund (RIDF) to meet the objective of 100% electrification. A new scheme called Accelerated Rural Electrification Programme (AREP), with provision for interest subsidy, is also being launched. With GoI promoting a number of schemes and programmes to accelerate the pace of village electrification, much-needed impetus may also come in from the international arena as in the past. For example, The United Nations Environment Programme (UNEP) has launched a major new $7.6 million initiative to offer 18,000 south Indian households low cost financing for solar generated electricity (Infraline.com, 2003).

The GoI has also initiated a number of measures for aiding access to electricity in the rural areas; some of these are highlighted below:

- The Kutir Jyoti Programme (KJP): launched by the GoI in 1988-1989 for the electrification of poor rural households. The Kutir Jyoti Scheme released in 1989 connected nearly 60 lakh households in 15 years or at a rate of approximately 4 lakh households per year.

- The Pradhan Mantri Gramodaya Yojana (PMGY): launched in 2000-2001, in order to achieve the objective of sustainable human development at the village level. The central government provides financing under the scheme in the form of loans (90%) and grants (10%). The PMGY envisages an assistance of about $ 320 Million in the last 4 years of the 10th five-year plan.

- Minimum Needs Programme (MNP): Central plan assistance by way of 100% loan for last mile connectivity has been made available to states under MNP and an amount of $155 Million has been released during the period 2001-2003 for rural electrification;

- The Accelerated Rural Electrification Programme (AREP): Under this, the GoI has announced an interest subsidy scheme in the Union Budget 2002-2003 and has approved the grant of interest subsidy of over $ 112 Million. Funds for rural electrification are available under the Rural Infrastructure Development Fund operated by National Bank for Agriculture and Rural Development (NABARD). In addition, loan assistance for electrification of villages, hamlets and socially deprived is also available.

- Rajeev Gandhi Grameen Vidyutikaran Yojana (RGGVY): Ministry of Power has introduced the scheme RGGVY in April 2005, which aims at providing electricity in all villages and habitations in four years and provides access to electricity for all rural households. Under RGGVY, electricity distribution infrastructure is envisaged to

[5] Carried out under the aegis of the Ministry of Rural Development, PMGY is a comprehensive Scheme that aims at reducing the shortage of houses for Below Poverty Line (BPL) families in the rural areas and also assists in the healthy development of the habitat in these areas.

establish Rural Electricity Distribution Backbone (REDB) with at least a 33/11KV sub-station, Village Electrification Infrastructure (VEl) with at least a distribution Transformer in a village or hamlet, and standalone grids with generation where grid supply is not feasible., This infrastructure would cater to the requirements of agriculture and other activities in rural areas including irrigation pumpsets, small and medium industries, khadi and village industries, cold chains, healthcare and education and IT (MoP, 2007). This would facilitate overall rural development, employment generation and poverty alleviation.

There is, however, a serious concern about the role of privatization and the impact of overall reforms programme on rural electrification development. In a recent study on the analysis of the impacts of the electricity reforms in the rural development of Orissa, Sharma et al (2002) reveal that during the restructuring period the rural electrification programs suffered serious setbacks.

The study concluded that the agricultural sector suffered the maximum with low growths in lift irrigation, energy availability to pump sets, etc. Also, the share of electricity provided for agriculture at the national level has decreased slightly from 29.90% in' 1992-93 to 28.78% in 2001-02, but in the states of Orissa and Haryana, it has substantially reduced from 5.60% to 1.81% and 27.20% to 19.61%, respectively, during the above period.

These concerns pose a serious threat to the all round development and to the development of the poor, and every possibility should be explored to make sure that overall reforms do not have a negative impact on the rural electrification. This assumes greater significance in agrarian economies where majority of the population resides in rural areas.

THE TASKS AHEAD: A ROADMAP TO SUCCESS

Since the existing institutional set-up has failed to deliver financially and operationally efficient distribution entities, there is an urgent need to introduce and institutionalize changes to bring about sustainable and pervasive improvements. With the introduction of the Electricity Act 2003, SEBs have to unbundle activities with regard to the generation, transmission and distribution. Although no rigid time frame is spelled out, yet most of the SEBs have already started this process, as this is the first step towards reform. A roadmap to the success of the yet to come reform measures must incorporate the following:

-   Strengthening the regulating commissions
-   Implementing the Multi-Year Tariff (MYT) Framework
-   Ensuring Universal Metering and Proper Billing
-   Reorganizing the distribution sector
-   Measuring efficiencies and appraising performances in the sector

These measures have been discussed in detail in the following sections.

STRENGTHENING THE ROLE OF REGULATORY COMMISSIONS

In the emerging deregulated regime in the Indian Power sector, the role of the Regulator shall be very crucial as happens in any free and open power market structure. The, ERC Act, 1998 has already laid the foundation of the Central Electricity Regulating Commission (CERC) at the central level and the State Electricity Regulating Commission (SERC) at the state level. The CERC is currently a functioning body, whereas twenty-two states have so far constituted the SERCs. The key function and responsibilities of the Regulatory Commission arc following:

- Tariff setting
- Licenses and setting performance standards.
- Monitoring the performance of regulated entities
- Gauging the environmental impacts of resource utilization
- Ensuring conservation and efficient use of utility and societal resources
- Enabling Consumer protection
- Assuring high system reliability
- Design of tools for incentives to utilities
- Adjudicating disputes in matters of electricity trade

As many as eighteen of the SERCs have issued tariff orders so far. It is, therefore, expected that the remaining states will implement the regulatory commissions soon and that the commissions will work in the true spirit as envisaged their formation. It is also essential that the Regulating Commissions be maintained as an independent body, free of political and business pressures and gain public acceptance for playing a unique role in synthesizing the competing interests of the utilities, the consumers and government.

IMPLEMENTATION OF MULTI-YEAR TARIFF (MYT) FRAMEWORK

The MYT is a system wherein the tariff setting is carried out through a single exercise applicable for a number of years. MYT, therefore, implies adherence to specific benchmarks that will prevail for a number of years, with the possibility of extension of principles governing the input costs and output prices for several years at a time. This is in contrast to the present system of annual determination of tariffs, a system that is too flexible giving undue freedom for arbitrary decision-making and political influence. The MYT leads to a reduction in regulatory effort on the part of the commissions, besides a regulatory uncertainty, and is a part of encouraging and fostering a transparent and stable system of incentives.

The high degree of tariff distortions that exist at present in India, need to be corrected in a time bound manner and the linkage of tariffs to the underlying cost of services needs to be established. Almost all reforming countries have invariably adopted Performance Based Regulation through Multi- Year Tariff (MYT) framework. In line with this, the Indian Electricity Act, 2003 requires the appropriate Commission to be guided by MYT principles. Survey results carried out by Indian Institute of Technology, Delhi indicate a near consensus for the view that a consistent framework on MYT should be implemented across the country. The framework should make the utilities accountable for all controllable cost and revenue elements, while passing through with the uncontrollable factors. Thus, implementation of performance based regulation/through MYT framework is by far the most important structural initiative required to minimize risks for utilities and consumers, to promote efficiency, and to attract investments in the distribution sector. The MYT framework shall be applied to both the public and private utilities.

In this context, the following require immediate attention:

- Instrument of MYT regulation needs to be precisely defined with little room for discretion and alternate interpretations.
- The framework should be kept simple, practical and may initially focus on the computation of revenue allowance rather than on retail tariff formulation across a multi-year period
- The MYT framework should feature sufficient incentives to encourage utilities to improve upon the regulatory targets. This would benefit both the utilities and the consumers and accelerate performance improvement and loss reductions
- Benefit sharing mechanisms between the utilities and consumers should be defined clearly and should be an integral part of MYT framework
- All calculations for determining revenue allowance should be based on actual levels and not the desired levels
- A number of researchers such as Ailawadi not necessary and Bhattacharyya (2002) have indicated that non-availability of data and information inadequacy is even faced by regulators and affects their working. Hence, it must be seen that availability of actual reliable data is ensured.

ENSURING UNIVERSAL METERING AND INITIATING PROPER BILLING PRACTICES

Inefficient billing and collection have been the major causes of commercial losses of the SEBs. At the national level, only 55% $ 124.00 Millions) of the total energy generated is billed out and only 41 % ($ 92.00 Millions) is realized (IT Task Force, 2003). Also, currently a very large numbers of consumers are supplied electricity without meters across various states. This leads to malpractices and electricity wastage by consumers, who either do not payer pay nominal flat rates. An essential prerequisite to ensure the success of reforms is to ensure effective revenue collection that can be reinvested for reduction of losses in the system. This highlights the need for 100% metering.

In this direction, several initiatives have been taken by various SEBs in the form of replacement of mechanical meters by electronics meter, digitization of meter reading, installation of pre-paid meters, introduction of handheld devices for meter reading and online metering. Maharashtra State Electricity Board (MSEB) has been a pioneer in innovation in the IT implementation in distribution sector (IT Task Force, 2003). The MSEB has developed a new software system called Consumer Monitoring System (CMS) for managing metering-billing-collection cycle at the sub-division level. Karnataka Power Transmission Company limited (KPTCL) has also successfully computerized the process of issue of consumer bills and collection in Banglore city for the past two years (IT Task Force, 2003). This practice has been extended to the surrounding areas of Banglore city subsequently and KPTCL is planning to extend it further to other parts of Karnataka. Another SEB, the West Bengal State Electricity Board (WBSEB) has implemented a fully operational Distribution Automation System in Jalpalguri Circle (IT Task Force, 2003).

The cost estimates for integrated billing system depend on a number of factors such as economies of scale (Numbers of meters to be installed in a defined region or circle), meter costs, meter installation costs, software implementation costs, and the costs of organization structure to reflect responsibility, authority and control. IT Task Force (2003) has estimated that based on the data assumption of the 16,000 installations of more than 10 kw load is $ 4. Table 2 illustrates the total cost estimates for the integrated billing system for the above data. It is evident that universal metering and installation of integrated billing systems will require enormous financial investments, and separate projects may have to be undertaken with the help of the government and the global aid agencies to achieve these goals. The Electricity Act 2003 has given two years of timeframe for achieving 100% metering. Assuming that this is achieved despite the financial constraints, there would still be the need to adopt appropriate IT measures on a priority basis to ensure that all metered consumers are billed correctly and promptly.

Table 2. Cost Estimates for Integrated Billing System

Cost breakdown (Million) Dollars	Initial Cost $	Year 1	Year 2
Meter costs Dollar U.S.	4.8	6.4	Nil
Installation costs	0.5	1.12	0.64
Software (SW) costs	0.2	0.72	0.10
Hardware (HW)costs	0.12	0.12	Nil
HW & SW Maintenance	Nil	0.02	0.02
Total Costs	**5.7**	**8.4**	**0.76**

Source: I T Task Force (2003).

Reorganizing the Distribution Sector

In the Indian context where the distribution companies have been a monopoly of the SEBs, unfurlment of the reforms imply large- scale SEBs reforms through initiation of an array of steps with the following change sequencing:

(a) Distribution zoning,
(b) Formation of optimal number of distribution companies (DISCOMs),
(c) Evolution of optimal zoning for the distribution companies based on influencing parameters such as size, sale and numbers and types of consumers, and
(d) Where feasible and necessary, privatization of DISCOMs in order to bring in investments and quality of service. A mix of privatized and government entities may also help foster competition to promote efficiency.

DISTRIBUTION ZONING

Unbundling is identified as a key requirement for promoting competition in a sector that has been monolithic so far. Unbundling involves breaking distribution regions into a number of zones, each managed by an independent player. This introduces the possibility of competition and hence performance enhancement amongst various entities and also gives the government or the regulator, the privilege of eliminating non-performing entities.

More specifically, the regrouping of distribution system of SEBs into smaller entities would have the following advantages:

- Creation of distribution zones of manageable sizes
- Possibility of inter-utility comparison of performance across the zones for fostering some level of competitive environment.
- Possibility of experimenting with the field application of different models (such as the management contracts, Bots, licenses, Joint Ventures, lease, Concession etc.) in various zones, giving the government /regulator greater choice and flexibility.
- Feasibility of the entry of smaller players/local entities that are well aware of local problems into the power market
- The choice of allocating resources preferentially in certain areas (zones) that are least developed such as the tribal areas or the areas infested by poverty.

The structure of distribution zones can be mixed or concentrated comprising different types of consumers like industrial, domestic or agriculture. Internationally, supply of electricity to rural areas is not given special dispensation, e.g., subsidies for capital investment in network expansion, and private distribution of electricity in rural areas is not prevalent in most countries. However in a few cases, like in Australia, rural and urban zones were segregated when distribution was privatized (Distribution Policy Committee Report, 2002). Similarly, in Argentina, large provincial distribution areas continued under state ownership when Buenos Aires was privatized (Distribution Policy Committee Report, 2002). In India, there is a need to approach rural electrification in a manner that addresses its special needs and also leverage the benefits of private and community enterprises to improve service in these areas. Cooperatives often provide an effective option for extending services to rural areas, especially with access to quality advice and help on technical, financial management, human resource development and other related activities.

Formation of Optimal Numbers of Distribution Companies (DISCOMs)

Requirements of the large investments and economics of scale indicate a preference towards larger and therefore, fewer DISCOMs. But the concerns about manageability, customer services, the need for regulatory comparisons and the need to attract a wider range of investors including the local and other small players, might suggest just the opposite (i.e., smaller and large numbers of operating entities). Based on a review of international privatized DISCOMs in terms of customer numbers, investment size, and MKWh sales, the Distribution Policy Committee set up by the Ministry Of Power, GoI, has suggested that for Indian conditions, the selection process should allow for DISCOMs with a maximum of about 3 million customers and a minimum of about 3500 MKWh of sales per year (Distribution Policy Committee Report, 2002).

Evolution of Optimal Zoning for DISCOMs Based on Influencing Parameters

The selection of the number and the location of the Distribution Companies is one of the most sensitive and crucial decisions to be made during the reforms programme and is the key to the success of the reforms and restructuring process. This exercise of structuring i.e. dividing the area under consideration into an appropriate number of zones, needs to be carried out with caution, as sub-optimal choices will lead to under-performance of distribution utilities. One of the major requirements to make every zone compatible is that the structure of each zone should be proportioned in terms of influencing parameters. Some of the major parameters that must be given consideration in order for the zoning to be effective could be:

1. Consumer numbers in each zone
2. Energy-sales in every zone
3. Type of consumers: Domestic/Industrial/Commercial/Agriculture
4. Similarities of lifestyles and cultural backgrounds including common language
5. Distribution Area of each zone
6. Connected load to various zones
7. Likely Revenue in each zone
8. Subsidy ratio amongst various consumers of each zone

A methodology to evaluate the optimal zoning has been demonstrated by Thakur et al (2004) for one of the largest states of India, the state of Madhya Pradesh (M.P.) by employing a Delphi analysis. With a total numbers of consumers at 6.1 million and total sale of 13369.9 MKwh (1999 figures), three DISCOMs were chosen and the state was divided in three Zones.

The zoning was carried out by employing parameters as illustrated in Table 3, A number of experts were consulted to decide the parameter weights (Table 3.) Figure 3 shows the final zoning based on the parameters for Delhi State. It is possible to refine this methodology and apply it with larger number of additional parameters such as connected load, revenue, subsidizing ratio etc. The outcome of such an analysis could be extremely useful in delineating optimal equitable distribution zones under any distribution sector reforms framework.

Table 3. Weights Given To Parameters for Optimal DISCOM Configuration

Sl.No.	Parameters	Weight age (%)
1.	Size Factor	10
2.	Geographical Area	10
3.	Number of Consumer	30
4.	Energy Sale	40
5.	Cultural Uniformity	10

Source: Thakur et al (2004).

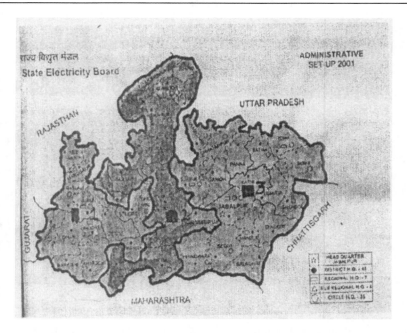

Figure 3. Final DISCOM Zoning on the Basis of Weights given to Parameters (Source: Thakur et al, 2004).

Benchmarking of Indian Power Distribution Utilities: The Need for Performance Appraisal

Once the unbundling has been carried out and the sector is reorganized on lines of optimal zoning, keeping track of the performance of the reforms and ensuring competition and efficiency in the sector should assume priority of the policy makers, planners and regulators. Benchmarking, as a technique for evaluation of performances across a number of utilities, is considered a potential methodology for efficiency improvements within organizations and sectors. Such appraisals form an important part of introducing competition and leveraging best practices, and in gauging the effectiveness and success of any reforms programme. In addition, by comparing the operating efficiencies of different distribution network owners with their national and international counterparts and with the best practices, it is possible to identify the scope for further efficiency improvements, and utilize the performance appraisal studies as a resource allocation tool. Such studies also enable the regulators to provide incentives to the well performing states and utilities. It is also possible to measure comparative improvements in the performance of a single entity over time, providing an indication of the rate of previous productivity gains and helping to establish the expected rate of productivity gains over the regulatory period. Around the world, benchmarking is receiving new attention, especially where it is being employed as a regulatory tool for setting the X factor in price cap regimes. In effect, benchmarking promises to form the core of the newly emerging regulatory regimes in the power sector.

Unfortunately, the concept of efficiency and effectiveness in power services has been alien to the Indian scenario. To make reforms a success story in India it is essential to review and compare the historical and current performances of state/private distribution utilities in terms of their levels and standards of service, the condition and serviceability of assets, the human resources, and the financial performances over time. Based on the productivity and efficiency analysis, benchmarks can be set, and utility efficiency scores can be obtained based on the set benchmarks. The utility efficiency scores need to be utilized for evolving strategic plans that mitigate the factors contributing to the system inefficiencies. Such studies can greatly help in avoiding structural and contractual inefficiencies in the emerging restructuring of the power sector. This. is especially crucial and significant currently as the important features of the sector (like tariff policy) are being redesigned in the ongoing reform process. With the liberal market attitude brought about by the introduction of Electricity Act, 2003, unbundling and restructuring is going to be the preferred choice, and to make this process effective, there is an urgent need to carry out scientific analysis of efficiency evaluation for the emerging structure of the distribution sector in India.

So far, besides the present work, only two studies on Indian power sector have been reported. The studies reported are:

1. The Power Finance Corporation (PFC) has given a project to The Credit Rating Information Services of India Limited (CRISIL) information and Credit Rating Agency (ICRA) to carry out a performance rating of the power sector across the states and give rating scores for state utilities. This is a preliminary study and no standard econometric method has been employed for calculating scores (CRISL/ICRA, 2006).

2. The NGO 'Prayas' has also carried out a preliminary study for six private distribution utilities (Prayas, 2003). Its occasional report compares six private distribution utilities of India on five aspects, namely, T &D losses, receivables, manpower, distribution investments, and distribution cost on the basis of easily available public data. Besides these studies, little has been done to evaluate the performance of the sector. There is thus an urgent need to carry out a scientific analysis of efficiency evaluation using advanced benchmarking techniques for the players in the Indian distribution sector. This need has been mainly addressed in the present paper.

PRIVATIZATION OF DISCOMs

Private sector participation in distribution sector is still in a nascent stage in India with only two states Orissa and Delhi having so far experimented with privatization. Poor SEB performances and financial constraints in meeting the targets for capacity addition have been the two major reasons to look for private participation in India. The privatization process has also been pushed through in view of the requirement of inducing efficiency in operation and services, as has happened in the case of Delhi state. The experiences in Argentina, Chile and Peru reveal significant reductions in energy losses within 2-6 years of privatization (Distribution Policy Committee Report, 2002), and hence there is some hope that the Indian power sector may benefit from its experiments in privatization. Given the specific conditions prevalent in India, these examples may not be completely replicable nevertheless, they do serve as useful guidelines for setting targets in the Indian context. The process of privatization requires considerable amount of preparatory work, including the tackling of the past liabilities, restructuring, retrenching/reemployment of existing' staff, and making provisions for financial support to the emerging entities. The latter would be required to create an environment that is conducive for investors, and so even if the states successfully sell off the DISCOMs, the private companies that buy these DISCOMs would still look for support during the period of transition. The following specific issues need to be addressed in India in order to lend credibility to the privatization programme:

- Willingness of the State governments for implementing and supporting the anti-theft legislations
- Assistance in enforcement of tariff collection from agriculture and domestic consumers
- A special policy for the poor who may not afford to pay for power in a no-subsidy environment
- Defining the role of the Regulator from. the perspective of sustainable long term development of power sector
- Bringing about an attitudinal change amongst the employees for improving the Sector performance through improved work culture
- Enforcing universal metering and ensuring that legislation prevents meter tampering with heavy penalties and the provisions of the legislation are actually enforced and implemented
- Ensuring the existence of effective price regulation for DISCOMs and other network companies, with the following at the core:
  - Revenue Adequacy (Does the tariff allow cost recovery?);
  - Appropriate Tariff Structure (Are costs allocated efficiently?); and
  - Transparency (Is the regulator required to use binding mechanistic rules and objective data to set tariffs?).

The current set-up in India is flawed with respect to all the three criteria spelled above.

Privatization of distribution would result in significant benefits only if it is properly structured and the process is well managed and regulated, with support from the government and public alike. It is important that all the stakeholders be taken into confidence while the privatization is being opted. This is necessary in the Indian context, as the supply of power is generally perceived as the responsibility of the government, and change in the government's role from that of being a service provider to that of a facilitator will not be smooth, or without the usual hurdles of acceptability in the Indian public mindset.

CONCLUSION

With the unfoldment of reforms initiatives, the Indian electricity sector is on the threshold of witnessing a gradual but certain transition towards competitive market. The distribution sector poses numerous challenges and a number of tasks outlined above need to be addressed. This chapter has endeavored to discuss the distribution reforms as being envisaged in India where they form the core issue in the post Electricity Act 2003 era. It has been emphasized that reforms have so far not yielded desired results because of the weak distribution link in the form of SEBs. Indeed to increase the pace of reforms further, it is required to urgently resolve the issues relevant to various stakeholders like restructuring of distribution zones, Tariff issues, metering issues and issues related to transfer of existing liabilities.

Some of the key recommendations that can lead to strengthening of the distribution sector are:

- The SEBs have to become accountable and viable. This can be achieved by unbundling their activities and gradually introducing competition.
- Alternative institutional structures are to be 'explored to meet the conflicting objective of coverage and efficiency, depending on the state's situation.
- During the process of unbundling, there is a need to consider issues like optimal sizing for distribution companies
- T &D losses need to be brought down. This can be done by increasing the efficiency of DISCOM and by strengthening proper metering and billing practices.
- The Regulatory environment must become strong to prevent misuse of monopoly and to solve legal/commercial/technical wrangles quickly.

A situation where tariffs are no more decided by the government and are not subject to political pressures (with regulatory commissions guarding the interest of all stakeholders), will ensure that the tariffs are set based on operational and financial parameters, and this will broaden the scope for introduction of the concept of efficiency in the sector. However, this would be possible only if sector performances are measured and benchmarked. Benchmarking studies can help identify the scope for efficiency improvements and explain differences -in electricity prices and service indicators, which vary from case to case: The variations arise because each electricity distribution network owner faces a particular set of circumstances (environmental factors), including market size, population density, system configuration and climatic factors. Associated' with these differences are advantages and disadvantages that impact on the comparative performance of distribution networks. Benchmarking studies account for all of the above, besides providing an indication of the levels of efficient operating, maintenance and capital expenditure. Benchmarking studies are essential to draw lessons that can greatly help us in avoiding structural and contractual inefficiencies in the emerging power sector. Around the world, benchmarking is receiving new attention, especially where it is being used as a regulatory tool to set the X-factor price cap regimes. Thus, benchmarking promises to form the core of the newly emerging regulatory regimes in the power sector for developing countries like India where the utilities belong to the public sector/government domain, the prime objective of power distribution enterprises (mostly the State Electricity Boards (SEBs)) is the address al of social concerns: of making power available to everyone; and the issues of making these utilities competitive remains largely unaddressed. Growing - customer dissatisfaction, mounting financial 'losses, growing awareness about consumer rights and overall economy-wide changes have now forced the government to take action and to introduce sweeping reforms in an otherwise monopolistic service structure. With the enactment of the Electricity Act- 2003, India has striven to hasten the restructuring of its power distribution sector. The improvements will envisage introduction of efficiency in the utilities, on a sustained basis to ensure efficient and economic power supply to the consumers. Herein comes the role of utility benchmarking.

The introduction of these reforms implies reforming utility operations and ways of management - financial, personnel and. technical, or to pave way for private investment and operation now actively being promoted by the World Bank and other multilateral and bilateral institutions, or to evolve public private partnerships. All of these would require prior appraisal of distribution enterprises and a continuous review of newly evolved public private mechanisms. To determine the feasibility of the choice for privatization a government needs to undertake a range of analysis including an analysis of the state of utility, an analysis of existing regulatory framework, an analysis of which stakeholders support privatization and which oppose it, and an analysis of the financial viability of alternative options. However, the first and the foremost key factor would be an analysis of the state of utility or the performance appraisal of existing institutions in terms of their current levels and standard of service, the condition and serviceability of assets, the human resources, and the financial performance. In short, this would mean analyzing existing institutions in terms of their performances, efficiencies and effectiveness and all of this would require evaluation in terms of certain key performance indicators to find out what these institutions are doing relative to other institutions or how an individual institution is performing on the time-scale.

While performance need to be monitored and evaluated to find the effect of greater investments on the sector, any improvements in internal efficiencies will also need to be quantified and measured. Internal efficiency improvements can free up resources, which can bring down the overall resource requirement for utilities. All of this would however, require formal sector benchmarking.

Furthermore, with the establishment of Regulatory Commissions and compulsory unbundling of all the state Electricity boards there is an urgent need for rigorous and in depth study of performance of distribution utilities in India. Efficiency measurement would be of particular interest to the regulators in the open market regimes. Efficiency measurement will also form the core for introduction of the incentive based regulatory regimes and in promoting yardstick competition amongst a number of utilities. As the power utilities get progressively freed from the government control, the regulators would invariably require sophisticated benchmarking tools and methodologies to regulate the monopolies and to introduce incentive regulation while determining tariffs. Thus benchmarking the distribution enterprises would be a primary step in the direction of ensuring sustenance in the power sector. The subsequent chapters therefore present frarmework for benchmarking the Indian Power utilities.

APPENDIX

Table A. 3 percentage contribution of the Government and the Private Sector in Power Sector (2006)

	Central Sector	State Sector	Private Sector
Generation	32.5	55.5	12
Transmission	15	84.6	0.4
Distribution	Nil	88	12

Source: MOP, 2007 (Ministry of Power, Government of India).
GOI- Government of India.

REFERENCES

[1]   Allerto, Gabriele, 2004, "Policy alternatives in reforming energy utilities in developing countries", *ENERGY POLICY*, 32, 1319- 1337.

[2]   Agrawal et. al., 2003, "The Delhi Electricity DISCOM Privatization: Some Observations and Recommendations for Future Privatization in India and Elsewhere". *WORLD BANK ENERGY and MINING SECTOR BOARD Discussion*, paper number 8. The World Bank, Washinton, DC.

[3]   Thakur Tripta, Deshmukh S.G., Kaushik S.C. , Tripathy S.C. (2004), "Optimal zoning for Distribution Sector under Deregulated Environment. A case study for the State of Madhya Pradesh, India, *Proc. 2nd IEEE Conference on Electric Utility Deregulation, Restructuring and Power Technology*, IEEE Hong Kong.

In: Research and Applications for Energy …
Editor: Riad Benelmir

ISBN: 978-1-62948-892-9
© 2014 Nova Science Publishers, Inc.

Chapter 2

BIOMASS AND FORESTRY: AN ANALYTICAL EVALUATION OF FUEL WOOD ENERGY

Freederick N. Onyango and Reccab Ochieng Manyala*
Centre for Research on New and Renewable Energies (CRNRE), Maseno University, Kenya

ABSTRACT

An analytical evaluation of energy from some fuelwood with potential for charcoal production is presented. Specifically, the major parameters: ash, fixed carbon, volatile matter and moisture content, which determine the magnitude of specific heat of charcoal derived from the fuelwood, are evaluated. The paper also presents analysis of how each parameter contributes to the specific heat of charcoal from a given fuelwood. A scientific method which can be used by decision-makers/ authorities, organizations or individuals in proper land-use for the enhancement of the environment by way of afforestation/agroforestry, while at the same time satisfying the energy needs of the rural and urban population, especially in the developing countries is thus presented.

Keywords: Fuelwood, energy, environment, afforestation, agroforestry, charcoal

1. INTRODUCTION

Wood and other forms of plant material have constantly been put under economic exploitation by mankind since time immemorial resulting in wanton degradation of the environment in many countries with devastating consequences. Certain types of trees have been endangered or brought to extinction through usage such as construction of homes, fencing of settlement areas to provide necessary protection of man and his domesticated animals in addition to adequate protection of crops against wild animals. More importantly,

---

* E-mail address: directorcrnre@maseno.ac.ke (Corresponding author)

wood has been used indiscriminately to provide fuel required for cooking and for house heating, especially in the rural areas.

Wood is composed of chemical compounds which, when burnt, decompose to simpler compounds and eventually water, carbon dioxide and gases. During the burning process, the intrinsic energy is released in the form of heat. This is the heat energy required for, *inter alia*, cooking process. Notwithstanding, other wood usages which require specific wood species for specific tasks on a non-routine basis, cooking consumes virtually all types of wood trees; and is a daily activity which contributes heavily to the degradation of the environment, particularly in developing countries.

Farming is yet another indirect way of destroying forests in many countries. With the global population explosion, particularly in the developing countries, the acreage of land prepared for food-crops increases every year. Consequently, large forests are destroyed to allow tilling of the land for this purpose.

2. A SURVEY OF FUELWOOD USAGE

The conventional source of heat energy such as kerosene, liquefied petroleum gas (LPG) or electricity is usually not easily available to the rural-poor in most developing countries where more than 90% of the population lives, mostly as peasants. In cases where the conventional sources of energy reach certain commercial centers, the cost is usually prohibitive to the peasants. Wood therefore, remains the only source of energy for all requirements in these areas. But even in the urban areas in most of the developing countries charcoal, the derivative of fuelwood, is still widely used in order to reduce the domestic bill for LPG, kerosene or electricity. Tables 1 and 2 show population in some developing countries by major cooking fuels and population versus sustainable forest yield respectively.

Table 1. Population x 10^6 by Major Countries [1]

Countrie	Locality	Commercial	Traditional	Total	Ratio
Africa South of Sahara	Urban	25	25	50	1:1
	Rural	10	280	290	1:28
India	Urban	40	90	130	4:9
	Rural	20	460	480	1:23
Middle East	Urban	80	10	90	8:1
	Rural	25	85	110	5:17
Latin America	Urban	170	25	195	34:5
	Rural	60	70	130	6:7

From Table 1, every 28 out of 29 people who live in the rural areas in Africa south of Sahara use traditional source of energy for cooking and other heating purposes followed by India where 23 out of every 24 people use the same source of heat energy.

A study of the Eastern and Central African region (Table 2) reveals, for example that in a country like Kenya, nearly seven people would scramble for a single tree for their entire wood requirement. This threat of the hazardous overuse of trees prompted the government of Kenya some time back to enact Tree Protection Legislation which has seen the implementation of systematic tree planting programmes. Consequently, various Government Departments, especially the one in charge of Forestry and Non-Governmental Organizations (NGOs) such as the Kenya Wood-fuel Development Programme (KWDP) supported by the GTZ, the Kenya Wood Cycle Project (KWCP) supported by the Swedish Berjer Institute, Kenya Energy Non-Governmental Organization (KENGO), Green Belt movement and many others took the lead in tree planting programmes. Some of these organizations were the pioneers of afforestation programmes in Kenya concerned with protection of the environment, provision and retention of soil nutrients and in some cases, provision of foliage and fodder.

Table 2. The Ratio of Population versus Sustainable Forest Yield in Certain African Countries [2]

	COUNTRIES	RATIO
1	Uganda	1.4:1.0
2	Burundi	2.5:1.0
3	Kenya	6.7:1.0
4	Ethiopia	18.9:1.0
5	Rwanda	1.0:3.5
6	Tanzania	1.0:3.5
7	Somali	1.0:9.9
8	Zaire	1.0:13.0
9	Congo	1.0:40.0

Later on, there emerged other bodies such as Kenya Forestry Research Institute (KEFRI) and International Centre for Research in Agroforestry (ICRAF) with a wider scope of forest research and management.

Although research and development (R&D) by organizations like KENGO and some Appropriate Technology groups was geared to construction and dissemination of economic cook stoves (*jikos*) for the rural poor, the main aim of these organizations were to reduce cost element of their stoves without necessarily considering which particular trees would provide the optimum energy charcoal.

To the best of our knowledge, no group has engaged in any study to identify which trees do possess high specific heat whose growth can be enhanced to match undue degradation of the environment.

3. EXPERIMENTAL

It is with the foregoing in mind that we embarked seriously on wood energy content research with the aim of, *inter alia*, enhancing agroforestry and the environment. Consequently our research objectives have been:

- to determine the specific heat values of trees that are likely to produce charcoal with high energy content;
- to formulate criteria governing the specific heat content of fuelwood;
- to ultimately help in advising authorities/organizations and individuals on the enhancement of the environment through agroforestry, etc.

Quantitatively, we set out to determine:

(i) **Moisture Content (MC)** which comprises the amount of water which the charcoal absorbs from the atmosphere or that which is released during combustion as a result of the nature of the chemical compounds which makes the woody component of the tree. It is the non-productive part of the charcoal heat formation since it absorbs heat to allow for its vaporization and consequent evaporation;

(ii) **Volatile Matter (VM)** which is that part of the woody material made of low molecular weight hydrocarbons with low combustion temperatures and therefore decomposes at low temperatures.

(iii) **Fixed Carbon (FC)** which is the major part of wood which gives rise to charcoal and is composed of high molecular weight hydrocarbons with high decomposition temperatures.

(iv) **Ash** which is the silvery grey material that remains after complete combustion. It is made up of inorganic salts, mainly the oxides of potassium, sodium, calcium, magnesium and iron whose decomposition temperatures are high and above the cooking temperatures.

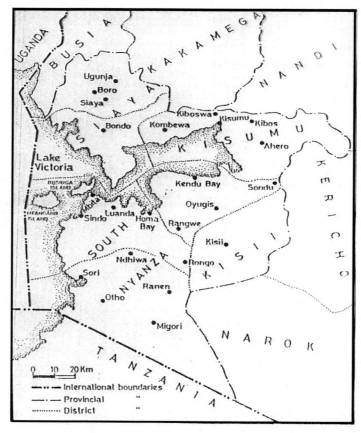

Figure 1. Area of study shown in dotted lines.

An area in the Lake Victoria region of Kenya with potential fuel wood crisis (Fig. 1) was identified for study. The area covers approximately 12,000 sq. km with an approximate population of 2,000,000 people giving rise to an average density of 170 persons per square kilometer.

The study area is total agrarian life as well as mixed farming. In some cases, there is a complex mixture of activities which include fishing. Consequently unplanned felling of trees to clear the land for farming, fish-smoking, tobacco drying, brick curing and routine cooking is quite intensive.

Staple foods in the region include maize, banana, sorghum, millet, cassava, potatoes and fish. Cash crops include cotton, pyrethrum, coffee, tea, tobacco and sugarcane all of which require clearance of large tracts of land for their production. Trees in this area are also cut to provide heat for fish-smoking, tobacco-curing, fencing material for the farms and provision for poles for rural building construction. Another activity which has recently risen in the area is brick curing. The local brick-curing process only uses wood fuel as a source of heat energy and has seen the destruction of many trees for the activity.

From the foregoing, the chosen area of study is prone to wanton destruction of trees, and hence was found suitable for the objectives of our study.

It is to be noted that the rural folk, especially those involved in charcoal trade were fully integrated into the study. After detailed interviews with stakeholders (charcoal dealers), a good deal of charcoal samples were collected from them and subjected to rigorous scientific investigation. The major apparatus used in the investigation were high temperature furnace and bomb calorimeter.

RESULTS AND DISCUSSION

Results of our study which were derived from various acacia tree species are shown in Figures 2, 3 and 4 respectively. Charcoal from these tree species were analyzed for the quality of ash, moisture, volatile matter and fixed carbon contents.

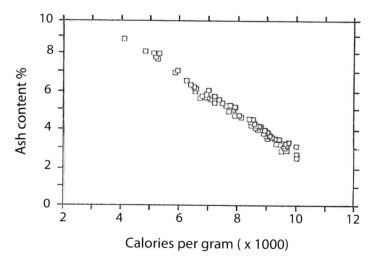

Figure 2. Ash content versus Energy.

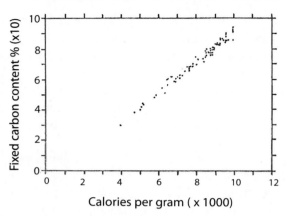

Figure 3. Fixed carbon content versus Energy.

It is evidently clear from both tables that there is a consistent correlation between the quantity of ash content and specific heat, that is, the ash content increases with corresponding decrease in the magnitude of specific heat. More importantly, the amount of fixed carbon has direct relationship with the magnitude of the specific heat (Figure 2), and conversely ash content bears indirect proportion to the energy values of all trees under investigation (Figure 1). It is thus discernible that either ash content or fixed carbon can be used as an indicative parameter for evaluation of calorific value of any given tree species.

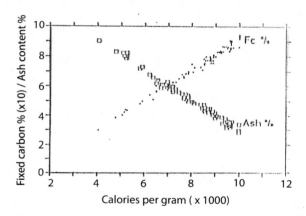

Figure 4. Ash and Fixed Carbon content versus energy.

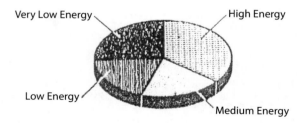

Figure 5. Pie chart of 68 indigenous fuelwood tress studied.

The merger of Figure 2 and 3 gives Figure 4 which clearly indicates the critical point for the determination of trees with high energy content using the outlined method with a given number of know tree species and families.

A pie chart (Figure 5) gives a four-segment representation of the specimens investigated, and can be used to classify trees into various grades of trees with respect to energy content. These results are certainly indicative of a powerful tool for the enhancement of agro forestry and/or afforestation.

CONCLUSION

From the results given in Figure 2 and 3, there is clear direct relationship between heat energy content (calorific values) and the magnitude of fixed carbon. There is also an inverse relationship between ash and energy content for all the trees investigated.

The merger of the two graphs (Figure 4) gives the critical point from where one can deduce trees that can be used in afforestation programme for charcoal purposes. The trees on the right hand side of the quadrant are able to give fixed carbon of not less than 60% capable of giving rise to charcoal with not less than 7,000 Cal/gmgrouped into three sub-groups: high, medium and low energy content trees. The rest of the trees falling on the left hand side of the quadrant in Figure 4 can be classified as having very low heat energy and are unsuitable for charcoal production. More importantly, the results of this investigation reveal a powerful tool which can be used in the process of agro forestry and afforestation.

REFERENCES

[1]   Hughart, D. 1979. Prospects for Traditional and Non-Conventional Energy Sources in developing Countries. World Bank Staff working Paper No. 346.

[2]   Cochran, W.G. 1977, *Sampling Techniques.* 3rd. Edition. John Wiley and Sons. New York.

[3]   Kenya Government 1993, *National Development Plan 1994-1966. Government Printers*-Nairobi Kenya.

[4]   Robinson, J H. 1967. *Organic Constituents of Higher Plants.* Burges Publishing Company, Mineapolis.

In: Research and Applications for Energy …
Editor: Riad Benelmir

ISBN: 978-1-62948-892-9
© 2014 Nova Science Publishers, Inc.

Chapter 3

MODELING ENERGY USAGE AND AUDITING BY MATRIX TECHNIQUE

Reccab M. Ochieng

Department of Physics and Materials Science,
Maseno University, Maseno, Kenya, East Africa

ABSTRACT

This paper presents a matrix method approach to modeling of energy usage and financial planning for households, industries, institutions and communities. A discussion is then presented on how the model can be modified and implemented for national or global use.

1. INTRODUCTION

For good financial planning and management of energy usage, it is necessary to know how much energy an individual or household uses hence the amount spent on different sources of energy on a daily, weekly, monthly or even on a yearly basis.

A model which can aid in this respect would, therefore help individuals, households, institutions or a country to do carry out good and proper planning and management of its energy sources and resources. In this paper we outline a model that has parameters which can be adjusted to accomplish the tasks. The model has been developed mathematically using matrix technique.

2. THEORY

In mathematics, a matrix (plural matrices) is a rectangular array of numbers, symbols, or expressions, arranged in rows and columns. The individual items in a matrix are called its elements or entries [1]. Matrices, though they may appear weird objects at first, are a very important tool in expressing and discussing problems which arise from real life cases. This may be for example economics. Indeed, consider two families A and B (though we may easily take more than two). Every month, the two families have expenses such as: utilities, health, entertainment, food, etc...

Let us restrict ourselves to: food, utilities, and health. How would one represent the data collected? Many ways are available but one of them has an advantage of combining the data so that it is easy to manipulate them. Indeed, we will write the data as follows [2]:

$$Month = \begin{pmatrix} Family & Food & Utilities & Health \\ A & a & b & c \\ B & d & e & f \end{pmatrix} \tag{1}$$

If there is no problem in confusing what the names are, then we may write

$$Month = \begin{pmatrix} a & b & c \\ d & e & f \end{pmatrix} \tag{2}$$

We can assume that the matrices for the first three months of the year for the three families are:

$$J = \begin{pmatrix} \alpha & \gamma & \beta \\ \delta & \varepsilon & \phi \end{pmatrix}, \; F = \begin{pmatrix} \varphi & \eta & \mu \\ \rho & \sigma & \varsigma \end{pmatrix}, \; M = \begin{pmatrix} \omega & \xi & \psi \\ \kappa & \theta & \chi \end{pmatrix} \tag{3}$$

With little algebra and matrix addition rule we can conclude that the two families spent a total of $(\gamma + \varepsilon) + (\eta + \sigma) + (\xi + \theta)$ on their utilities for the first quarter of the year. The utilities may include gas, electricity, water, and sewage charges, however as the data is presented, it is difficult to know what each family spent on different energy sources they used. We can still use the same method of data presentation in matrix form to determine this as stated in the abstract by modeling the energy usage. We shall restrict ourselves to one family which, say uses electricity, solar, kerosene, Liquified Petrolium Gas (LPG), firewood and many other forms (sources). These can be presented in a row as

$$S_{11}, S_{12}, S_{13}, \cdots\cdots, S_{1n} \tag{4}$$

where n determines the number of sources or forms of energy that the family uses.

The varying unit cost of the different sources such as the cost of crude oil per barrel and cost of electricity per kilowatt hour and many others may be given by

$$u_{11}, \; u_{21}, u_{31}, \cdots\cdots u_{n1} \tag{5}$$

From the two expressions, (4) and (5) it is possible to calculate the total amount spent on fuel on an hourly basis or daily basis or even a monthly basis depending on the need. The total unit cost is then given by

$$\text{Total Unit Cost (T1)} = \begin{pmatrix} S_{11}^1 & S_{12}^1 & S_{13}^1 & \cdots & S_{1n}^1 \end{pmatrix} \cdot \begin{pmatrix} h_1 u_{11} \\ h_2 u_{21} \\ h_3 u_{31} \\ \cdot \\ \cdot \\ \cdot \\ \cdot \\ \cdot \\ h_n u_{n1} \end{pmatrix} \tag{6}$$

This can be expressed in a compact form as

$$T1 = \sum_{j=1}^{n} \left(S_{1j}^1 \right) \left(h_j u_{j1} \right) \tag{7}$$

where $h_1, h_2, h_3, \cdots, h_n$ represent the time used for each source or form of energy. It is seen that $0 \le h_n \ge 100\%$ and may take fractional or integral values.

Equation (7) represents the total amount of energy used by household 1 for say, a day. For several households, say N, it is possible to write

$$T_{Total(H)} = TN = T1 + T2 + T3 +, \cdots, + TN = \sum_{\substack{j=1 \\ \alpha=1}}^{N} \left(S_{1j}^\alpha \right) \left(h_j^\alpha u_{j1} \right) \tag{8}$$

for the N households and the subscript (H) stands for household.

3. DISCUSSION

This simple but compact formula (8) is useful enough to help households in a community plan for their energy needs and demands. It can be extended to cover a province or a district for household energy usage. A similar expression for industries within a locality can be obtained to find out how much the industries consume in an hour, a day, a week or a month. It is necessary to factor in the seasonal variations for h_n^α so that one comes up with the correct times spent for particular energy sources. Since these are percentages, they must be converted into actual time values when carrying out the calculations. They will in fact, depend on the time scales used. For industrial calculations one would then modify (8) to read

$$T_{Total(I)} = \sum_{\substack{j=1 \\ \lambda=1}}^{F} \left(M_{1j}^\lambda \right) \left(h_j^\lambda u_{j1} \right) \tag{9}$$

where the M_{1j}^λ's are similar to S_{1j}^α's say, for industry 1 but for a total of F industries with varying seasonal cost factors h_n^α.

CONCLUSION

It is reasonable to conclude that by using the matrix method technique it is possible to do an energy audit for a household, institution or a community for sound and good financial planning. The method can easily reveal which source of energy is used most and how much it costs to use that source or form of energy for a certain prescribed period of time. It is also possible to use the method for projections to know how much will be spent over a period of time and thus, control the usage or spread the usage over other cheaper sources and forms.

REFERENCES

[1]   *http://en.wikipedia.org/wiki/Matrix_*(mathematics). Accessed on June 15, 2012.
[2]   *http://www-groups.dcs.st-and.ac.uk/~history/HistTopics/Matrices_and_determin-ants.html*. Accessed on June 18, 2012.

In: Research and Applications for Energy ...
Editor: Riad Benelmir

ISBN: 978-1-62948-892-9
© 2014 Nova Science Publishers, Inc.

Chapter 4

MODELING THE EFFECTS OF MERGERS IN THE RETAIL SECTOR - A PARSIMONIOUS MULTILATERAL APPROACH

Niels Blomgren-Hansen*

Department of Economics, Copenhagen Business School,
Porcelænshaven 16.1, 2000 Frederiksberg, Denmark

Abstract

According to EU competition law, mergers that significantly impedes effective competition, particularly by creating or strengthening a dominant position are prohibited. To identify these cases, authorities need a quantifiable model of the relationship between the variables that are affected by the merger and some measure of competition. Furthermore, the authorities must make their decision quickly, rendering deliberate data collection and econometric analyses infeasible in practice. The decision must be based on easily accessible data.

In this paper, a simple model of the interaction between the retail and wholesale markets is constructed, calibrated and simulated based on a concrete case (the acquisition and merger of 250 shops previously organized in a voluntary chain of shops comprising roughly half of the market for high-end cosmetics in Denmark).

Model simulations predicts that the merger would most likely significantly affect retail prices. The harmful effects are markedly intensified through the possible abuse of buyer power to raise barriers to the market and curb the competitiveness of minor rivals. However, the dominant position is vulnerable if increased profits induce the entrance to the sector of more independent competitors. The competition authorities were justified in conditioning its approval on the removal of contract-based barriers to entry.

Analytically, the main results of this work are the following: (1) In a linear model characterized by heterogeneous products and constant marginal costs, the optimal (Nash equilibrium) wholesale price is unaffected by the structure in the retail sector. (2) The effect of buyer power- induced quantity discounts depends crucially on the specific design of the rebate scheme: A relative discount on the list price that the independent shops are charged *increases* the average retail price, whereas a fixed

*E-mail address: nbh.eco@cbs.dk

reduction relative to the pre-merger price *reduces* the average retail price. (3) Buyer power-induced retail price maintenance (RPM) increases the average retail price. RPM increases the competitiveness and profits of the merged shops only if the producers keep the wholesale prices unchanged. If the producers adjust their wholesale prices, then RPM hurts both the merged and the independent shops and benefits only the producers. The harmful effects on consumer welfare and efficiency are intensified.

1. Introduction

According to the Danish Competition Act, the Competition Council (CC) should validate a merger that does not impede competition significantly, particularly by creating or strengthening a dominant position. The CC may condition its approval on the commitment of the merging firms to take specific actions to remove the potentially harmful effects of the merger. Most other countries' anti-trust acts have equivalent wording.

The formulation requires a conceptual clarification. What, exactly, is meant by 'the competition is impeded'? In practice, most analyses focus on the short or medium term effects on consumer prices. However, as important as this variable may be from a welfare theoretical viewpoint, it may be equally important to assess the effect on the efficiency and the dynamics of the sector in question.

Logically, the assessment of whether the competition is impeded 'significantly' requires a quantified evaluation of the likely effects of the merger. To produce this evaluation, we must build, calibrate and simulate a quantifiable model of the sector involved. The model must be consistent with the pre-merger market facts and data and sufficiently specific to create a quantitative evaluation of the effects of the merger not only the sector immediately affected, but also adjacent up- or down-stream sectors. Equally important is that the model must be sufficiently simple to be useful in practice, given the narrow time limits for the authorities' decision that are stipulated in the Competition Act. Finally, it must be possible to calibrate the model using easily accessible data, i.e. primarily the information included in the material submitted by the merging firms, public statistics and 'guesstimates' from experienced competition economists.

In setting up and calibrating the model several highly simplifying assumptions are unavoidable. This point is not a relevant criticism – it is a condition. The central question is whether the simplifications result in (strongly) misleading predictions with regard to the effects of the merger. This troublesome question should be an inspiration for improving the models rather than an excuse for rejecting consistent models in favor of unstructured market descriptions, general non-quantified theoretic reasoning and impulse.

The model simulation approach to merger effect analyses is not new. Werden and Froeb [15] provide an excellent and thorough survey of the literature on the unilateral competitive effects of horizontal mergers based on the classical structure- conduct-performance paradigm. See also Hovenkamp [6].

The contributions of this chapter are (a) presenting an analysis of a merger in the retail sector based only on accounting data ('a parsimonious approach') and (b) extending the analysis beyond the short-run case by allowing the number of competitors to adjust to the increase in profits, and (c) considering the effects of the merged company's possible/likely abuse of buyer-power in relation to its suppliers and (indirectly) its smaller competitors.

The analyzed abuses are (i) buyer power-induced volume discounts and (ii) buyer power-induced retail price maintenance (RPM) in the form of 'guiding' (effectively) binding the minimum retail prices).

2.   The Case

In 2007 a capital fund (CVC) bought almost all of the 294 shops cooperating within a voluntary chain called Matas[1]. The shops had previously been managed by 180 individual owners, most of whom only had a single shop. The Matas shops are dominant in the market for high-end cosmetics. Their market share is approximately 50 percent.

Legally, the Matas shops were independent units; thus, CVC's acquisition of the shops was considered a merger. However, the competition was already mellowed by the fact that, collectively, the shop owners held a strong brand, benefitted from joint marketing activities, and bought most of their supplies through a jointly owned wholesale company. Nevertheless, the Competition Council (CC) found that the merger might be harmful to competition[2]. The (limited) competition between the Matas shops is eliminated, when the prices are set centrally; when the suppliers are denied access to the shops; when the merger empowers Matas to make suppliers and owners of shopping malls accept conditions that discriminate against independent competitors and/or raise barriers to entry in the market.

The conclusion that the merger would most likely have a significant effect is supported by this analysis. If the previous chain of independent Matas shops were, effectively, a cartel, acting as a single profit maximizing company, we would expect the Matas shops to have charged higher prices than the independent shops, and the individual Matas shop owners to have had a strong incentive to underbid the chain. The Matas chain would not have been a stable cartel. Most likely, the Matas chain was solely a chain of shops benefiting from a common brand and a joint-purchasing company, as it claimed.

As is the case in most mergers the competition authorities consider the information about the market is limited. From the material supplied by the merging shops we know that total sales of high-end cosmetics in the 250 shops accounted for approximately 1 billion Danish krones (Dkr) and that the gross profit / price ratio is close to one. In addition, we know that there are approximately ten (mostly foreign) larger wholesale suppliers of high-end cosmetics. Most of these suppliers are considered 'must carry' suppliers. Accounting statistics indicate that the margin / price ratio at the production or wholesale stage is in the order of one.

3.   The Model

The first step is to consider: (a) the structure of the retail and wholesale markets; (b) the competition in the markets; (c) the functional form of demand and cost functions.

This chapter is based on the following assumptions:

---

[1] Konkurrencerådet (CC) 2007.

[2] The Competition Council found evidence of competition among the Matas shops, for example, by selling at campaign prices after a mutual sales campaign had come to an end. The council also found that the prices of selected products were lower in cities with more than one Matas shops.

- all shops are of equal size and evenly distributed geographically

- the brands are considered differentiated products and every shop sells every brands (i.e., all of the brands are considered 'must carry' products)

- the consumers consider the shop services to be differentiated, partly due to the differences in the distance from home

- consequently, both retailers and producers engage in differentiated Bertrand competition

- the marginal costs are constant (and all shops and producers have some excess capacity)

- the market demand function for high-end cosmetics is linear, and

- in the short run, the number of shops is unaffected by the merger; however, in the absence of barriers to the market the number of independent shops is assumed to increase as a reaction to the increase in profits resulting from the merger.

In particular, the assumed functional form (curvature) of the market demand function is likely to be crucial to the predicted price effect of the merger. Werden and Froeb [15] demonstrate that the predicted price increase in a simple two-firm merger case might be as much as four times higher if the demand function is assumed to be isoelastic rather than linear [3]. The choice of the linear demand function is based on the following considerations: (a) simplicity; (b) the isoelastic demand function's unreasonable implication that the creation of a monopoly renders the price indeterminate (increases to infinity) if the elasticity of demand is less than one, which is likely to be the case in the market for high-end cosmetics; and (c) the fact that the competition authorities have the burden of proof if they challenge the merger. Consequently, the produced evidence should be robust and not easily rejected by the court as being based on biased speculations.

Finally, we need to choose a metric to be able to measure the quantity of high-end cosmetics sold one-dimensionally. We will arbitrarily choose to measure the quantities in units that sell at the same price of 100 Dkr. This (arbitrary) metric is in accordance with a specific product, a bottle of perfume, described in the analysis produced by the CC. The implication of one-dimensionality in the measurement of sales is *not* the implicit assumption that one bottle of perfume costing 100 Dkr is a perfect substitute to two bottles costing 50 Dkr each or to one half of a bottle costing 200 Dkr. The brands are imperfect substitutes. The one-dimensionality only implies that the shops are indifferent whether they sell one bottle of expensive perfume or four bottles of cheap perfume and that the margin/price ratios are the same. This simplifying assumption is not crucial for the approximate validity of the predicted effects of the merger.

Based on the limited information available and the above-mentioned (hopefully reasonable) assumptions, we can derive the following pre-merger market 'data': (1) Number of units sold: $Q = 20.000.000$; (2) Retail price: $P = 100$; (3) Whole sale price: $Z = 50$;

---

[3]In their example, the logit demand curve is almost similar to the linear demand curve, and the AIDS (almost ideal demand system) demand function is almost similar to the isoelastic demand curve.

(4) Marginal production cost: $C = 50$; (5) Number of shops: $n = 500$; and (6) Number of producers (brands): $m = 10$.

3.1. The Pre-Merger Retail Market

The first step is to model the retail market before the merger, i.e. a market consisting of n identical, competing, and independent shops.

As mentioned above, we will assume that the market demand function is linear:

$$Q = A - b \cdot P \tag{1}$$

Each of the n retailers sells all m brands. This assumption implies $n \cdot m$ demand functions. However, due to the symmetry and one-dimensionality assumptions the number of demand functions reduces to n, one for each shop.

The demand function of the ith shop is as follows:

$$
\begin{aligned}
Q_i &= \frac{A}{n} - \frac{b}{n} \cdot P_i - c \cdot (P_i - P_1) - c \cdot (P_i - P_2) - - - c \cdot (P_i - P_n) \\
&= \frac{A}{n} - \left(\frac{b}{n} + (n-1) \cdot c \right) \cdot P_i + (n-1) \cdot c \cdot P_{-i}
\end{aligned} \tag{2}
$$

where P_{-i} is the price charged by its competitors, c is a measure of the competition among the individual shops, and $(n-1) \cdot c$ is a measure of the competition that the individual shop faces from its $(n-1)$ competitors.

The ith shop sets its price to maximize its gross profit:

$$\Pi_i = Q_i \cdot (P_i - Z_i) \tag{3}$$

where Z_i is the wholesale price paid by the ith shop.

The FOC is:

$$\frac{\partial \Pi_i}{\partial P_i} = Q_i - \left(\frac{b}{n} + (n-1) \cdot c \right) \cdot (P_i - Z_i) = 0 \tag{4}$$

Because all n shops are assumed to be identical, they are charged the same wholesale price, $Z_i = Z$, and they all peg the same retail price, $P_i = P_{-i} = P$:

$$P = \frac{1}{2 \cdot b + n \cdot (n-1) \cdot c} \cdot A + \frac{b + n \cdot (n-1) \cdot c}{2 \cdot b + n \cdot (n-1) \cdot c} \cdot Z \tag{5}$$

By substituting 5 for P in 2, we may derive the quantity sold as a function of the wholesale price Z, the number of shops n, and the intensity of competition among shops c:

$$
\begin{aligned}
Q &= \omega \cdot (A - b \cdot Z) \tag{6} \\
\omega &\equiv \frac{b + n \cdot (n-1) \cdot c}{2 \cdot b + n \cdot (n-1) \cdot c} \simeq \frac{b + n^2 \cdot c}{2 \cdot b + n^2 \cdot c} \tag{7}
\end{aligned}
$$

The parameter ω measures the ratio between the quantity actually sold given the imperfect competition in the retail market before the merger and the quantity sold in the hypothetical case of perfect competition, i.e. if $(n-1) \cdot c \to \infty$ and, consequently, $P = Z$.

3.2.   The Pre-merger Wholesale Market

Similar to the retail market, the producer (or wholesale) market is assumed to be characterized by monopolistic competition. The m producers are of equal size and face identical marginal costs, C. As in the retail market, the symmetry and one-dimensionality assumptions reduce the effective number of demand functions from $n \cdot m$ to the number of producers, m.

The representative jth supplier's demand function is as follows:

$$
\begin{aligned}
Q_{Pj} &= \frac{\omega}{m} \cdot (A - b \cdot Z_j) - d\omega(m-1) \cdot (Z_j - Z_{-j}) \\
&= \frac{\omega}{m} \cdot [A - (b + dm(m-1)) \cdot Z_j + dm(m-1) \cdot Z_{-j}]
\end{aligned} \tag{8}
$$

The parameter d is a measure of the competition among the individual producers, and $d \cdot (m-1)$ is a measure of the competition that the individual producer encounters from his $(m-1)$ competitors.

Producer no. j sets his wholesale price Z_j to maximize his gross profit:

$$
\Pi_{Pj} = Q_{Pj} \cdot (Z_j - C)
$$

under the assumption that his $(m-1)$ competitors do not change their prices. The FOC is:

$$
\frac{\partial \Pi_{Pj}}{\partial Z_j} = Q_{Pj} - \frac{\omega}{m} \cdot (b + dm(m-1)) \cdot (Z_j - C) = 0 \tag{9}
$$

From the assumption that all of the producers face identical demand and costs functions, the common wholesale price Z reduces to:

$$
Z = \frac{1}{2b + dm(m-1)} \cdot A + \frac{b + dm(m-1)}{2b + dm(m-1)} \cdot C \tag{10}
$$

It is worth noting that the common wholesale price is unaffected by the variables that define the competition in the retail market (n and c), when the marginal costs are constant. The Nash equilibrium wholesale price will be the same if the retail market is characterized by either a monopoly ($n = 1$) or a large number of competitors ($n \to \infty$), and if the products are either perfect substitutes ($c \to \infty$) or imperfect substitutes ($c < \infty$).

However, the derivation of this conclusion is based on the assumption that all shops are identical. It is not clear that this assumption holds true if several of the shops merge because the conditions of the merged shops and the independent shops are no longer identical. This question will be addressed in section 4.2.

Furthermore, the conclusion that the level and structure of the wholesale prices are unaffected by a merger in the retail sector is clearly inaccurate, if wholesale prices are determined via bargaining between the producers and retailers rather than unilaterally by the producers, cf. Mazzaotto [10]. This situation is addressed in section 5.

3.3. Model Calibration

The model contains four parameters to be determined:, A, b, c, and d. However, we have only three independent relationships: The two first-order conditions determining retail and wholesale prices, (5) and (10) and one of the three demand functions: for the whole market (1), the individual retailer (2), and the individual producer (8). Consequently, these three relationships must be supplemented with a fourth relationship.

In principle, one might make an econometric estimate of any of the three demand functions. However, the necessary data are not available. In addition, even in cases in which we do have data and attempt to estimate the price elasticity, the estimate is almost always so uncertain that it does not effectively provide much of a restriction on reasonable guesstimates.

From the margin/price ratio, $(P-Z)/P = 1/\varepsilon_i = 0.5$, we know the price (point) elasticity of the representative retailer's demand curve $\varepsilon_i = 2$. The elasticity of the total market ε is clearly significantly less and most likely less than one.

Our best guesstimate is that the (point) market elasticity of demand ε is close to 0.5. We base this guesstimate primarily on two indications: (a) the CC found that the sale of high-end cosmetics had grown significantly more rapidly in recent years than the sale of low-end cosmetics (and there is no reason to believe that this faster growth rate is due to a decrease in the relative price of high-end cosmetics) and (b) the Dorfman-Steiner condition[4] and the fact that the market for high-end cosmetics is characterized by high marketing and development costs. However, our guess is no doubt uncertain. As a check of the robustness of our central predictions, we derive the likely effects assuming, alternatively, that $\varepsilon = 1$ and $\varepsilon = 0.25$.

Substituting ε for $b \cdot P/Q$ and utilizing the descriptive market data ($Q = 20.000.000$; $P = 100; Z = 50; C = 25; n = 500$ and $m = 10$) we obtain the following parameter value:

	$\varepsilon = 0.25$	$\varepsilon = 0.5$	$\varepsilon = 1$
$A = (1+\varepsilon) \cdot Q$	25×10^6	30×10^6	40×10^6
$b = \varepsilon \cdot \frac{Q}{P}$	50000	100000	200000
$c = \frac{Q}{P-Z} \cdot \frac{1-\varepsilon \cdot \left(1-\frac{Z}{P}\right)}{n \cdot (n-1)}$	1.4028	1.2024	0.8016
$d = \frac{Q}{Z-C} \cdot \frac{(1+\varepsilon)-\varepsilon \cdot \left(2 \cdot \frac{Z}{P}-\frac{C}{P}\right)}{m \cdot (m-1)}$	9444	10000	11111

4. The Post-Merger Markets

The first step is to model the post-merger retail market, i.e. determine the retail prices charged by the merged shops and the independent shops (P_K and P_U, respectively) and the corresponding quantities sold (Q_K and Q_U) as functions of the wholesale prices that the producers charged the merged and the independent shops (Z_K and Z_U, respectively). The

---

[4]Profit maximization requires that the share of marketing costs as a fraction of the price is equal to the ratio of the elasticity of the marketing costs and that of the price. Tesler [13] finds that the marketing costs as a percent of total revenue are are 3-4 times greater in the cosmetics industry than in the average of 44 consumer product industries. See also Rosenthal et al. [11] and Fornell and Robinson [4] for analyses of the relationship between non-informative advertising and price competition.

second step is to determine the wholesale prices as functions of the retailers' reactions to the merger. Throughout this section we assume Nash behavior.

4.1.   The Retail Market

We assume that a share α of the n shops are bought by the capital fund and merged and that the remaining $(1-\alpha) \cdot n$ shops continue as independent shops. In this section the number of outlets is assumed to be unaffected.

The demand function of the merged shops is determined by adding the demand functions of the $\alpha \cdot n$ participating shops as follows:

$$Q_K = \alpha n \left(\frac{A}{n} - \left(\frac{b}{n} + (1-\alpha)nc \right) P_K + (1-\alpha)ncP_U \right) \tag{11}$$

The capital fund pegs P_K to maximize its gross profit:

$$\Pi_K = Q_K \cdot (P_K - Z_K) \tag{12}$$

given the wholesale price Z_K and the price charged by the independent shops P_U. The FOC is defined by the following:

$$2 \left(\frac{b}{n} + (1-\alpha)nc \right) P_K - (1-\alpha)ncP_U = \frac{A}{n} + \left(\frac{b}{n} + (1-\alpha)nc \right) Z_K \tag{13}$$

The demand function of the representative ith independent shop is only affected by the merger because $\alpha \cdot n$ competitors charge the same price P_K, while the remaining $(1-\alpha) \cdot n - 1 \simeq (1-\alpha)$ independent competitors charge the price P_{U-i}:

$$Q_{Ui} = \frac{A}{n} - \left(\frac{b}{n} + nc \right) P_{Ui} + \alpha ncP_K + (1-\alpha)ncP_{U-i} \tag{14}$$

Maximization of the gross profit:

$$\Pi_{Ui} = Q_{Ui}(P_{Ui} - Z_{Ui}) \tag{15}$$

provides the FOC:

$$2 \left(\frac{b}{n} + nc \right) P_{Ui} = \frac{A}{n} + \alpha ncP_K + (1-\alpha)ncP_{U-i} + \left(\frac{b}{n} + nc \right) Z_{Ui} \tag{16}$$

In symmetric equilibrium ($Z_{Ui} = Z_{U-i} = Z$ and $P_{Ui} = P_{U-i} = P_U$) (14) and (16) reduce to:

$$Q_U = (1-\alpha)n \left(\frac{A}{n} - \left(\frac{b}{n} + \alpha nc \right) P_{Ui} + \alpha ncP_K \right) \tag{17}$$

$$\left(2\frac{b}{n} + (1+\alpha)nc \right) P_U - \alpha ncP_K = \frac{A}{n} + \left(\frac{b}{n} + nc \right) Z_U \tag{18}$$

4.2. The Wholesale Market

The analysis of the effect of the merger in the retail market on the price setting in the wholesale market turns out to be surprisingly laborious. The derivation is given in the appendix.

The conclusion of the analysis is that the level and the structure of wholesale prices are unaffected by the merger in the retail sector (and by the pre-merger point elasticity of demand ε).

$$Z_K = Z_U = Z = \frac{1}{2b + d \cdot m \cdot (m-1)} \cdot A + \frac{b + d \cdot m \cdot (m-1)}{2b + d \cdot m \cdot (m-1)} \cdot C \tag{19}$$

This conclusion is not trivial (as it would be if the merger simply intended to divide the market into two separate markets catering to identical consumers). In our case, the merger reduces the competition. However, the two retail channels still compete.

The result depends crucially on the assumption that the wholesale prices are set unilaterally by the producers (Nash equilibrium). If the wholesale prices are determined via bargaining the resulting price vector will reflect the bargaining power of the parties as demonstrated in Mazzarotto [10]. In sections 6 and 7 below we analyze the likely effects of the merged shops' increased buyer power.

5. The Merger Effects as a Function of the Share of the Merged Shops

Inserting the parameter values determined in section 3.3, we can assess the consumer price effect of the merger as a function of the share of the merged shops α. The result is illustrated in figure 1. The graph is drawn on the assumption that the market point elasticity of demand is $\varepsilon = 0.5$. The upper line is the price charged by the merged shops, the lower line is the price charged by the independent shops, and the thick line is the average consumer price.

The graph indicates that a merger that involves less than 30 percent of the shops has a limited effect on the average consumer price. If the merger comprises 40 percent of the market, the price effect is appreciable (slightly more than 5 percent). This finding supports the competition authorities' rule-of-thumb that a merger comprising 40 percent of the market is likely to create a dominant position that impedes the competition. The function is strongly progressive. If the merger comprises 50 percent of the market (as in the case analyzed) the price increase is estimated to be 9 percent, which is approximately three times greater than the price increase if the merger is limited to 30 percent of the market. The authorities' suspicions of the legality of the proposed merger appear to be justified.

Table 1 provides estimates of the effects of the merger on prices, quantities sold and profits. The share of merged shops is $\alpha = 0.5$.

In the central case of ($\varepsilon = 0.5$) the model simulation indicates that he merged shops raise their price by 16 percent and the independent shops raise their price by 4 percent. The increase in the (weighted) average retail price is 9 percent and the resulting fall in the quantities sold through the two channels is 5 percent. However, the effects on the merged shops' and the independent shops' sales and profitability differ significantly. Reflecting a

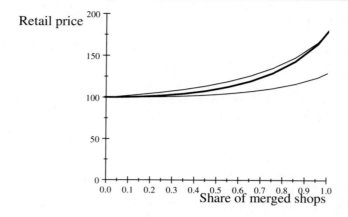

Figure 1. Effect on retail prices of the share of merged shops.

Table 1. The effects of the merger on retail prices, quantities sold and profits

		Pre-m	$\varepsilon = 0.25$	Post-m $\varepsilon = 0.5$	$\varepsilon = 1$
P_K	Dkr	100	121.7	**116.1**	108.5
P_U	Dkr	100	106.0	**103.7**	101.2
P	Dkr	100	112.6	**109.1**	104.6
Q_K	mill	10.0	8.081	**8.266**	8.782
Q_U	mill	10.0	11.225	**10.748**	10.248
Q	mill	20.0	19.306	**19.014**	19.030
Π_{Ki}	kDkr	2000	2318	**2184**	2055
Π_{U_i}	kDkr	2000	2516	**2307**	2098

relative increase of 12 percent in their relative price the merged shops realize a 17 percent fall in sales, whereas the independent shops sell 7 percent more at a 4 percent higher price. As a consequence of these diverging effects on prices and sales the independent shops' profit gain is significantly larger than that of the merged shops, 15 percent and 9 percent, respectively.

How robust are these results with respect to our uncertain guess that the pre-merger point elasticity of market demand is $\varepsilon = 0.5$?

The alternative simulations based on $\varepsilon = 0.25$ and $\varepsilon = 1$, respectively, provide some indication.

If the elasticity is in the low end of the likely range ($\varepsilon = 0.25$), the average price will increase by almost 13 percent (compared to 9 percent) and total sales will fall by approximately 3 percent (compared to 5 percent). The implication for the resulting profit gains is even more significant. The merged shops gain 16 percent (compared to 9 percent) and the independent shops 26 percent compared to 15 percent).

If alternatively the elasticity is in the high end ($\varepsilon = 1$), then the estimated price effect of the merger will be only half as high as in the central case (less than 5 percent compared to 9 percent), whereas the estimated effect on the quantities sold is approximately identical. However, the profit gains from the merger are much smaller: the merged shops gain less than 3 percent and the independent shops about 5 percent.

How critical is the accuracy of the assumed market elasticity of demand in assessing the validity of the merger? That depends on the focus of the CC. If the CC primarily focuses on consumer prices and consumer welfare, then the accuracy is a matter of concern. If, on the contrary, the CC focuses on efficiency (roughly proportional to the decline in quantities sold), then the accuracy appears to be of minor significance.

6.   Dynamic Effects of the Merger

So far we have assumed that the number of shops is unaffected by the merger. This assumption is common in most merger analyses but clearly unreasonable in the absence of strong barriers to entry.

We do not know how to measure the height of the barriers to entry. However, model simulations allow us to answer a number of related questions such as: How many entrants are required to erode the merged shop's excess profit? What are the the long-run effects of the merger, if there are no persistent barriers to entry? How robust are the answers to these questions on the assumed elasticity of market demand?

In doing so we will assume (a) that the market was in equilibrium before the merger in the sense that the gross profit earned by a representative shop, 2 mill Dkr, is exactly what is required to keep the actual number of outlets constant and (b) that the increase in profit earned by independent shop owners due to the merger induces the establishment of new independent shops until the profit has fallen to its equilibrium level.

To solve the model we need to reformulate the equations (11), (14), (13), (16), (12) and (3) as functions of number of merged shops n_K (unchanged, 250) and the number of independent shops n_U. The number of independent shops is determined such that the profit of the representative independent shop is back to its pre-merger level $\Pi_{Ui} = 2000$ kDkr.

The solution is given in table 2.

Qualitatively the results of the model simulation may not surprise: The number of independent shops increases, which drives down the retail prices and stimulates demand. However, the quantitative assessment of the effects are noteworthy. In the central scenario ($\varepsilon = 0.5$) the additional number of shops necessary to eliminate the independent shops' excessive profit is only 36 (14 percent of the number of independent shops or 7 percent of the total number of outlets before the merger). In the absence of high barriers to entry it does not appear unrealistic that the number of outlets may increase by 7 percent within a period of a few years. The increased number of shops will reduce the increase in the average retail price due to the merger to approximately 3 percent or a third of the estimated price hike if barriers to entry were insurmountable. The initial fall in quantities sold is reduced by 60 percent. However, that does not mean that the initial efficiency loss it reduced in proportion. The reason is that the number of units sold per shop falls from 38.000 if the number of shops had remained constant to 36.500 in new equilibrium.

These estimates are rather robust to the assumed market elasticity of demand. If the elasticity is low ($\varepsilon = 0.25$), then the initial price increase is larger, but so is the incentive to

Table 2. The effect of the merger if the number of independent shops adjusts until profit has fallen to its pre-merger level

		Pre-m	Post-m $\varepsilon = 0.25$	Post-m $\varepsilon = 0.5$	Post-m $\varepsilon = 1$
n_K		250	250	**250**	250
n_U		250	293.4	**285.7**	268.3
P_K	Dkr	100	110.9	**109.90**	107.1
P_U	Dkr	100	98.4	**99.06**	99.96
P	Dkr	100	103.2	**103.46**	103.2
Q_K	mill	10.0	7.665	**7.940**	8.578
Q_U	mill	10.0	12.128	**11.648**	10.742
Q	mill	20.0	19.793	**19.588**	19.320
Π_{Ki}	kDkr	2000	1867	**1902**	1959
Π_{Ui}	kDkr	2000	2000	**2000**	2000

open new shops. The necessary accessions of new shops is only slightly larger, 43 compared to 36. Conversely, if the elasticity is high ($\varepsilon = 1$), then the additional number is smaller, only 18.

The losers are the merged shops. Provided no permanent barriers to entry the simulations predict that the profit per shop eventually falls *below* the pre-merger level, regardless of the elasticity of demand[5]. The fall in profits reflects increased excess capacity in the merged shops as well as declining prices. In the central scenario, the number of units sold per shop is reduced by more than 20 percent.

This development is not consistent with the assumption that the pre-merger profit left no excess profit to the shop owners. The merged shops are forced to react to the declining sale and profit by reducing the number of shops. But it is a loosing strategy. The more shops the owner of the merged shops closes, the more new independent shops will open. This process will continue until the owner of the merged shops is left with a single shop. If the elasticity of accession to the market is infinite at the assumed minimum level of profit per shop (2 million Dkr), then it is simply not possible for any group of colluding or merged shops to earn an excess profit, regardless of size and the market elasticity of demand. The merged shops may be dominant in the sense that it has a large market share. Unless they can impose barriers to entry their market power is temporary.

Theoretically, this result is trivial. The contribution from model simulations is to demonstrate that the number of entrants necessary to erode the market power of the merged shops is rather small and, consequently, that the CC need not be too concerned about the merger as such, provided that it can prohibit the merged shops from establishing barriers to entry in the market.

---

[5]The number of entrants necessary to erode the merged shops' excess profit is only little more than half of the number of entrants necessary to erode the independent shops' excess profit. In the central scenario ($\varepsilon = 0.5$) 23 entrants will do the job (29 if ε is low, and 10 if ε is high).

7.   Stackelberg Behavior

So far we have assumed that the merged shops as well as the independent shops take competitors' and suppliers' prices as given (Nash behavior). This is not reasonable. Having a market share of 50 percent the merged shops know and take into account that the price they set will affect the prices set by the minor, independent competitors.

If the merged shops in setting their own price take into account that their independent competitors will react by raising their prices as well (Stackelberg behavior), then the resulting consumer prices will be higher. The interesting question is, by how much?

To answer these questions we insert P_U as determined in (18) into (11) and derive the value of P_K that maximizes the merged shops' profit Π_K and simulate the resulting model.

The conclusion is that strategic behavior matters. In the central scenario ($\varepsilon = 0.5$, unchanged number of shops) the average consumer price is estimated to increase by additional 2.5 percent and total sales to drop by additional 2 percent. The loss in consumer welfare and efficiency is significantly higher than if the merged shops 'play Nash'.

Table 3. The effect of merger in case of Nash and Stackelberg behavior

	P_K	P_U	P	Q_K	Q_U	Q	Π_{Ki}	Π_{Ui}
	Dkr	Dkr	Dkr	mill	mill	mill	kDkr	kDkr
Nash	116.1	103.7	109.1	8.266	10.748	19.014	2184	2307
Stack.	121.4	104.9	111.7	7.693	10.994	18.687	2196	2414

However, the most telling result of the simulation is that Stackelberg behavior has a very limited effect on the merged shops' profit whereas the independent shops gain markedly. The reason is that the merged shops' sales drop by additional 7 percent due to an additional 5 percent increase in the merged shops' *relative* price.

This result indicates that short-sighted strategic behavior might not be in the interest of the capital fund that owns the merged shops. Most likely the (small) profit gain is very temporary because the independents shops' increased profit markedly enhances the incentive for potential entrants to open new shops. To avoid complicating the analysis unnecessarily, we will assume in the following that the merged shops take the price set by the independent shops as given.

8.   Buyer Power and Volume Discount

In section 4.2 above we stated (and in appendix we have proved) that unilaterally determined wholesale prices are unaffected by the merger in the retail sector, if the marginal costs are constant[6].

---

[6]Concentration in the retail sector might have a strong effect on wholesale prices, if the concentration in the retail sector induces concentration upstream (Lustgarten [9]). In our case a reduction from ten producers to five would more than double the unilaterally determined wholesale price from 50 to 106. Of course, the CC should consider the risk of a negative effect of the merger on the competition in the upstream sector, but in the case of a merger in the retail market for high-end cosmetics, this outcome is unlikely. The producers of high-end

Nevertheless, volume discounts that are not cost-based prevail in many markets. Why[7][8]?

An obvious answer is that producers do not peg the price that they charge large customers unilaterally. The producers and the dominant retailer's purchasing manager negotiate, and the resulting price is often a (considerable) price discount relative to the list price that the minor purchasers with no buyer power must pay. The size of the discount depends not only on the size of the order, but also on the relations between the parties, their market knowledge, and their negotiating skills[9]. A large organization is clearly in a much stronger position than a small player[10].

Dobson et al. [2] call attention to the fact that mergers in the retail sector strengthen both the merged shops' market power and buyer power, resulting in opposing influences on consumer prices. Snyder [12] finds that the merger will result in *lower* prices for both the merged shops and the (minor) independent competitors. In contrast, the CC [8] argues that a discount may result in *higher* prices. However, the CC does not elaborate on the necessary conditions for this phenomenon to occur.

It is not evident how to model the bargaining[11]. Here, we will simply assume that the merged shops obtain better conditions than the minor independents shops. In stead we will focus on the question of the effect of the design of the rebate scheme.

8.1. A Relative Discount

Assume that the merged shops obtain a volume discount of 10 percent of the list price paid by the independent shops, i.e. $Z_{Kj} = 0.9 \cdot Z_{Uj}$ and $Z_{K-j} = 0.9 \cdot Z_{U-j}$.

In the central scenario ($\varepsilon = 0.5$ and unchanged number of shops) the functions (30) de-

---

cosmetics have built strong must-carry brands through developing costs and expensive advertising (Tesler [13], Fog [3] and Dobson et al [2]).

[7]Buchanan [1] explains a quantity discount as an imperfect alternative to two-part pricing. Ideally, the producer would like to charge all customers the same price (his marginal cost) and require a fee determined as all or some fraction of the retailers' profits. Two-part pricing would be efficient in the sense that the sum of the producer's surplus and the retailers' surplus would be maximized. However, it is difficult to interpret a normal discount scheme as anything equivalent to joint profit maximizing two-part pricing (Weng [14]). The small retailers pay more than the bigger retailers and fees, if any, go the opposite direction from the producer to the retailers, often as a payment for having the products exposed on the shelves or in flyers

[8]Fog [3] finds that price discrimination is much less prevalent than predicted by theory. He offers a number of explanations: (i) Price discrimination is considered unfair and harmful to the good name of the producer; (ii) Well-known esteemed buyers abstain from 'conspicuous exploitation' of their buyer power because they consider it more important to develop stable long term relations to the producer; and (iii) Retailers of 'must-carry'- brands have limited bargaining power.

[9]Fog [3] quotes a manager in saying that 'our discount depends on the size of the order and the imprudence of the buyer.'

[10]Mazzarotto [10]

[11]The literature offers a number of theoretical, often strongly simplified models in the search of an explanation of non-cost based discount schemes. Inderst and Wey [7] assume one seller, one large buyer and a number of small buyers. The producer faces a convex cost function. The contracts between the producer and the retailers are complex and efficient. They share the resulting maximum joint profit. The sharing depends on the buyer power of the retailers, which in turn, depends on their market share.

termining the jth producer's sale to each of the two retail channels reduce to

$$Q_{Kj} = 9.917 \times 10^5 + 24546 \cdot Z_{U-j} - 27273 \cdot Z_{Uj}$$
$$Q_{Uj} = 1.2893 \times 10^6 + 40910 \cdot Z_{U-j} - 45455 \cdot Z_{Uj}$$

The wholesale price vector is derived by maximizing the representative jth producer's profit:

$$\Pi_{Pj} = Q_{Uj} \cdot (Z_{Uj} - 25) + Q_{Kj} \cdot (0.9 \cdot Z_{Uj} - 25)$$

with respect to his list price Z_{Uj}. The resulting FOC is:

$$\frac{\partial \Pi_{Pj}}{\partial Z_{Uj}} = 4099200 + 65456 \cdot Z_{U-j} - 142730 \cdot Z_{Uj} = 0$$

from which we deduce the list price $Z_U = Z_{Uj} = Z_{U-j}$ and the corresponding discounted price Z_K that the merged shops are charged:

$$Z_U = 53.048; \quad Z_K = 0.9 \cdot Z_U = 47.743$$

The model simulation predicts that a 10 percent discount to the dominant buyer is partially offset by an increase of 6 percent in the list price that the smaller shops must pay. Consequently, the merged shops receive a discount of 4.5 percent rather than 10 percent relative to the pre-merger price (or the post-merger Nash equilibrium price). However, the competitive position of the merged shops improves, and their market share increases indicating that a buyer power-induced discount may be an effective strategy for curbing the competitiveness of the minor competitors. The average wholesale price *increases* by 1.3 percent from 50 to 50.67, and the average consumer price *increases* by additional 0.8 percent (see table 4).

8.2. A Fixed Discount

Alternatively, the merged shops may demand a fixed discount of 10 percent relative to the pre-merger (or Nash equilibrium) price, i.e. a reduction of Z_K from 50 til 45.

In this case, the functions determining the representative jth producers sale are the following:

$$Q_{Kj} = 9.917 \times 10^5 - 0.9 \cdot 24793 \cdot Z_{U-j} + 0.9 \cdot 57851 \cdot 45 + 24793 \cdot Z_{Uj} - 57851 \cdot 45$$
$$= 731370 - 22314 \cdot Z_{U-j} + 24793 \cdot Z_{Uj}$$
$$Q_{Uj} = 12.893 \times 10^5 + 0.9 \cdot 67769 \cdot Z_{U-j} - 0.9 \cdot 24793 \cdot 45 - 67769. \cdot Z_{Uj} + 24793 \cdot 45$$
$$= 1400900 + 60992 \cdot Z_{U-j} - 67769 \cdot Z_{Uj}$$

Maximization of the profit:

$$\Pi_{Pj} = Q_{Kj} \cdot (45 - 25) + Q_{Uj} \cdot (Z_{Uj} - 25)$$

with respect to Z_{Uj} provides the FOC:

$$\frac{\partial \Pi_{Pj}}{\partial Z_{Uj}} = 24793 \cdot (45 - 25) + 1400900 + 60992 \cdot Z_{U-j} - 67769 \cdot Z_{Uj} - 67769 \cdot (Z_{Uj} - 25) = 0$$

which in symmetric equilibrium reduces to:

$$Z_U = 48.171$$

The simulation predicts that a fixed discount reduces the wholesale price for both the dominant buyer, who exerts buyer power, *and* the minor players. The reason is that the discount to the merged shops makes the producers earn less from selling a unit to the merged shops than to the independent shops. Consequently, the producers want to sell more to the independent shops and lower Z_U to do so.

Table 4 summarizes the estimated effects of a buyer power-induced discount. The row marked N reproduces the results in case of Nash behavior. The row marked R represents the solution if the merged shops obtain a proportional (relative) volume discount of 10 percent of the list price and the row marked F represents the solution if the merged shops obtain a fixed discount of 10 percent of the pre-merger price.

Table 4. The effects of a relative discount (R) and a fixed discount (F)

	P_K Dkr	P_U Dkr	P Dkr	Q_K mill	Q_U mill	Q mill	Π_{Ki} kDkr	Π_{Ui} kDkr	Π_{Pj} kDkr
N	116.1	103.7	109.1	8.26	10.74	19.00	2186	2309	47381
R	115.5	105.5	110.0	8.47	10.48	18.95	2296	2198	48664
F	113.1	101.9	106.8	8.51	10.74	19.25	2318	2309	41911

In contrast to the case of a relative discount a fixed discount is beneficial for the consumers by reducing the average retail price by slightly more than 2 percent.

Consequently, if the parties agree on a discount scheme that is designed as a fixed rebate relative to the pre-merger price, Snyder is correct in conjecturing that the isolated effect of buyer power is beneficial to the consumers. However, Dobson's stronger allegation that the beneficial effect from buyer power might outbalance the harmful effect from market power is not substantiated in this exercise. A rough calculation indicates that, in our case, the discount should be of the order of 40 percent for this to occur.

A fixed discount and the resulting lower retail prices may appear an unlikely outcome. The design of the rebate scheme is determined either unilaterally by the producers or as the result of negotiations between the producers and the merged shops' purchasing manager. The model simulation indicates that the producers have a strong interest in offering a proportional (relative) discount that actually increases their profit rather than a fixed discount that is a severe financial burden. For the merged shops a relative discount a relative discount is also preferable because it is an effective strategy for reducing the incentive for entrants to open new shops.

Consequently, in our case the beneficial effect for the consumers of buyer power that Snyder, Dobson and Mazzarotto imagine is a mirage. On the contrary, the CC are correct in conjecturing that a buyer power-induced volume discount is harmfull to consumer welfare as well as to the competition.

9.   Retail Price Maintenance

The request for a significant volume discount is one way in which the merged shops may exploit their buyer power. Another and more sophisticated (ab)use of buyer power is to persuade the producers to raise their guiding retail prices and put pressure on the smaller, independent shops not to underbid the guiding retail prices, at least not significantly and/or systematically, thereby curbing the independent shops' ability to compete.[12].

Assume that the merged shops demand that the producers refuse to sell to the independent shops that charge a retail price below a guiding price of, say, $P_U^* = 110$ Dkr. This price is significantly above the price that the independent shops would charge in Nash equilibrium ($PU = 103.7$ Dkr) but also significantly below the price charged by the merged shops ($P_K = 116.1$ Dkr.). The Competition Act prohibits retail price maintenance (RPM), but not guiding retail prices. A guiding retail price at this level is unlikely to provoke reaction from the competition authorities. If they should worry about the possible harmful effects and conduct an analysis of the market, they would most likely conclude that the prices charged by the merged shops and the independent shops differ significantly and argue that this fact is a strong indication of effective competition and, consequently, that the guiding prices are not harmful to the consumers.

9.1.   Unchanged Wholesale Prices

The effect of binding minimum retail prices depends crucially on whether the producers keep wholesale prices constant or adjust wholesale prices to reflect the changed market conditions.

In our central scenario ($\varepsilon = 0.5$, unchanged number of shops) the binding retail price ($P_U^* = 110$) reduces the merged shops' and the independent shops demand functions, (11) and (17), respectively, to the following:

$$
\begin{aligned}
Q_K &= 1.5 \times 10^7 - 125000 \cdot P_K + 75000 \cdot P_U^* = 23250000 - 125000 \cdot P_K \\
Q_U &= 1.5 \times 10^7 + 75000 \cdot P_K - 125000 \cdot P_U^* = 1250000 + 75000 \cdot P_K
\end{aligned}
$$

If the wholesale price that the merged shops are charged remains constant, $Z_K = 50$, then the merged shops' profit maximizing retail price is:

$$
P_K = \frac{23250000}{2 \cdot 125000} + \frac{1}{2} \cdot Z_K = 118
$$

The model simulation indicates that RPM is beneficial to both the merged shops, which sell 3 percent more to at a slightly higher price, and the independent shops, which sell 6 percent less at a 6 percent higher price (see table 5 below). The explanation why it is beneficial to the independent shops to be 'forced' to raise their price is that the binding minimum price effectively makes the independent shops act as a cartel. The difference is that a cartel

---

[12]See Dobson et al. [2] and Gilligan [5]. The Danish Competition Council [8] mentions the possibility that the suppliers react to a merger in the retail sector and the resulting increase in consumer prices by raising their guiding prices on their own initiative.

organized by the independent shops themselves would have been unstable because each of the 250 independent shops would have a strong incentive to not to comply with an agreed cartel price, and the cartel would have no means to sanction the non-compliers. In the case of RPM, the 'cartel' members are policed by the producers.

The losers are the consumers and the producers. The average retail price increases by almost 5 percent more than in Nash equilibrium and total sales fall by additional 2 percent. The profit earned by the producers fall in proportion if, as assumed in this subsection, the producers keep wholesale prices unchanged.

9.2. Adjusted Wholesale Prices.

But why should they? The assumption that the producers should keep wholesale prices unchanged in case of RPM appears unreasonable. From the viewpoint of the individual producer, the independent shops' demand becomes less elastic because these shops will not raise their retail prices in response to an increase in the wholesale price (up to a level at which the optimum retail price exceeds the minimum price). Thus, theoretically we deduce that producers will react to RPM by raising their wholesale prices. The interesting question for the CC to consider is by how much.

To assess this question we rewrite

$$\begin{bmatrix} P_K \\ P_U \end{bmatrix} = \begin{bmatrix} 79.340 \\ 64.463 \end{bmatrix} + \begin{bmatrix} 0.573720 & 0.19834 \\ 0.12397 & 0.66116 \end{bmatrix} \begin{bmatrix} Z_K \\ Z_U \end{bmatrix} \tag{20}$$

to express P_K and Z_U as functions of $P_U^* = 110$:

$$Z_U = 1.5125 \cdot P_U^* - 0.1875 \cdot Z_K - 97.5 = 68.875 - 0.1875 \cdot Z_K \tag{21}$$
$$P_K = 60 + 0.5 \cdot Z_K + 0.3 \cdot P_U^* = 93 + 0.5 \cdot Z_K$$

Substituting $68.875 - 0.1875 \cdot Z_K$ for Z_U reduces (23) to the following:

$$\begin{bmatrix} Q_K \\ Q_U \end{bmatrix} = \begin{bmatrix} 1.1625 \times 10^7 - 62500 \cdot Z_K \\ 8.225 \times 10^6 + 37500 \cdot Z_K \end{bmatrix} \tag{22}$$

The jth representative producer's sales to the merged shops and the independent shops are given by:

$$Q_{Kj} = 1.1625 \times 10^6 - 62500 \cdot Z_{Kj} + 0.9 \cdot 62500 \cdot Z_{K-j}$$
$$Q_{Uj} = 8.225 \times 10^5 + 37500 \cdot Z_{Kj} - 0.9 \cdot 37500 \cdot Z_{K-j}$$

Maximizing the jth producers profit

$$\Pi_{Pj} = Q_{Kj} \cdot (Z_{Kj} - 25) + Q_{Uj} \cdot (68.875 - 0.1875 Z_{Kj} - 25)$$

with respect to the wholesale price that he charges the merged shops, Z_{Kj}, result in the FOC:

$$\frac{\partial \Pi_{Pj}}{\partial Z_{Kj}} = 0 = 1.1625 \times 10^6 - 62500 \cdot Z_{Kj} + 0.9 \cdot 62500 \cdot Z_{K-j} - 62500 \cdot (Z_{Kj} - 25)$$

$$- 0.1875 \cdot (8.225 \times 10^5 + 37500 \cdot Z_{Kj} - 0.9 \cdot 37500 \cdot Z_{K-j})$$
$$+ 37500 \cdot (68.875 - 0.1875 Z_{Kj} - 25)$$

which in symmetric equilibrium $(Z_{Kj} = Z_{K-j} = Z_K)$ reduces to $Z_K = 55.124$. As conjectured, the wholesale price that the independent shops are charged is even higher, $Z_U = 68.875 - 0.1875 \cdot Z_K = 58.539$.

The effect on retail prices, sales and profit of RPM is given in table 5. The row marked 'RPM fixed' refers to the case where the wholesale prices remain unaffected, and 'RPM adj'. to the case where the producers react to the RPM by raising the wholesale prices.

Table 5. The effect of the merger in case of retail price maintenance

	P_K Dkr	P_U Dkr	P Dkr	Q_K mill	Q_U mill	Q mill	Π_{Ki} kDkr	Π_{Ui} kDkr	Π_{Pj} kDkr
Nash	116.1	103.7	109.1	8.26	10.74	19.00	2186	2309	47381
RPM fixed	118.0	110.0	113.7	8.50	10.10	18.60	2312	2424	46500
RPM adj.	120.6	110.0	114.7	8.18	10.29	18.47	2141	2119	59159

The simulation predicts that buyer power-induced binding minimum retail prices may increase the negative effects of the proposed merger on consumer welfare and the efficiency significantly .

Buyer power-induced RPM is especially harmful to consumers if the producers adjust wholesale prices to 'expropriate' most of the increase in the total profits resulting from the merger.

However, the most salient prediction is that RPM results in the merged shops being slightly (2 percent) worse off and the independent shops being significantly worse off (8 percent) worse off than in Nash equilibrium if producers adjust their wholesale prices, in contrast to the case in which wholesale process are assumed unaffected.

One might conclude that the merged shops' possible (ab)use of buyer power to force the producers to impose and police the minimum guiding prices in order to curb the competitiveness of the independent competitors is an unrealistic scenario because they should know that the producers have a strong incentive to adjust wholesale prices and that, if the producers do so, the merged shops stand to lose.This inference is likely too optimistic and based on the assumption that the merged shops are sufficiently sophisticated to realize that the immediate gain (at unchanged wholesale prices) is turned into a loss when, eventually, the producers adjust their prices.

Conversely, the 'morale' is that RPM in the form of effectively binding 'guiding' retail prices is a risk that the competition authorities should consider when assessing a proposed merger, regardless of whether the RPM is induced by the merged shops' buyer power or initiated by the producers themselves as a response to increased retail prices.

In Denmark, retailers of luxury specialties appear to be 'disciplined' to a degree that resembles tacit collusion. The problem is attenuated by the fact that the competition authorities have limited means of sanctioning (legal) guiding prices that support and are supported by tacit collusion. Guiding retail prices are likely the most sincere competition problem in the trade in specialties.

10.   Conclusion

In the case analyzed in this chapter the Danish Competition Council decided not to prohibit the merger of approximately 250 shops previously organized in a voluntary chain even
though the shops with a share of around 50 percent were already dominant in the market for
high-end cosmetics and the merger would almost by definition strengthen their dominant
position and impede the competition. The acceptance of the merger was conditioned on the
removal of certain contract-based covenants in restraint of trade.

The purpose of this chapter is not to criticize the decision as such but call attention to
the weak analytical premises for the decision. The material on which the decision was made
presented several relevant reflections but practically no quantitative assessment of the likely
effects of the merger. This is a problem as the wording of the Competition Act implies a
quantitative assessment of whether the merger impedes the competition 'significantly'.

The reason for the inadequate quantitative analysis is likely not only lack of data and
time but equally much the analysts' reluctance to engage in consistent quantitative modeling
because this activity unavoidably and mercilessly reveals to themselves and opponents the
shaky foundation of their recommendations.

As convincingly argued by prominent antitrust economist like Werden and Froeb
[15]and others the way to improve the basis for decisions in merger cases is to build, calibrate and simulate quantitative models. Models provide analytical consistency to predictions.

The model presented in this chapter adds to the literature by being parsimonious in
its data requirements and, nevertheless, allowing quantitative assessment of not only the
static unilateral effects of the merger but also of the likely dynamic effects and the strategic
interaction between the retail sector and the wholesale sector.

The conclusion is that the merger of the 250 shops in the Danish market for high-end
cosmetics has the potential of being harmful to the consumers by raising retail prices. However, it also demonstrates that the market power of the merged shops is vulnerable to attack
from the opening of new shops induced by increased profit due to the merger. The number
of entrants required to erode excess profit appears surprisingly low. As a consequence the
merged shops are likely to pursue a strategy of (ab)using their buyer power to curb the independent shop's ability to compete and raise entry barriers. The analysis indicates that buyer
power-induced volume discounts and retail price maintenance may be effective defensive
strategies and have severe negative effects on consumer welfare, efficiency and market dynamics. The likely increased prevalence of these phenomena should be a matter of concern
for the competition authorities.

Appendix

The effect on a merger in the retail sector on unilaterally determined wholesale
prices.

The two retail demand equations (11) and (14) and the two retail price equations (13)
and (18) may be conveniently reformulated as the following:

$$\begin{bmatrix} Q_K \\ Q_U \end{bmatrix} = A \cdot \begin{bmatrix} \alpha \\ 1-\alpha \end{bmatrix} - \Phi \cdot \begin{bmatrix} P_K \\ P_U \end{bmatrix} \tag{23}$$

$$\Phi \equiv \begin{bmatrix} (b \cdot \alpha + h) & -h \\ -h & (b \cdot (1-\alpha) + h) \end{bmatrix}$$

$$h \equiv \alpha \cdot (1-\alpha) \cdot n^2 \cdot c$$

and

$$\begin{bmatrix} P_K \\ P_U \end{bmatrix} = \Gamma^{-1} \cdot \left[A \cdot \begin{bmatrix} \alpha \\ 1-\alpha \end{bmatrix} + \Lambda \cdot \begin{bmatrix} Z_K \\ Z_U \end{bmatrix} \right] \tag{24}$$

$$\Gamma \equiv \begin{bmatrix} 2 \cdot (\alpha \cdot b + h) & -h \\ -h & 2 \cdot b \cdot (1-\alpha) + (1 + \frac{1}{\alpha}) \cdot h \end{bmatrix}$$

$$\Lambda \equiv \begin{bmatrix} (\alpha \cdot b + h) & 0 \\ 0 & ((1-\alpha) \cdot b + \frac{h}{\alpha}) \end{bmatrix}$$

From 23 and 24 we derive the demand faced by the two retail channels as functions of wholesale prices

$$\begin{bmatrix} Q_K \\ Q_U \end{bmatrix} = A \cdot \begin{bmatrix} \Sigma_K \\ \Sigma_U \end{bmatrix} - \begin{bmatrix} \Omega_{KK} & \Omega_{KU} \\ \Omega_{UK} & \Omega_{UU} \end{bmatrix} \cdot \begin{bmatrix} Z_K \\ Z_U \end{bmatrix} \tag{25}$$

$$\begin{bmatrix} \Sigma_K \\ \Sigma_U \end{bmatrix} \equiv [I - \Phi \cdot \Gamma^{-1}] \begin{bmatrix} \alpha \\ 1-\alpha \end{bmatrix} = \theta \cdot \begin{bmatrix} 2\alpha(h + b\alpha) \\ 2h + 2b\alpha - h\alpha - 2b\alpha^2 \end{bmatrix} \tag{26}$$

$$\theta \equiv \frac{h + b\alpha - b\alpha^2}{\alpha \cdot \Delta_\Gamma}$$

$$\begin{bmatrix} \Omega_{KK} & \Omega_{KU} \\ \Omega_{UK} & \Omega_{UU} \end{bmatrix} \equiv \Phi \cdot \Gamma^{-1} \Lambda \tag{27}$$

$$= \theta \begin{bmatrix} (h + b\alpha)(h + 2b\alpha) & -h(h + b\alpha) \\ -h(h + b\alpha) & 2bh + h^2 + 2b^2\alpha - 2b^2\alpha^2 \end{bmatrix} \tag{28}$$

By comparing 26 and 27 we realize that

$$\begin{bmatrix} \Sigma_K \\ \Sigma_U \end{bmatrix} = \frac{1}{b} \cdot \begin{bmatrix} \Omega_{KK} & \Omega_{KU} \\ \Omega_{UK} & \Omega_{UU} \end{bmatrix} \cdot \begin{bmatrix} 1 \\ 1 \end{bmatrix} \tag{29}$$

$$\Omega_{KU} = \Omega_{UK}$$

and, consequently, that the demand system 25 reduces to

$$\begin{bmatrix} Q_K \\ Q_U \end{bmatrix} = \frac{1}{b} \cdot \begin{bmatrix} \Omega_{KK} & \Omega_{KU} \\ \Omega_{UK} & \Omega_{UU} \end{bmatrix} \cdot \begin{bmatrix} A - b \cdot Z_K \\ A - b \cdot Z_U \end{bmatrix} \tag{30}$$

which is the two-dimensional equivalent to 6.

The representative jth producer sells to both the merged shops and the independent shops. The corresponding demand functions are

$$
\begin{bmatrix} Q_{Kj} \\ Q_{Uj} \end{bmatrix} = \frac{1}{bm} \begin{bmatrix} \Omega_{KK} & \Omega_{KU} \\ \Omega_{UK} & \Omega_{UU} \end{bmatrix} \begin{bmatrix} A - (b+e)Z_{Kj} + eZ_{K-j} \\ A - (b+e)Z_{Uj} + eZ_{U-j} \end{bmatrix} \tag{31}
$$

$$
e \equiv dm(m-1)
$$

By maximizing his profit

$$
\Pi_{Pj} = Q_{Kj} \cdot (Z_{Kj} - C) + Q_{Uj} \cdot (Z_{Uj} - C) \tag{32}
$$

with respect to Z_{Kj} and Z_{Uj}, we derive the two first-order conditions

$$
Q_{Kj} - \Omega_{KK} \cdot \frac{b+e}{b \cdot m} \cdot (Z_{Kj} - C) - \Omega_{UK} \cdot \frac{b+e}{b \cdot m} \cdot (Z_{Uj} - C) = 0 \tag{33}
$$
$$
Q_{Uj} - \Omega_{KU} \cdot \frac{b+e}{b \cdot m} \cdot (Z_{Kj} - C) - \Omega_{UU} \cdot \frac{b+e}{b \cdot m} \cdot (Z_{Uj} - C) = 0
$$

In symmetric equilibrium ($Z_{Kj} = Z_{K-j} = Z_K$ and $Z_{Uj} = Z_{U-j} = Z_U$) 33 reduces to

$$
(\Omega_{KK} + \Omega_{UK}) \cdot (A + (b+e) \cdot C) = (2b+e) \cdot (\Omega_{KK} \cdot Z_K + \Omega_{KU} \cdot Z_U)
$$
$$
(\Omega_{UK} + \Omega_{UU}) \cdot (A + (b+e) \cdot C) = (2b+e) \cdot (\Omega_{UK} \cdot Z_K + \Omega_{UU} \cdot Z_U)
$$

which we may write as

$$
(2b+e) \cdot \Omega \cdot \begin{bmatrix} Z_K \\ Z_U \end{bmatrix} = \Omega \cdot \begin{bmatrix} 1 \\ 1 \end{bmatrix} \cdot (A + (b+e \cdot C)) \tag{34}
$$

$$
\begin{bmatrix} Z_K \\ Z_U \end{bmatrix} = \begin{bmatrix} 1 \\ 1 \end{bmatrix} \cdot \frac{A + (b+e) \cdot C}{2b+e}
$$

(34) implies that the producers charge the merged shops and the independent shops the same price and that the price level is unaffected by the merger:

$$
Z_K = Z_U = Z = \frac{1}{2b + d \cdot m \cdot (m-1)} \cdot A + \frac{b + d \cdot m \cdot (m-1)}{2b + d \cdot m \cdot (m-1)} \cdot C \tag{35}
$$

References

[1] Buchanan, J. M. (1953), The Theory of Monopolistic Quantity Discounts. *The Review of Economic Studies*, Vol. 20:3, pp. 199-208.

[2] Dobson, P. W. et al (2001), Buyer Power and its Impact on Competition in the Food Retail Distribution Sector of the European Union. *Journal of Industry, Competition and Trade*, 1:3, pp. 247-281.

[3] Fog, Bjarke (1994), *Pricing Theory in Theory and Practice*. Handelshøjskolens Forlag.

[4] Fornell, C. and W. T. Robinson (1983), Industrial Organization and Consumer Satisfaction/Dissatisfaction. *Journal of Consumer Research*, Vol. 6 pp 1-26.

[5] Gilligan, T. W.(1986), The Competitive Effects of Retail Price Maintenance. *The RAND Journal of Economics*. Vol 17:4.

[6] Hovenkamp, Herbert J. (2009), *Analyzing Horizontal Mergers: Unilateral Effects in Product-Differentiated Markets*. University of Iowa Legal Studies Research Paper, No. 09-12.

[7] Inderst, R. and C. Wey (2007), Buyer Power and Supplier Incentives. *European Economic Review*. Vol 51, pp 647-667.

[8] Konkurrencestyrelsen (2007), *CVC's overtagelse af Matas og en række Matasbutikker*. www.ks.dk.

[9] Lustgarten, S. H.(1975), The Impact of Buyer Concentration in Manufacturing Industries. *The Review of Economics and Statistics*. Vol. 57:2, pp 125-132.

[10] Mazzarotto, Nicola (2004), *Retail Mergers and Buyer Power*. CCR Working Paper CCR 04-3.University of East Anglia.

[11] Rosenthal, M.-B. et al (2003), Demand Effects of Recent Changes in Prescription Drug Promotion. *Forum for Health Economics and Policy*. Vol. 6, pp. 1-26.

[12] Snyder, C. M. (1996), A Dynamic Theory of Countervailing Power. *The RAND Journal of Economics*. Vol. 4, pp. 747-769.

[13] Tesler, L. G., (1964), Advertising and Competition. *Journal of Political Economy*. Vol 72, pp. 537-562.

[14] Weng, Z. K. (1995), Channel Coordination and Quantity Discounts. *Management Science*. Vol. 41:9, pp. 1509-1522.

[15] Werden, Gregrory J. and Froeb, Luke M. (2006): Unilateral Competition Effects of Horizontal Mergers. In Paolo Buccirossi, ed., *Handbook of Antitrust Economics*. MIT Press.

Chapter 5

NaOH and KOH for Preparing Activated Carbons Used in Energy and Environmental Applications

A. Linares-Solano[*], M. A. Lillo-Ródenas, J. P. Marco-Lozar, M. Kunowsky and A. J. Romero-Anaya

Dpto. Química Inorgánica, Universidad de Alicante, Alicante, Spain

ABSTRACT

Alkaline hydroxides, especially sodium and potassium hydroxides, are multi-million-ton per annum commodities and strong chemical bases that have large scale applications. Some of them are related with their consequent ability to degrade most materials, depending on the temperature used. As an example, these chemicals are involved in the manufacture of pulp and paper, textiles, biodiesels, soaps and detergents, acid gases removal (e.g., SO_2) and others, as well as in many organic synthesis processes. Sodium and potassium hydroxides are strong and corrosive bases, but they are also very stable chemicals that can melt without decomposition, NaOH at 318ºC, and KOH at 360ºC. Hence, they can react with most materials, even with relatively inert ones such as carbon materials. Thus, at temperatures higher than 360ºC these melted hydroxides easily react with most types of carbon-containing raw materials (coals, lignocellulosic materials, pitches, etc.), as well as with most pure carbon materials (carbon fibers, carbon nanofibers and carbon nanotubes). This reaction occurs via a solid-liquid redox reaction in which both hydroxides (NaOH or KOH) are converted to the following main products: hydrogen, alkaline metals and alkaline carbonates, as a result of the carbon precursor oxidation. By controlling this reaction, and after a suitable washing process, good quality activated carbons (ACs), a classical type of porous materials, can be prepared.

Such carbon activation by hydroxides, known since long time ago, continues to be under research due to the unique properties of the resulting activated carbons. They have promising high porosity developments and interesting pore size distributions. These two properties are important for new applications such as gas storage (e.g., natural gas or

---

[*] Corresponding author: E-mail address: linares@ua.es; Fax: +34 965903454.

hydrogen), capture, storage and transport of carbon dioxide, electricity storage demands (EDLC-supercapacitors-) or pollution control. Because these applications require new and superior quality activated carbons, there is no doubt that among the different existing activating processes, the one based on the chemical reaction between the carbon precursor and the alkaline hydroxide (NaOH or KOH) gives the best activation results.

The present article covers different aspects of the activation by hydroxides, including the characteristics of the resulting activated carbons and their performance in some environment-related applications. The following topics are discussed: i) variables of the preparation method, such as the nature of the hydroxide, the type of carbon precursor, the hydroxide/carbon precursor ratio, the mixing procedure of carbon precursor and hydroxide (impregnation of the precursor with a hydroxide solution or mixing both, hydroxide and carbon precursor, as solids), or the temperature and time of the reaction are discussed, analyzing their effect on the resulting porosity; ii) analysis of the main reactions occurring during the activation process, iii) comparative analysis of the porosity development obtained from different activation processes (e.g., CO_2, steam, phosphoric acid and hydroxides activation); and iv) performance of the prepared activated carbon materials on a few applications, such as VOC removal, electricity and gas storages.

1. INTRODUCTION

Alkaline hydroxides, especially those from sodium and potassium, are multi-million-ton per annum commodity chemicals that have great ability to degrade many materials [1,2]. Both are strong caustic metallic bases that are widely used in many different topics, for example organic synthesis processes (acting as catalysts or as nucleophilic reagents), demineralization of coals and other carbon materials, disaggregating agents in analytical chemistry, as well as in large scale applications such as the manufacture of pulp and paper, textiles, tissue digestion, biodiesels, soaps and detergents, acid gases removal (e.g., SO_2), drinking water treatment and others [1-5]. Although KOH and NaOH can be used interchangeably in a large number of applications, NaOH is preferred by the industry because of its lower cost. Hence the worldwide production of NaOH is about one hundred times higher than for KOH (e.g., for 2005, the production of NaOH was 70 million tonnes, whereas it was approximately 700,000 tonnes for KOH) [1, 2, 6, 7].

Although these two hydroxides are strong and corrosive bases, NaOH and KOH are interestingly stable chemicals that melt without decomposition at 318°C and at 360°C, respectively [7]. However, at these temperatures both melted hydroxides are even stronger caustic bases, as a result of which they react with most materials and even start reacting with the quite inert carbon materials. At temperatures about their melting points, these melted hydroxides strongly react with most types of carbon containing raw materials (coals, lignocellulosic materials, pitches, etc.), as well as with most pure carbon materials (carbon fibers, carbon nanofibers and carbon nanotubes) [8-10]. The reaction between the carbon precursor and the hydroxide can be controlled by means of many experimental variables (e.g., the nature of the precursor and the hydroxide, the reaction temperature and time, or the hydroxide carbon ratio, among others). The resulting solid products of the reaction are mixtures formed by the remaining carbon, alkaline carbonates and, depending on the reaction conditions, unreacted hydroxides. If such residue is washed, filtered and dried, the remaining carbon material results to be a super activated carbon (AC) [10].

Such activation reaction occurs via a solid-liquid redox reaction in which the hydroxides (both NaOH and KOH) are converted to the following main products: hydrogen, alkaline metals and alkaline carbonates, as a result of the carbon precursor oxidation [8-10], and some remaining carbon reactant. This remaining carbon is the objective of such type of reaction in which the number of pores of the carbon precursor used has increased considerably, as well as the size of the existing ones. Hence, by this hydroxide-carbon reaction we can prepare superior class activated carbons having high adsorption capacities. Therefore, under these experimental conditions, sodium and potassium hydroxides become very useful chemical agents for the carbon activation process and hence for preparing superior quality super-activated carbons [10-13].

Since the pioneer patent of Wennerberg et al. [14] a considerable work has been done over the years related to chemical activation with hydroxides [11-13, 15-39]. In this large number of papers, we can see that most of the variables affecting this activation process have been analyzed, specially the precursor and the hydroxide/carbon ratio. From all these papers it can be stated that carbon activation by alkaline hydroxides is a promising process. This statement is confirmed by industrial production of very high surface area activated carbons (e.g., Maxsorb series, commercialized by Kansai Coke and Chemical Company, Japan [13]).

The present article shows and discusses the reaction of two strong caustic chemicals (i.e., NaOH and KOH) with a large variety of carbon precursors, in order to highlight their specific use for preparing good quality "super-activated" carbons.

Considering the increasing interest in the use of alkaline hydroxides as activating agents, and the large number of published papers related to the variables affecting this activation process, this article reviews and updates the most important aspects of this activation process. This article, covering the most important aspects of the hydroxide-carbon reaction, will be useful for the reader to understand such activation process and the unique properties of the resulting ACs.

These properties and their performance in some environment-related applications will be analyzed, discussing the following topics: i) variables of the preparation method (e.g., the nature of the hydroxide, the carbon precursor, the hydroxide/carbon precursor ratio, the mixing procedure (impregnation or mixing of solids), the reaction temperature and time), analyzing their effect on the resulting porosity, ii) analysis of the main reactions occurring during the activation process, iii) comparative analysis of the porosity development obtained from different activation processes (e.g., CO_2, steam, phosphoric acid and hydroxides activation), and iv) performance of the prepared activated carbon materials on a few applications which are related to energy and environment, such as VOC removal, electricity and gas storages.

2. ACTIVATED CARBONS

The term activated carbon (AC) corresponds to a large group of carbonaceous adsorbents which are mainly formed by carbon atoms and have the peculiarity of possessing valuable, and tunable, properties such as: adsorption capacities, apparent surface areas and porosities (from low to very high) and porous textures with tunable pore size distributions. All these characteristics, including their different morphologies (powder, granular, pellet, fiber, monoliths, cloth and others) can be tailored and developed according to their final applications.

As a result of these tunable properties, ACs are the adsorbents which are mostly used in a large number of industrial applications and its world consumption is steadily increasing, being estimated this consumption around 650,000 tons in 2007 [40]. Furthermore, they are among the best candidates for emerging applications, particularly related to the environmental pollution remediation [41]. However, since ACs are not present in nature, they have to be prepared artificially, especially considering the consumption increase expected in the next five years [40].

2.1. Characterization

Considering the variety of fields in which activated carbons are used, their porous textures require a suitable characterization. Such complex characterization needs a combination of techniques, allowing to control and to optimize the performance of an AC for a given application. Amongst others, the following techniques should be underlined: physical adsorption of gases, mercury porosimetry, small angle neutron and X-ray or neutron scattering, transmission and scanning electron microscopy, scanning tunnel microscopy or immersion calorimetry. From them, undoubtedly physical adsorption of gases (e.g., N_2, CO_2 and many others) is the main technique and N_2 (at 77 K) the gas most widely used. Its main advantage is that it easily covers a wide relative pressure range (from 10^{-8} to 1). However, it has the disadvantage of having possible problems of N_2 diffusion inside the narrow porosity (size < 0.7 nm). To overcome this problem, the use of other adsorptives has been proposed, CO_2 adsorption at 273 K being an easy alternative to N_2 for the assessment of such narrow microporosity [42-45]. When the micropore volumes, deduced from both N_2 (77 K) and CO_2 (273 K) adsorption isotherms, are compared by applying a suitable equation (e.g., the DR equation) three cases can be found; i) a CO_2 micropore volume ($V_{DR}(CO_2)$) higher than the N_2 micropore volume ($V_{DR}(N_2)$, ii) a similar value ($V_{DR}(N_2) \approx V_{DR}(CO_2)$) and iii) a lower $V_{DR}(CO_2)$ value than $V_{DR}(N_2)$. The first case indicates that the porosity of the carbon sample is very narrow (micropore size < 0.7 nm), causing diffusion problems to the N_2 molecules to reach it. Case ii) indicates that the carbon sample has an homogeneous, and narrow, micropore size distribution (with a size of about 0.7 nm), and case iii) the higher is the difference between these two values, the wider and heterogeneous is the carbon samples' porosity, with well developed supermicroporosity and mesoporosity [25,46-55].

For a better understanding of the porosity results presented in the following sections of this article, all our activated carbons have always been characterized by both N_2 (77 K) and CO_2 (273 K) adsorption isotherms.

2.2. Preparation

For obtaining these ACs it is necessary to select the precursor and the method of preparation. Both have great importance as they determine the final porous textures of the resulting ACs. In relation to the former, any carbonaceous precursor with high carbon atoms content in its composition can be used. Examples of the most used ones are the "classical precursors" such as wood, coconut shells and coals [56-58], while less used precursors include agricultural by-products, waste residues, pitches, polymers and so on [56-58]. Once a given precursor has been selected, the method of preparation to be used needs to be analyzed. In general, depending on the precursor used, different activation methods and activating agents will be chosen. The activation of a carbon precursor, with the objective of increasing the raw precursors porosity and hence its adsorption capacity, can be carried out by any of the so-called "physical activation" and/or "chemical activation" processes [10,16,56-60].

The "physical activation" process is a controlled gasification in which the carbon precursor (previously carbonised or not) is activated at temperatures between 800-1000°C using carbon dioxide or steam. Both of these activating agents are commonly used and both react endothermally with the carbon atoms of the precursor according to the following reactions:

$$C + CO_2 \leftrightarrow 2\, CO, \Delta H = 159.0 \text{ kJ/mol} \tag{1}$$

$$C + H_2O \leftrightarrow CO + H_2, \Delta H = 118.5 \text{ kJ/mol} \tag{2}$$

In the course of the two reactions (1) and (2) shown before, carbon atoms from the precursor are oxidized and hence removed, starting with the less ordered, and most reactive, carbon atoms. For a suitable activation process (creation of micropores and/or size widening of the existing ones) such carbon atoms removal must take place predominantly inside the carbon particles, not in the outside part, to allow a suitable porosity and adsorption capacity.

On the contrary, the "chemical activation" process consists of mixing a carbonaceous precursor with a chemical activating agent and heating the mixture in an inert atmosphere, similarly to a pyrolysis process. After such thermal treatment and after a subsequent washing process, the obtained carbon material is richer in carbon content, and, ideally, has a well developed porous structure. Different compounds can be used for such type of activation; amongst others, H_3PO_4, KOH, or NaOH, have been reported in the literature [56-60].

In general, "chemical activation" presents advantages over "physical activation" that can be summarized as: i) it uses lower temperatures and pyrolysis times, ii) it usually consists of one stage and iii) it renders higher activation yields. Nevertheless, it also presents disadvantages as the need of a washing stage and the corrosiveness of some of the chemical agents used.

In both activation processes ("physical activation" and "chemical activation") it is important to have a deep knowledge of different preparation variables (less numerous in the "physical" activation process than in the "chemical" one) that affect the porous texture development (surface area, pore size and pore size distribution). The knowledge of the effect of these preparation variables on the porous texture of the resulting activated carbons will allow to select them and, hence, the properties of the prepared ACs.

2.3. Carbon Activation by Alkaline Hydroxides

Carbon activation by alkaline hydroxides is known since long time ago (mainly restricted to KOH) and the research on such activation process increases continuously [11-13,15-39]. Nowadays, ACs obtained by this activation have started to be industrially used (about 100 tonnes per year). These ACs possess three unique characteristics that make them very attractive for new and potential applications. These are: i) their low ash content, even using precursors having high ash contents, ii) their very high adsorption capacity and iii) their controlled narrow porosity distribution (not possible to achieve using other activation agents). As a result, there is no doubt that among the different existing activating processes, the chemical activation by NaOH or KOH is among the most powerful ones.

As it is shown later on, new applications and/or potential ones, such as gas storage (e.g. natural gas and hydrogen), capture, storage and transport (e.g. of carbon dioxide), electricity storage (EDLC, supercapacitors) or pollution control require unique properties which are provided by superior quality activated carbons, prepared by alkaline hydroxides.

2.4. Understanding the Main Reactions of the Hydroxide-Carbon Reaction

The main reactions occurring during the carbon activation with hydroxides are of interest in order to understand the unique features of the resulting activated carbons, as it is discussed on subsequent sections. By a combination of techniques (FTIR, "in situ" XRD and mass spectrometry), thermodynamic data and theoretical calculations (Gibbs Free Energy) we have analyzed the changes occurring in both chemical reactants (carbon and hydroxides), as well as the composition of the gaseous and solid reaction products [8-10,61]. From these results, and with a mass balance that accounts for more than 90 wt. % of the analyzed products, it has been shown that the hydroxide activation of carbon occurs via the following reaction:

$$6 \text{ MOH} + 2 \text{ C} \leftrightarrow 2 \text{ M} + 3 \text{ H}_2 + 2 \text{ M}_2\text{CO}_3 \tag{3}$$

where M: Na, K

It can be seen that this reaction is a solid-liquid redox reaction in which the hydroxides are converted to the following main products: hydrogen, alkaline metals and alkaline carbonates, as a result of the carbon precursor oxidation [8-10, 61].

Frequently, this reaction (3) is carried out in a temperature range of 700°C to 900°C and using lower hydroxide/carbon ratios than would be required for stoichiometry. Therefore, the hydroxide is the limiting reactant and, hence, some unreacted carbon will always remain. Much higher hydroxide/carbon weight ratios (about 10/1 for NaOH and 14/1 for KOH) would have to be used to avoid such hydroxide limitation.

2.5. Variables Affecting the Hydroxide-Carbon Reaction

Although many works have analyzed the variables of the hydroxide-carbon reaction [11,12,16,17,25-27,29,32,62], often the ACs obtained have not been similarly characterized. Thus, it is difficult, or even impossible, to compare results from different authors and hence to get conclusions. In a recent study [10], we reviewed the variables of the carbon activation by hydroxides in samples similarly prepared and characterized. In the present article, we summarize and update the fundamentals of the carbon activation by alkaline hydroxides and revisit it, adding new data obtained after this publication.

As it happens in most chemical reactions, the kinetics and extent of a reaction are generally affected by many variables, for example the reactants' concentrations, the reaction temperature and time. Contrarily to most chemical reactions, the key point regarding reaction (3) is the characteristics of the remaining carbon (i.e., its porosity development). Hence, it is important to know these variables and how they affect the porosity development of the remaining carbon material.

Amongst others, the most relevant variables for carbon activation by alkaline hydroxides affecting the final porous texture of ACs are: i) the reactivity of the carbon precursor, ii) the way of mixing both reactants, iii) the nature of the hydroxide, iv) the hydroxide carbon ratio, v) the maximum reaction temperature and v) two additional parameters that have recently been reported as the flow and type of gas used during the heat-treatment [8, 10-12].

2.5.1. Reactivity of the Carbon Precursor

The importance of the carbon precursors' reactivity is summarized next, using some examples extracted from our study with 16 carbonaceous precursors. This study covers a large variety of different carbon precursors (coals, lignocellulosic materials and carbon materials) and their heat treatment previous to their activation by hydroxide. The main conclusion is that the reactivity of the carbon precursor itself (estimated by TG analysis in air) controls its reactivity in reaction (3), and hence the extent of the reaction and the degree of activation reached, as well as the subsequent properties of the prepared ACs [9,10]. Thus, Table 1 compiles some results related to the reactivity of the carbon-NaOH reaction (the same happens with KOH) such as: i) the air reactivity (estimated as the temperature at which 20 wt. % of the carbon precursor is burnt), ii) the temperature at which reaction (3) starts (estimated from coupled TG-MS) and iii) the wt. % of the reacted carbon. These results show, as expected, that the reactivity decreases as the coal rank increases (lignite > subbituminous > anthracite) and that a heat treatment in the carbonaceous precursors previous to the activation reaction causes a decrease in their subsequent reactivity. Interestingly, the extent of the reaction (wt. % of carbon reacted) also depends on the reactivity of the starting carbon, decreasing from lignite to subbituminous coal to anthracite. The use of a pre-heat treatment step, prior to activation, provokes a more ordered carbon material and, hence, a less reactive one, as results of which the activation process becomes much more difficult [9, 10].

Table 1. Results related to the reactivity of the carbon precursor in relation to reaction (3)

Carbon Precursor	T (°C) (20% wt loss)	T (°C) (H_2 appears)	Reacted carbon (% wt)
L	266	250	9.0
SB	438	375	6.0
A	582	475	2.0
L850	445	450	5.2
A-1000	639	575	0.3

In addition to the reactivity of the precursor, other characteristics (especially its starting porosity) also affect the reaction. As stated above, the hydroxide-carbon activation depends very much on the reaction variables, as it is shown later on.

Figure 1 presents the N_2 adsorption isotherms at 77 K of precursors which have different structures and textural properties. They are activated by KOH (Figure 1a) and by NaOH (Figure 1b), keeping constant the other variables (physical mixing; hydroxide/precursor ratio

2/1 (weight); heating rate 20°C/min up to 750°C; soaking time 1 h; N_2 flow rate during heat treatment 500 ml/min).

These N_2 adsorption isotherms clearly show that the precursor influences remarkably the resulting adsorption capacity, although in a different manner depending on the hydroxide used.

Thus, the observed adsorption capacity sequence of Figure 1 varies considerably depending on the nature of hydroxide used. It can be seen that, in general, when KOH is used, the structural order of the precursor favours the activation results (e.g., anthracite > subbituminous > lignite ≈ almond shell). However, when NaOH is used the low structural order of the precursor favours the activation (e.g., lignite > almond shell > subbituminous > anthracite).

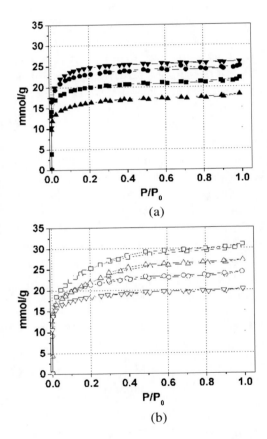

Figure 1. N_2 adsorption isotherms at 77 K for precursors activated similarly by (a) KOH ((!) Lignite, (,) Sub-bituminous, (B) Anthracite and (7) almond shell) and by (b) NaOH (empty symbols).

2.5.2. Way of Mixing the Hydroxide and the Carbon Precursor

The way of mixing the carbonaceous precursor with the alkaline hydroxide influences the properties of the prepared activated carbons. Most studies related to activation with alkaline hydroxides are based on the impregnation method and on the exclusive use of KOH. Impregnation consists of mixing by stirring, at a given temperature, the precursor with different volumes of a hydroxide solution [10,11].

After the impregnation process, the samples are heat-treated for activation. In contrast to this method, our research group has deeply investigated an alternative and more efficient method: the direct mixing, at room temperature, of the hydroxide and the carbonaceous precursor (i.e., in absence of water) [10,12]. Such method has shown to be very effective in all the carbon precursors used [10,12].

Additionally, and of special interest, is the observation that the mixing of NaOH with the carbon precursor can render comparable or even better results than with KOH (contrarily to what was assumed initially), with the advantage of its lower cost in comparison with KOH.

2.5.3. The Nature of the Hydroxide

Figure 2 presents the N_2 adsorption isotherms of two precursors (anthracite and almond shell) similarly activated with KOH (Figure 2a) and NaOH (Figure 2b).

The importance of the nature of the carbon precursor can be well observed; their activation behaviour and hence their adsorption capacities are different, due to their remarkable different reactivity and structural order. Additionally, these activation results depend on the nature of the hydroxide. This is shown in Figure 3, where the results of Figure 2 are presented, keeping constant the precursor used (Figure 3a for the anthracite and Figure 3b for almond shell).

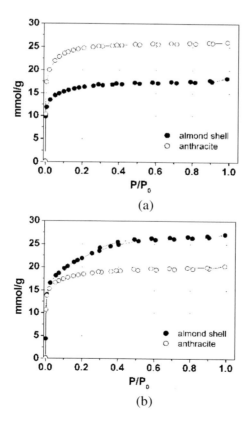

Figure 2. N_2 adsorption isotherms at 77 K for an anthracite and for an almond shell, both activated using the same experimental conditions by (a) KOH and (b) NaOH.

It can be seen that the results are not the same, depending on the nature of the activating agent used. KOH is much more effective than NaOH for activating ordered precursor (e.g., an anthracite), but the contrarily happens for less ordered lignocellulosic materials (e.g., almond shell), for which NaOH gives much better results.

The conclusion that could be obtained from Figure 3a is that KOH is a better activating agent than NaOH, as it is usually done in the literature. However, this cannot be generalized, as shown in Figure 3b and in Figure 1.

During many years, and without explanation, it has been stated that KOH is the best hydroxide activating agent for carbon activation and that NaOH was not a suitable one. The results of Figures 1 to 3, in line with many other results from our research group [10,33,53], show that the relative effectiveness of both hydroxides depends on the precursor used and that for some of them better activation results are obtained with NaOH than with KOH. The erroneous observation that confused the scientific community during many years, is due to the importance of the structural order of the precursor, that was not previously considered, and allows us to conclude that NaOH is better for carbons with poor structural order, whereas KOH produces better results for those having some structural order.

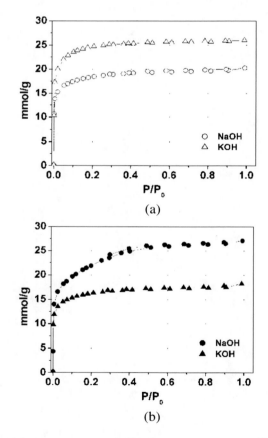

Figure 3. N_2 adsorption isotherms at 77 K showing the effect of the precursor used; (a) an anthracite and (b) an almond shell, both similarly activated by KOH or NaOH.

2.5.4. The Hydroxide/Carbon Ratio

The effect that the hydroxide/carbon ratio plays on the porosity development is analyzed next, taking as example a given carbon fiber (Donacarbo SL-242 provided by Osaka Gas, Japan). Such carbon fiber (CF) is activated at 750°C using NaOH or KOH at different ratios. Figures 4a and 4b show the effect that this variable has on the N_2 adsorption isotherms (77 K) and of their corresponding apparent BET surface areas. Table 2 (limited, as an example, only to KOH activation) also shows the important effect that the hydroxide/CF ratio has on the resulting ACFs properties.

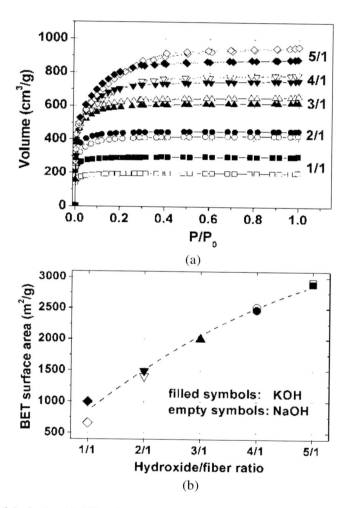

Figure 4. Effect of the hydroxide/CF ratio on: (a) the N_2 adsorption isotherms and (b) the BET surface area (empty symbols for NaOH and filled symbols for KOH) (redrawn from [63]).

The isotherms in Figure 4a are typical for microporous solids (type I) having most of the pores size below 2 nm. For the two lowest hydroxide/CF ratios (1/1 and 2/1) the porosity is mainly due to narrow micropores (< 0.7 nm), which implies that their micropore size distributions are quite narrow.

As the ratio increases, the knee of the adsorption isotherm widens which indicates the presence of supermicroporosity (0.7 - 2 nm), and hence the widening of their pore size distribution.

It should be pointed out that i) as shown in Table 2, the starting CF porosity has almost no adsorption of N_2 at 77 K, while contrarily its adsorption of CO_2 at 273 K is noticeable. This is due to the well known diffusion problem of the N_2 molecules at 77 K, which impedes them to get into the porosity at this low adsorption temperature [42,43] ii) the porosity of the starting CF develops very well upon activation with both hydroxides, reaching a comparable maximum high BET value (about 3000 m^2/g) for both hydroxides at a ratio of 5/1, iii) with the increase on the hydroxide/CF ratio, the extent of the reaction increases and, hence, also the resulting adsorption capacity, and iv) contrarily to most carbon precursors, it can be observed that with this Donacarbo SL-242 precursor the adsorption capacity developed by both hydroxides is the same.

**Table 2. Porous texture data, yields and packing density of ACFs
prepared at different KOH/CF ratios**

Sample	S_{BET} (m²/g)	$V_{DR}(N_2)$ (cm³/g)	$V_{DR}(CO_2)$ (cm³/g)	Yield (%)	*Packing ρ (g cm⁻³)
CF	7**	0.003	0.11	---	0.99
KOH 1/1	999	0.46	0.47	83	0.74
KOH 2/1	1491	0.71	0.65	80	0.74
KOH 3/1	2004	0.94	0.79	74	0.67
KOH 4/1	2472	1.13	0.71	65	0.58
KOH 5/1	2888	1.23	0.80	55	0.56

*Data used later (Hydrogen storage application)
** Low value due to N_2 diffusion problems at 77 K.

Additionally, Table 2 confirms that for low ratios, the volumes of micropores deduced from CO_2 adsorption are quite similar to those deduced from N_2 adsorption; however, for higher ratios, the micropore volumes deduced from CO_2 and N_2 differ, being much lower for CO_2. Both observations indicate the widening of the pore size distribution due to the presence of larger pores (supermicropores, between 0.7 and 2 nm and mesopores, between 2 and 7 nm). Similar results were also obtained by NaOH activation for most of the carbon precursors analyzed [10,12,53].

Particularly important from an economic point of view is the activation yield. This parameter is compiled in Table 2 and, interestingly, high values are obtained, covering a range between 83 % and 55 %. It can be seen that with the increase of the KOH ratio reaction the activation yield decreases. When NaOH is used, lower yields are reached [53].

2.5.5. Maximum Reaction Temperature (A Misleading Variable)

The literature shows that a large range of activation temperatures (from about 700°C to 1000°C) is being used for the carbon activation by hydroxides, without paying attention to its importance. However, the activation temperature is a very important parameter that merits much more attention. Of course, for higher activation temperatures, the extent of the reaction will be higher and hence the activation degree.

Nevertheless, according to reaction (3), one product of the reaction is the alkaline carbonate which, at temperatures higher than about 800°C, decomposes, evolving CO_2, following the reaction (4). In presence of the remaining carbon such CO_2 evolution causes an additional type of carbon activation, due to reaction (1).

$$M_2CO_3 \leftrightarrow MO + CO_2 \tag{4}$$

In reaction (1) the carbon activation takes place through a different mechanism (CO_2 gasification), as a result of which a much broader widening of the porosity is observed, as well as a decrease of the reaction yield. These two observations, which depend very much on the hydroxide and carbon precursor used, disturb two of the main advantages of the hydroxides activation as it will be commented later on: the reaction yield and the narrow pore size distribution. Consequently, an activation temperature higher than 800°C is not at all recommended, especially when narrow micropore size distributions are desired.

2.5.6. Flow and Type of Gas Used During the Heat-Treatment

Little attention has been paid to the flow rate of the gas used during the heat treatment process. During the hydroxide-carbon reaction H_2 is evolved (see reaction (3)), hence the gas flow is a variable that purges the system, shifts the reaction towards the products and influences the porous texture of the ACs. It has been shown [10,12] that changing the N_2 flow rate from 80 to 800 ml/min increases the microporosity development. Thereby, the micropore volumes and surface areas of the produced ACs are doubled; however, and interestingly, the micropore size distribution is not changed [10]. Nitrogen, argon and helium have been studied as purging atmospheres, using similar flow rates. The main observation is that the sample porosity development increases with the efficiency of these three gases to remove the reaction products (i.e., their molecular weight), following the order He < N_2 < Ar which confirms that they act in the reaction only as purging gases [8].

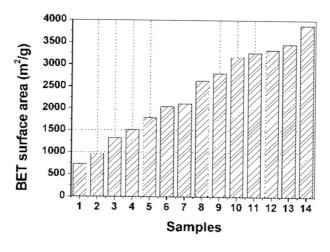

Figure 5. Apparent BET surface area development obtained varying experimental variables of the carbon-hydroxide activation. Numbers indicate different types of variables used.

2.5.7. Concluding Remarks

As it has been shown above, the carbon reaction with hydroxides depends on a large number of variables (much more variables than for physical activation).

By a suitable control of these variables, the characteristics of the resulting ACs can be selected, as it is summarized in Figure 5. The figure shows, for a fixed carbon precursor (anthracite), the large range of BET surface areas that can be obtained (≈ 4000 m^2/g) changing the variables of the hydroxide-carbon reaction.

3. COMPARISON OF NaOH, KOH, STEAM AND PHOSPHORIC ACID ACTIVATIONS

According to the above comments, the suitable selection of the experimental conditions of the hydroxide-carbon reaction allows to prepare ACs with well developed porosity. However, for some applications (as it is discussed later on) it is necessary not only to develop porosity (pore volume and surface area), but also to control the pore size distributions (PSD) of the prepared ACs. For a given precursor, it is difficult to control simultaneously porosity and pore size distribution for the activated carbons prepared either by physical activation (e.g., CO$_2$ or steam) or by chemical activation with conventional activating agents (e.g., phosphoric acid). In both cases, as the pore volume is developed, there is a subsequent widening of the PSD. Interestingly, with a suitable selection of the experimental preparation variables, carbon activation by hydroxides (HA) allows, simultaneously, to develop activated carbons with large porosity without a noticeable PSD widening. In the present section we compare the singularity of the porosity developed by hydroxide activation with the two most used activation procedures, first with physical activation (PA) and secondly with phosphoric acid activation (PAc).

3.1. General Feature of the Physical Activation (PA)

Using N$_2$ (77 K) and CO$_2$ (273 K) adsorption data of a large series of ACs, the general feature of the physical activation process (i.e., development of the micropore volume accompanied by widening of the PSD) is discussed. For it, ACs from different carbon precursors such as lignocellulosic materials, coals, Saran polymer, carbon fibers, activated with steam or with CO$_2$ at different degrees of activation are used as examples. Figure 6 presents the obtained results, plotting their micropore volumes (V$_{DR}$(N$_2$)) and narrow micropore volumes (V$_{DR}$(CO$_2$)), both calculated from DR equation, versus their apparent BET surface area. High surface areas (with maximum BET values in the range of 2500-3000 m^2/g) can easily be prepared by physical activation. As expected, a linear relation is found between the micropore volumes (V$_{DR}$(N$_2$)) and the BET values. This can be explained due to the fact that, although both equations differ on their fundamentals, they both analyze the same adsorption isotherm (N$_2$ at 77 K) and, hence, both give related results, as shown in Figure 6. Thus, as the activation degree increases (from a small percentage to 90 %) both, the V$_{DR}$(N$_2$) and the apparent BET surface area, increase similarly and linearly.

However, this is not the case for V$_{DR}$(CO$_2$), which only increases linearly up to a certain degree of activation or apparent BET (never above 1000 m^2/g). The carbon precursor that gets the highest $V_{DR}(CO_2)$ is the Saran sample, as shown in Figure 6, for which that linearity extends up to ≈ 0.6 cm^3/g.

The maximum $V_{DR}(CO_2)$ is much lower for the other carbon precursors used, decreasing from Saran in the following order: carbon fibers, lignocellolusic materials and finally coals.

These observations indicate that $V_{DR}(N_2)$ and $V_{DR}(CO_2)$ develop differently with the activation degree. $V_{DR}(CO_2)$ develops at low activation degrees, whereas at higher burn-offs wider micropores (supermicropores) appear. From these results we can conclude that, by physical activation, it is indeed difficult to prepare ACs with apparent surface areas higher than 1000 m^2/g having simultaneously similar $V_{DR}(N_2)$ and $V_{DR}(CO_2)$ values. Above ≈ 1000 m^2/g physical activation produces an important widening of the porosity.

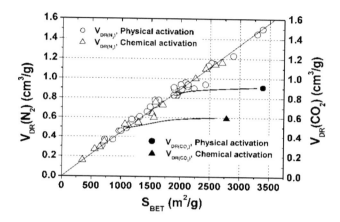

Figure 6. Comparative micropore volume ($V_{DR}(N_2)$) and narrow micropore volume ($V_{DR}(CO_2)$) evolutions vs apparent BET surface area for samples activated by physical and chemical activation.

3.2. Physical Activation (PA) vs Hydroxide Activation (HA)

The comparison between these two activation processes can also be deduced from Figure 6, where the $V_{DR}(N_2)$ and $V_{DR}(CO_2)$ are plotted versus the apparent BET surface area for a large series of ACs prepared by KOH activation.

It can be observed that, contrarily to what happened by physical activation, the $V_{DR}(CO_2)$ can reach linearity for activated carbons having BET surface areas much higher than 1000 m^2/g, allowing to prepare ACs with more than 2000 m^2/g, having simultaneously $V_{DR}(N_2) \approx V_{DR}(CO_2)$. These results confirm that hydroxide activation develops porosity in a different way than physical activation and shows an important advantage of the carbon activation by hydroxides. To strengthen the comparison between physical and chemical activation processes, three ACFs prepared by KOH, NaOH, and CO$_2$ activation from milled coal tar pitch-derived carbon fibers (Donacarbo S-241 precursor, supplied by Osaka gas Co., Ltd) with similar apparent surface areas have been selected. Table 3 compiles the characterisation results of the three ACFs and Figure 7 presents their PSD.

Table 3. ACFs prepared by CO$_2$, NaOH and KOH

Sample	S_{BET} (m^2/g)	Yield (%)

CF	---	---
CO_2	2487	6
NaOH	2541	40
KOH	2420	50

Two observations merit to be pointed out: i) the activation yield of the CO_2 activation is low, in comparison with the ones obtained for hydroxide activations, and ii) the PSD results obtained from the three activation agents show a noticeable dependence on the activation method used, the narrowest one being obtained for KOH, followed by NaOH and finally by CO_2.

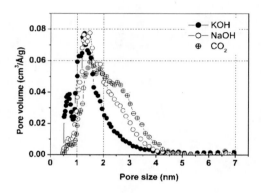

Figure 7. PSD of these ACs (redrawn from [10]).

In summary, the previous examples show that carbon activation by hydroxides is advantageous over physical activation because, in addition to its higher activation yields, ACs with both, high porosity development and narrow PSD, can be prepared. These characteristics are very interesting for some specific applications, as it is discussed later on.

Table 4. Commercial ACs prepared from different activation processes

Sample	Activation	S_{BET} (m²/g)	$V_{DR}(N_2)$ (cm³/g)	$V_{DR}(CO_2)$ (cm³/g)
A20, Osaka Gas	Physical act.	2206	0.79	0.43
Kynol ACF-25	Physical act.	1989	0.87	0.62
GF45, Norit	Chemical act. (H_3PO_4)	1718	0.75	0.35
A1100, Westvaco	Chemical act. (H_3PO_4)	1757	0.67	0.36
Maxsorb, Kensai Chemical	Chemical act. (KOH)	3178	1.20	0.69
AX21, Anderson Co.	Chemical act. (KOH)	2513	0.93	0.68
UA*	Chemical act. (KOH)	2122	0.92	0.89

* KOH activated anthracite prepared in the University of Alicante.

The advantage of the hydroxides activation in relation to other activation processes, in terms of porosity and pore size distributions, can also be inferred from Table 4, which compiles the adsorption characteristics of well-known commercial ACs prepared from different activation processes and precursors. These commercial ACs are: two ACFs prepared by physical activation (from Osaka Gas (A20) and from Kynol (ACF-25)), two phosphoric acid activated carbons (from Norit (GF45) and from Westvaco (A1100)), and two KOH activated carbons (Maxsorb3 and AX21). The table also includes a KOH-activated anthracite which was prepared in our laboratory. The selected commercial samples cover apparent BET surface areas from about 2000 m^2/g to 3000 m^2/g. From these data, it can be concluded that commercial ACs or the one prepared in the laboratory by KOH activation posses much higher $V_{DR}(CO_2)$ than those obtained by phosphoric acid or by physical activation. For example, the sample prepared in our laboratory has a BET surface area above 2000 m^2/g and, interestingly, similar $V_{DR}(N_2) \approx V_{DR}(CO_2)$.

3.3. General Feature of the Phosphoric Acid Activation (PAc)

The main feature of the phosphoric acid activation is the development of ACs with a large volume of supermicropores and mesopores [64,65]. These features lead to special applications (e.g., in gasoline car canisters for gasoline evaporation control [66]). Using a series of ACs prepared by phosphoric acid or alkaline hydroxide (KOH or NaOH) activation, their N_2 (77 K) and CO_2 (273 K) adsorption data are compared, in terms of porosity development.

3.4. Phosphoric Acid Activation (PAc) vs Hydroxide Activation (HA)

Using a given precursor, its activation by H_3PO_4, NaOH and KOH is compared in the present section. The precursor is a coconut fiber matting (CFM) waste, generated in the commercial production of coconuts (*Cocos nucifera*) in Salvador. In phosphoric acid activation, the precursor has been impregnated drop by drop with a given H_3PO_4 solution to prepare different H_3PO_4/precursor ratios (1.7/1, 3.0/1, and 4.1/1) [67], whereas for NaOH and KOH activations three hydroxide/precursor ratios have been used (1/1, 1.5/1 and 2/1) and the physical mixing method has been employed [12].

Figure 8a presents the N_2 adsorption isotherms (77 K) for ACs activated with NaOH and KOH (ratios from 1/1 to 2/1) and Figure 8b shows the isotherms of the ACs prepared with H_3PO_4 at three ratios (from 1.7/1 to 4.1/1). As the activating agent/precursor ratio increases, the resulting adsorption capacity increases for the three activating agents. However, they develop differently the samples' porosity, as evidenced by the different isotherm shapes: type I for samples activated with hydroxides (microporous samples) and type I + IV for samples activated with H_3PO_4 (microporous and mesoporous samples).

Table 5 compiles the textural properties of activated carbons prepared by activation with NaOH, KOH or H_3PO_4. It can be seen that the three activating agents used are very effective for developing high porosity, especially NaOH. The achieved porosities are remarkable, considering the low activating agent/precursor ratios used.

Table 5. Characteristics of ACs obtained by chemical activation with NaOH, KOH and H₃PO₄

Activating agent	Sample CFM	S_{BET} (m²/g)	$V_{DR}(N_2)$ (cm³/g)	$V_{DR}(CO_2)$ (cm³/g)	V_{Meso} (cm³/g)
NaOH	Na1/1	1437	0.62	0.45	0.12
NaOH	Na1.5/1	1927	0.82	0.54	0.17

NaOH	Na2/1	2622	0.97	0.57	0.41
KOH	K1/1	1178	0.58	0.46	0.04
KOH	K2/1	1888	0.91	0.76	0.05
KOH	K1.5/1	1570	0.78	0.62	0.04
H_3PO_4	P1.7/1	2285	0.94	0.48	0.47
H_3PO_4	P3.0/1	2320	0.89	0.46	0.67
H_3PO_4	P4.1/1	2569	1.01	0.49	0.86

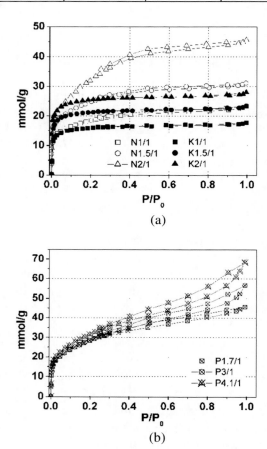

(a)

(b)

Figure 8. N_2 adsorption isotherms at 77 K for ACs prepared from coconut fiber matting (CFM) activated by (a) NaOH or KOH, and (b) H_3PO_4.

Also, it can be observed that the development of narrow microporosity increases in the order: H_3PO_4 < NaOH < KOH, whereas the mesoporosity develops in the order: KOH < NaOH < H_3PO_4, being especially relevant for H_3PO_4 activation. For a better comparison of these activation results, Figure 9 presents the PSDs of some selected ACs which have similar S_{BET} surface areas (K2/1, N1.5/1 and P1.7/1 samples). The PSDs clearly confirm the conclusions deduced from the N_2 adsorption isotherm shapes. Thus, the ACs prepared with H_3PO_4 have the widest pore size distributions, whereas the ACs obtained with NaOH and, especially, KOH have narrow pore size distributions.

From the previous results we can conclude that NaOH, KOH and H$_3$PO$_4$ are good activating agents which allow to obtain highly porous ACs. However, they develop different kinds of porosity. Thus, large mesopore volumes are obtained with H$_3$PO$_4$ activation, whereas narrow microporosity is obtained with KOH.

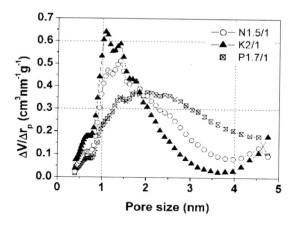

Figure 9. Pore size distributions of CFM samples prepared with KOH, NaOH and H$_3$PO$_4$ having similar BET surface area (around 2000 m^2 g^{-1}).

In order to improve the ACs performance according to their application, it is necessary to develop a suitable porosity. For example, the development of narrow microporosity is important in applications such as volatiles organic compounds (VOC) removal at low concentration [27,68,69] or gas storage [59,60] and high development of mesoporosity is interesting for example in gasoline vapour recovery [66].

4. THE USE OF ACs PREPARED BY HYDROXIDE ACTIVATION IN SELECTED POTENTIAL APPLICATIONS

The importance of the narrow microporosity (pores < 0.7 nm), which can be well developed with the activation by alkaline hydroxides (especially with KOH) is the controlling key for some specific applications of the ACs, as it is commented in the following sections.

4.1. VOC Removal at Low Concentration

As an example, Figure 10a plots the relationship between benzene adsorption capacity at 200 ppmv in helium (at 25°C) and the volume of narrow micropores for a series of ACs. These samples comprise a group of granular or powdered activated carbons.

Most of them were prepared by chemical activation with hydroxides, and some activated carbon fibers were prepared by steam or carbon dioxide activation [68,69]. From the results of this figure, it can be seen that the development of high narrow micropore volumes (pore < 0.7 nm) is highly beneficial for VOCs removal.

Figure 10a seems to suggest, at a first glance, that those adsorbents with fibrous morphology present higher VOC removal capacities than the others. However, the surface oxygen groups content of the materials have to be taken into account since, as discussed elsewhere, the presence of surface oxygen groups decreases the VOC removal [27,68,69].

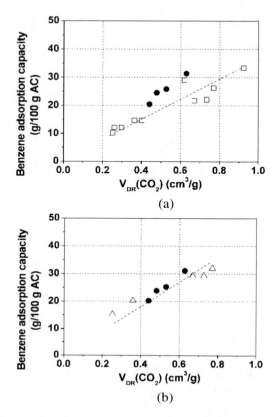

(a)

(b)

Figure 10. Relationship between benzene adsorption capacity, at 200 ppmv (and 25°C), and the volume of narrow micropores, redrawn from [68, 69], for: (a) ACFs (black circles) and pristine ACs (open squares) and (b) ACFs (black circles) and heat-treated ACs (open triangles).

Thus, results from Figure 10a can be understood considering that these ACFs, which present higher benzene adsorption, have lower oxygen surface groups than the other materials tested. This can be confirmed in Figure 10b in which all the AC samples (except ACFs) have been heat-treated to reduce their oxygen surface content.

Because all the samples of Figure 10b have similar oxygen contents, benzene adsorption depends only on their corresponding narrow micropore volumes [68].

Therefore, it is necessary to further improve the development of larger narrow micropore volumes for getting even better adsorption capacities. The results also emphasize the importance of having a low content of surface oxygen groups in order to enhance low-polarity VOC adsorption at low concentration.

4.2. Electricity Storage (EDLC-Supercapacitor-)

The electric double layer capacitor (EDLC) is an increasingly popular energy storage device. Due to its high energy and power densities it bridges the gap between batteries and classical electric capacitors [70]. An example of the application of alkaline hydroxides to prepare suitable ACs as electrodes for supercapacitors will be presented using activated carbon nanofibers (ACNFs) [71].

These materials were prepared from polymer blend-based CNFs which were activated with potassium hydroxide at different KOH/precursor ratios (from 0.5/1 to 3/1), as shown in Figure 11.

Their use as supercapacitor electrodes has been studied in cells having different electrolytes. Figure 11b presents their specific capacitance versus their apparent BET surface area in two electrolyte solutions (aqueous KOH, and aqueous H_2SO_4) [71].

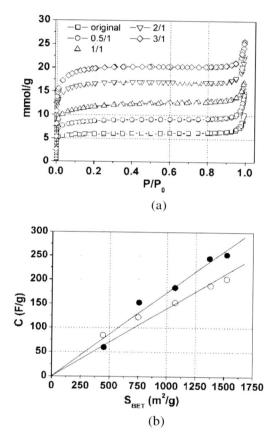

(a)

(b)

Figure 11. (a) N_2 adsorption isotherms, and (b) specific capacitance of ACNFs measured at 1mAcm^{-2} (C) vs. BET specific surface area (S_{BET}) in two electrolytes: H_2SO_4 (black circles) and KOH (open circles) (redrawn from [71]).

It can be seen that an increase in the KOH/CNFs ratio causes an enhancement of the adsorption capacity. Furthermore, a linear relationship exists between the apparent BET surface area and the specific capacitance, as it is shown in Figure 11b, which is also confirmed by results in the literature [72]. Considering that the apparent surface areas of these samples are < 1500 m^2/g, their capacitance results are high, presumably due to their relatively high conductivity. Thus, they present enhanced specific capacitances, in relation to conventional ACFs (fibers with diameters of about 10 μm), because of their nanometric size diameters. Additionally, their capacitances were less dependent on the current density in comparison with conventional ACFs. These advantages, useful for EDLC application, were attributed to a faster adsorption-desorption rate in the micropores of the ACNFs, thanks to their smaller diameters [71, 73].

4.3. Gas Storage

The high pressure storage of gases such as hydrogen, methane, carbon dioxide and others has a special interest for their potential use as fuel (e.g., hydrogen) or in the case of carbon dioxide for its capture and truck transport to its final storage, for example in a geological reservoir. The storage principle is the use of a high pressure adsorption process (or physisorption), as a supercritical gas (e.g., H_2) or as a subcritical one (e.g., CO_2). Such adsorption process has some advantages: a high storage capacity (very much depending on the surface area, porosity and pore size of the material), a fast kinetic of storage and release (reversibility), a short refueling time, a low heat evolution and an efficient cyclability. As shown above, ACs prepared by hydroxides activation present interesting properties such as very high porosity, different morphologies and tunable characteristics (sizes and shapes). Additionally, they possess good chemical stability, a suitable packing density and have relatively low cost.

4.3.1. Hydrogen Storage by High Pressure Adsorption

For a future energy sector, hydrogen is considered an ideal secondary energy carrier and a clean alternative to other fuels. For example, in fuel cells it can be used to provide electricity with high efficiency, emitting only water. However, its storage is one of the main drawbacks, due to its low density. In order to use hydrogen as a fuel in transportation, a number of different technologies are considered today [74-77]. Among them, the high pressure storage in adsorbent materials is a promising technology. Of course, the type of adsorbent plays the most relevant role, ACs being the most suitable candidates [75].

Two main alternatives can be used for storing hydrogen by high pressure adsorption; i) at room temperature and very high pressures (from 10 MPa to 70 MPa) and/or ii) at low temperatures (cryogenic temperatures) and moderate pressures (< 4 MPa).

As an example of the performance of the ACs to store hydrogen, we have selected the results obtained with the Donacarbo SL-242 carbon fiber (CF), activated with KOH at different KOH/CF ratios that were commented before (see Table 2). Such series of KOH-activated carbon fibers cover a wide range of porosity, providing high volumes of narrow micropores (< 0.7 nm), which are especially important to store hydrogen.

The hydrogen adsorption isotherms of the investigated materials, measured at 298 K, are shown in Figure 12a. The unactivated fiber precursor already adsorbs over 0.4 wt%. By chemical activation with KOH, the adsorption amount can be increased significantly. The hydrogen adsorption amount increases with the KOH/fiber ratio up to a ratio of 4/1, reaching the maximum adsorption amount of 1.1 wt%. When the ratio is further increased to 5/1, no significant increase in hydrogen adsorption is observed. Probably, this is due to a destruction of the narrow microporosity which controls the hydrogen uptake at room temperature and 20 MPa.

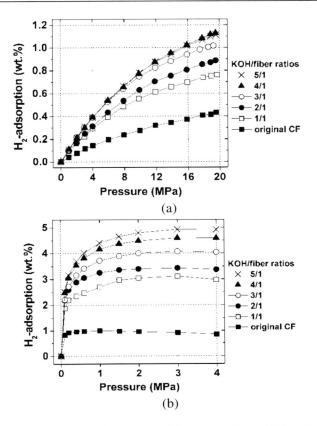

Figure 12. Gravimetric H_2 excess adsorption measured for an unactivated CF, and ACFs that were activated with KOH using KOH/fiber ratios between 1/1 and 5/1 (a) at 298 K, and (b) at 77 K (redrawn from [63]).

The hydrogen adsorption isotherms at 77 K and up to 4 MPa of the same samples are shown in Figure 12b. The unactivated carbon fiber already adsorbs 1 wt% of hydrogen at 77 K, due to a small amount of narrow microporosity. As expected, the adsorption increases significantly when the precursor is chemically activated with KOH. Thus, the adsorption capacities of the activated samples continuously increase with the KOH/fiber ratio. The highest adsorption amount of around 5 wt% is reached for a KOH/fiber ratio of 5/1.

It is a common practice to try to find correlations between porosity and hydrogen adsorption [63, 78-87]. In Figure 13a, the gravimetric H_2 adsorption values, obtained at 298 K and 20 MPa, are plotted versus the narrow micropore volume, $V_{DR}(CO_2)$. The hydrogen uptake values were taken from Figure 12, as well as from other ACF materials [72]. A linear relationship can be observed between $V_{DR}(CO_2)$ and the gravimetric hydrogen uptakes at room temperature. This is in agreement with findings from previous studies [63, 78-80, 87, 88].

In the case of hydrogen adsorption at 77 K and 4 MPa, previous studies found a better correlation with the total microporosity (< 2 nm) [63,78,79]. Accordingly, in Figure 13b, the maximum adsorption amounts at 77 K are plotted versus the total micropore volume, $V_{DR}(N_2)$. Also at 77 K the expected linear relationships with micropore volumes larger than 0.1 cm^3/g can be observed, being in agreement with previously reported results [63,78-83,87].

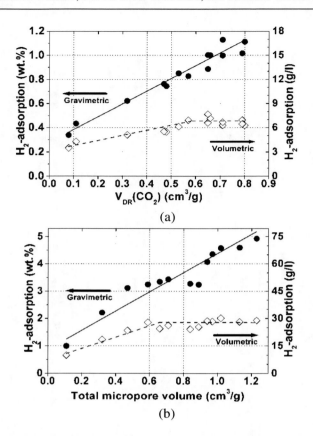

(a)

(b)

Figure 13. Maximum H_2 excess adsorption (redrawn from [63]) (a) at 298 K and up to 20 MPa vs the volume of narrow micropores ($V_{DR}(CO_2)$) and (b) at 77 K and up to 4 MPa vs the total micropore volume ($V_{DR}(N_2)$) for a large number ACFs. The H_2 excess adsorption is given on a gravimetric (left axis), as well as on a volumetric basis (right axis).

In addition to the gravimetric adsorption amounts, also the excess adsorption on a volumetric basis is correlated in Figures 13a and 13b. The volumetric adsorption amounts were calculated by multiplying the gravimetric values by the corresponding packing densities from Table 2. In contrast to what was found for the gravimetric values at both adsorption temperatures, no linear trend can be observed for the volumetric adsorption amounts. Interestingly, these results clearly indicate that also adsorbents with less developed porosity are able to obtain high volumetric adsorption values, if they have higher densities. In volumetric terms, an optimum relation between developed porosity and packing density needs to be found.

Until now, only gravimetric and volumetric excess adsorption of H_2 has been discussed. However, for practical applications, it is of interest to determine the amount of hydrogen that can be stored inside a determined tank design. Real adsorbents always contain certain amount of void space, and its contribution to the total storage needs to be taken into account in order to estimate the total storage capacity of a material. Therefore, the effort has to be made to reduce the void space as much as possible by increasing the packing density of the material. The void space can be estimated by means of the following formula: $V_{Void} = 1 - (\rho_{Pack}/\rho_{Skel})$ [63,78,79,87,89,90], where V_{Void} is the void space, ρ_{Pack} the packing density, and ρ_{Skel} the skeleton density of the material. When applied to the adsorption isotherms in Figure 12, high total hydrogen storage capacities are obtained: 17.1 g/l at 298 K, and 38.6 g/l at 77 K, respectively. Clearly, not only the porosity of the material, but also its packing density is of particular importance for the total amount of hydrogen stored. Continuing with this concept of total hydrogen storage, all the data shown in Figure 13 reaches considerably higher total hydrogen capacities than the plotted values. As an example, the two highest values obtained at 298 K (1.1 wt%) and at 77 K (4.9 wt%), give total hydrogen capacities of 2.8 wt% and 6.4 wt%, respectively. All these results indicate that interesting hydrogen storage materials can be synthesized by carbon fibers activation with hydroxides, although more work is required to further improve them.

4.3.2. Carbon Dioxide Storage by High Pressure Adsorption

According to the IPCC´s report, there are unequivocal evidences which indicate that the climate-change is a reality attributable to the human activity [91].

Nowadays, carbon capture, storage and transport (for short-term CO_2 storage in CCS technologies) are some of the technological options that are being studied in order to control CO_2 emissions to the atmosphere and, hence, to reduce climatic change effects [91].

Among them, high pressure adsorption on porous materials has a special interest and hence, both, the properties of the adsorbents (mainly surface area, micropore volume and narrow micropore volume) and the storage pressure used will control the final storage capacity. The use of solid adsorbents (porous materials) has been established as a potentially valid alternative for the CO_2 capture.

There is a large variety of available porous materials and, among them, activated carbon materials have emerged as promising adsorbents within CCS technologies [92-98]. This is due to their unique properties such as high pore volumes and surface areas, high stability and low chemical reactivity [56]. These properties make activated carbons attractive materials, not only in the CO_2 capture, but also in its transportation.

Capture and discontinuous transport of CO_2 have been investigated for years in our research group by using activated carbons obtained by different activation procedures (physical and chemical activation). Our results conclude that those ACs prepared by alkaline hydroxides show significant advantages for this application since their textural properties and porosity can be perfectly controlled and tailored, as it has been previously discussed.

In this section we illustrate the CO_2 uptake at room temperature (298 K) using a large number of activated carbons prepared from several precursors (i.e., lignocellulosic precursors and coals) and different activation variables (e.g., the use of NaOH or KOH as activating agents or the hydroxide/precursor ratios).

Consequently, these ACs have a wide variety of textural properties which allow to analyze the relationship between the amount of CO_2 adsorbed and their textural properties. Figure 14 presents their large range of adsorption capacities: (a) narrow micropore volume ($V_{DR}(CO_2)$), (b) total micropore volume ($V_{DR}(N_2)$), and (c) BET surface area (ranging from about 500 m^2/g to more than 3000 m^2/g).

The high pressure device and the procedure used to store CO_2 on ACs are described elsewhere [78,99]. Figure 15 presents the storage results obtained in these ACs at different pressures (up to 4 MPa), showing the influence that the sample properties have on the results. Thus, Figure 15a relates the narrow micropore volume with the CO_2 uptake. It shows that the adsorption capacity controls the uptake and that a well defined linear relationship exists between these two parameters when the pressure range is limited to 0.1 and 1 MPa. Hence, at this pressure range the amount of CO_2 adsorbed is controlled by the narrow micropore volume (< 0.7 nm).

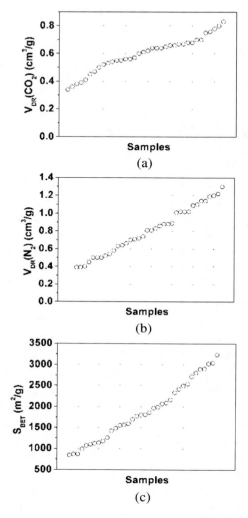

Figure 14. Textural properties obtained from the characterization of the chemically activated carbons. (a) narrow micropore volume, (b) total micropore volume, and (c) BET surface area.

For pressures higher than 1 MPa, such linear tendency is not observed anymore (see the bad defined correlation for 4 MPa). This indicates that, at higher pressures, the filling of larger pores is taking place. This is confirmed in Figure 15b where a linear relationship between the CO_2 uptake and the total micropore volume (or apparent BET surface area) is observed for the higher pressure range studied (from 1 to 4 MPa). In summary, these results show that CO_2 uptake at room temperature is sensitive to both, the pore size distribution and the storage pressure used. From an application point of view, the density of the ACs is needed to determine their CO_2 storage per unit volume. ACs prepared by hydroxide activation (as shown above) present interesting packing densities (i.e., density obtained by applying a certain pressure). An example is shown in Figure 16 where the total, the adsorbed and the compressed CO_2 is presented per unit of volume (g CO_2/l).

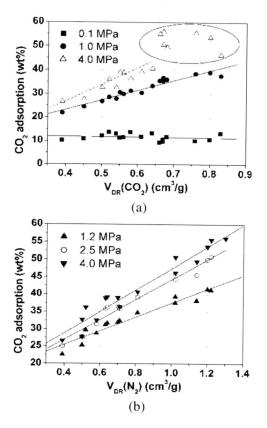

(a)

(b)

Figure 15. Influence of the different textural properties as a function of the pressure used for the adsorption process of CO_2 at 298 K versus (a) narrow micropore volume, $V_{DR}(CO_2)$, and (b) total micropore volume, $V_{DR}(N_2)$.

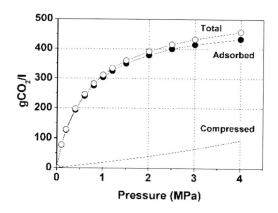

Figure 16. Comparison between CO_2 stored by compression and by adsorption on an activated carbon.

The amount of CO_2 stored per unit of volume in a tank vessel that contains activated carbon is higher than the CO_2 stored in the same tank by compression (empty vessel). For example, at 2 MPa, a tank filled with activated carbon could store almost 400 g/l, while the amount stored by compression would be only 40 g/l. Thus, the adsorption process can store more than 9 times the amount stored by compression, which is an important advantage for transport. At 4 MPa the CO_2 storage is indeed large, reaching for some monolithic samples 500 g/l.

CONCLUSION

In addition to the many large scale uses of alkaline hydroxides, this article analyzes and claims attention to a relatively new one: the hydroxide activation of carbon materials.

It is based on the strong reactivity of NaOH and KOH when they are mixed and heat-treated with carbon precursors. These strong chemical alkaline bases react with most carbon precursors, modifying their original porosities through a solid-liquid redox reaction. In this reaction, carbon is oxidized to carbonate and the hydroxide is mainly reduced to alkaline metal and hydrogen. Hence, both reactants are converted to hydrogen, alkaline metals, alkaline carbonates, and to a reacted carbon product, which remains due to the use of a low hydroxide stoichiometry.

After washing the reaction products, a super class activated carbon (AC) can be obtained from the resulting carbon material.

The main features of the ACs obtained by this process are their high adsorption capacities and their narrow pore size distributions, which make them suitable for different applications. As it happens in most chemical reactions, the kinetics and the extent of the hydroxide-carbon reaction are generally affected by many variables.

However, contrarily to most chemical reactions, the key point of such reaction is the porosity characteristics of the remaining carbon. Hence, this article analyzes, in different sections, how the most relevant reaction variables affect the porosity of the prepared ACs.

The main conclusions which can be extracted from the analyzed variables (among others, the reactivity of the carbon precursor, the nature of the hydroxide and the hydroxide/carbon ratio) are: 1) all of them have important effects on the reaction extent and on the carbon activation degree, which determine the properties of the resulting activated carbons. 2) The porosity development of the ACs prepared by such hydroxide activation process is quite singular in terms of porous texture and pore size distribution. 3) When compared with other activation processes, the characteristics of the resulting ACs can be controlled much more efficiently by the activation with hydroxides. 4) NaOH, as well as KOH, are among the most powerful known activating agents to prepare super high quality ACs and 5) the unique characteristics of the ACs prepared by hydroxide activation (high microporosity including a well developed narrow micropore volume) are very useful for most of the applications related to energy and environmental concerns which are discussed in this article (e.g., VOC removal, supercapacitors, hydrogen storage, as well as capture, storage and transport of carbon dioxide).

ACKNOWLEDGMENTS

The authors thank the Spanish MICINN (MAT 2009-07150), the Generalitat Valenciana (project Prometeo/2009/047) and FEDER for financial support.

REFERENCES

[1]   Kirk-Othmer, R. E. *Kirk-Othmer Encyclopedia of Chemical Technology;* John Wiley and Sons: New York, NY, 2007 (57th edition).

[2]   Greenwood, N. N.; Earnshaw, A. *Chemistry of the Elements;* Butterworth-Heinemann: Oxford, 2003 (2nd edition).

[3]   Holleman, A. F.; Wiberg, E. *Inorganic Chemistry;* Academic press: San Diego, CA, 2001.

[4]   Shriver, D. F.; Atkins, P. W. *Inorganic Chemistry;* Oxford University Press: Oxford, 2002.

[5]   Housecroft, C. E.; Sharpe, A. G. *Inorganic Chemistry;* Pearson Prentice Hall: New York, NY, 2008.

[6]   Kurt, C.; Bittner, J. In *Ullmann's Encyclopedia of Industrial Chemistry*; Wiley-VCH: Weinheim, DE, 2005.

[7]   Bailar, J. C.; Eméleus, H. J.; Nyholm, R.; Trotaman-Dickenson, A. F. *Comprehensive Inorganic Chemistry* vol I; Pergamon Press: Oxford, 1973.

[8]   Lillo-Ródenas, M. A.; Cazorla-Amorós, D.; Linares-Solano, A. *Carbon.,* 2003, 41(2), 267-275.

[9]   Lillo-Ródenas, M. A.; Juan-Juan, J.; Cazorla-Amorós, D.; Linares-Solano, A. *Carbon.,* 2004, 42(7), 1365-1369.

[10] Linares-Solano, A.; Lozano-Castelló, D.; Lillo-Ródenas, M. A.; Cazorla-Amorós, D. *Chem. Phys. Carbon.,* 2008, 30, 1-62.

[11] Lozano-Castelló, D.; Lillo-Ródenas, M. A.; Cazorla-Amorós, D.; Linares-Solano, A. *Carbon.,* 2001, 39(5), 741-749.

[12] Lillo-Ródenas, M. A.; Lozano-Castelló, D.; Cazorla-Amorós, D.; Linares-Solano, A. *Carbon.,* 2001, 39(5), 751-759.

[13] Otowa, T.; Tanibata, R.; Itoh, M. *Gas. Sep. Purif.,* 1993, 7(4), 241-245.

[14] Wennerberg, A. N.; O'Grady, T. M. (1978) US patent, 4,082,694.

[15] Ahmadpour, A.; Do, D. D. *Carbon.,* 1996, 34(4), 471-479.

[16] Juan-Juan, J.; Lozano-Castelló, D.; Raymundo-Piñero, E.; Lillo-Ródenas, M. A.; Cazorla-Amorós, D.; Linares-Solano, A. In *Solutions in dioxin and mercury removal*; Editors, Cazorla, D.; Wirling, J.; Publicaciones Universidad de Alicante: *Alicante,* 2003; pp 91-112.

[17] Illán-Gómez, M. J.; García-García, A.; Salinas-Martínez de Lecea, C.; Linares-Solano, A. *Energy Fuels,* 1996, 10(5), 1108-1114.

[18] Hayashi, J.; Watkinson, A. P.; Teo, K. C.; Takemoto, S.; Muroyama, K. In *Coal Science 1*; Editors, Pajares, J.A.; Tascón, J.M.D.; Elsevier Science: The Netherlands, 1995; pp 1121-1124.

[19] Ahmadpour, A.; Do, D. D. *Carbon.,* 1997, 35(12), 1723-1732.

[20] Evans, M. J. B.; Halliop, E.; MacDonald, J. A. F. *Carbon.,* 1999, 37(2), 269-274.

[21] Teng, H.; Hsu, L. Y. *Ind. Eng. Chem. Res.*, 1999, 38(8), 2947-2953.

[22] Perrin, A.; Celzard, A.; Albiniak, A.; Kaczmarczyk, J.; Marêché, J. F.; Furdin, G. *Carbon.*, 2004, 42(14), 2855-2866.

[23] Teng, H.; Yeh, T. S.; Hsu, L. Y. *Carbon.*, 1998, 36(9), 1387-1395.

[24] Guo, J.; Lua, A. C. *Micropor. Mesopor. Mat.*, 1999, 32(1-2), 111-117.

[25] Zou, Y.; Han, B. X. *Adsorpt. Sci. Technol.*, 2001, 19(1), 59-72.

[26] Lozano-Castelló, D.; Cazorla-Amorós, D.; Linares-Solano, A. *Fuel Process. Technol.*, 2002, 77-78, 325-330.

[27] Lillo-Ródenas, M. A.; Carratalá-Abril, J.; Cazorla-Amorós, D.; Linares-Solano, A. *Fuel Process. Technol.*, 2002, 77-78, 331-336.

[28] Park, S. J.; Jung, W. Y. *J. Colloid Interf. Sci.*, 2002, 250(1), 93–98.

[29] Park, S. J.; Jung, W. Y. *J. Colloid Interf. Sci.*, 2002, 250(1), 196–200.

[30] Carvalho, A. P.; Cardoso, B.; Pires, J.; de Carvalho, M. B. *Carbon.*, 2003, 41(14), 2873-2876.

[31] Diaz-Teran, J.; Nevskaia, D. M.; Fierro, J. L. G., Lopez-Peinado, A. J.; Jerez, A. *Micropor. Mesopor. Mat.*, 2003, 60(1-3), 173-181.

[32] Guo, J.; Lua, A. C. *Chem. Eng. Res. Des.*, 2003, 81(A5), 585-590.

[33] Maciá-Agulló, J. A.; Moore, B. C.; Cazorla-Amorós, D.; Linares-Solano, A. *Carbon.*, 2004, 42(7), 1367-1370.

[34] Tseng, R.-L.; Tseng, S.-K. *Journal of Colloid and Interface Science*, 2005, 287 (2), 428-437.

[35] Fierro, V.; Torné-Fernández, V.; Celzard, A. *Microporous and Mesoporous Materials*, 2007, 101 (3), 419-431.

[36] Wang, H.; Gao, Q.; Hu, J. *Journal of the American Chemical Society*, 2009,131 (20), 7016-7022.

[37] Basta, A.H.; Fierro, V.; El-Saied, H.; Celzard, A. *Bioresource Technology*, 2009, 100 (17), 3941-3947.

[38] Sevilla, M.; Mokaya, R.; Fuertes, A. B. *Energy Environ. Sci.*, 2011, 4(8), 2930-2936.

[39] Zheng, M. D.; Zhang, X. Y.; Li, R. C.; Wu, M. B.; Geng, Y. J.; He, X. *J. Adv. Mat. Res.*, 2011, 197-198, 1253-1257.

[40] Roskill Information Services. *The Economics of Activated Carbon*; Roskill Information Services Ltd.: London, 2008.

[41] Linares-Solano, A.; Cazorla-Amorós, D. In *Handbook of Advanced Ceramics*, Eds. Somiya, S.; Kaneno, M. 2nd Edition. In press.

[42] Cazorla-Amorós, D.; Alcaniz-Monge, J.; Linares-Solano, A. *Langmuir*, 1996, 12(11), 2820-2824.

[43] De La Casa-Lillo, M.A.; Alcañiz-Monge, J.; Raymundo-Piñero, E.; Cazorla-Amorós, D.; Linares-Solano, A. *Carbon.*, 1998, 36(9), 1353-1360.

[44] Rodríguez-Reinoso, F.; Linares-Solano, A. In *Chemistry and Physics of Carbon*; Thrower, P. A.; Ed.; Marcel Dekker: New York, NY, 1989; Vol. 21, pp 1-146.

[45] Cazorla-Amorós, D.; Alcañiz-Monge, J.; De la Casa-Lillo, M. A.; Linares-Solano, A. *Langmuir.*, 1998, 14(16), 4589-4596.

[46] Lozano-Castelló, D.; Cazorla-Amorós, D.; Linares-Solano, A.; Quinn, D. F. *J. Phys. Chem., B* 2002, 106(36), 9372-9379.

[47] Lozano-Castelló, D.; Cazorla-Amorós, D.; Linares-Solano, A. *Carbon.*, 2004, 42(7), 1233-1242.

[48] Lozano-Castelló, D.; Cazorla-Amorós, D.; Linares-Solano, A.; Hall, P. J.; Fernández, J. J. *Studi. Surf. Sci. Catal.,* 2000, 128, 523-532.

[49] Lozano-Castelló, D.; Raymundo-Piñero, E.; Cazorla-Amorós, D.; Linares-Solano, A.; Müller, M.; Riekel, C. *Carbon.,* 2002, 40(14), 2727-2735.

[50] Lozano-Castelló, D.; Raymundo-Piñero, E.; Cazorla-Amorós, D.; Linares-Solano, A.; Müller, M.; Riekel, C. *Studi. Surf. Sci. Catal.,* 2002, 144, 51-58.

[51] Lozano-Castelló, D.; Cazorla-Amorós, D.; Linares-Solano, A. *Chem. Eng. Technol.,* 2003, 26(8), 852-857.

[52] Lillo-Ródenas, M. A.; Cazorla-Amorós, D.; Linares-Solano, A.; Béguin, F.; Clinard, C.; Rouzaud, J. N. *Carbon.,* 2004, 42(7), 1305-1310.

[53] Lillo-Ródenas, M. A., Marco-Lozar, J. P., Cazorla-Amorós, D., Linares-Solano, A. *J. Anal. Appl. Pyrol.,* 2007, 80(1), 166-174.

[54] Vilaplana-Ortego, E.; Lillo-Ródenas, M. A.; Alcañiz-Monge, J.; Cazorla-Amorós, D.; Linares-Solano, A. *Carbon.,* 2009, 47(8), 2141-2142.

[55] Vilaplana-Ortego, E.; Lillo-Ródenas, M. A.; Alcañiz-Monge, J.; Cazorla-Amorós, D.; Linares-Solano, A. *Fuel Process. Technol.,* 2010, 91(2), 145-149.

[56] Bansal, R. C.; Donnet, J. B.; Stoeckli, F. *Active Carbon;* Marcel Dekker: New York, NY, 1988.

[57] Jankowska, H.; Swiatkowski, A.; Choma, J. *Active Carbon,* Ellis Horwood: New York, NY, 1991; pp 29-38.

[58] Marsh, H.; Heintz, E. A.; Rodríguez-Reinoso, F. *Introduction to Carbon Technologies;* Servicio de Publicaciones de la Universidad de Alicante: Alicante, 1997.

[59] Kyotani, T. In *Carbon Alloys. Novel Concepts to Develop Carbon Science and Technology;* Yasuda, E.; Inagaki, M.; Kaneko, K.; Endo, M.; Oya, A.; Tanabe, Y.; Eds.; *Elsevier Science*: Oxford, 2003; pp 109-142.

[60] Burchell, T. D. *Carbon Materials for Advanced Technologies;* Pergamon: Amsterdam, 1999.

[61] Raymundo-Piñero, E.; Azaïs, P.; Cacciaguerra, T.; Cazorla-Amorós, D.; Linares-Solano, A.; Béguin, F. *Carbon.,* 2005, 43(4), 786-795.

[62] Maciá-Agulló, J. A.; Moore, B. C.; Cazorla-Amorós, D.; Linares-Solano, A. *Proceeding of Carbon Conference,* 2003, Oviedo, 2003.

[63] Kunowsky, M.; Marco-Lozar, J. P.; Cazorla-Amorós, D.; Linares-Solano, A. *Int. J. Hydrogen Energy,* 2010, 35(6), 2393-2402.

[64] Molina-Sabio, M.; Rodríguez-Reinoso, F. *Colloids and Surfaces A: Physicochemical and Engineering Aspects,* 2004, 241 (1-3), 15-25.

[65] Puziy, A. M.; Poddubnaya, O. I.; Martínez-Alonso, A; Suárez-García, F.; Castro-Muñiz, A.; Tascón, J. M. D. *Adsorpt. Sci. Technol.,* 2008, 26(10), 843-851.

[66] Philips, J. J.; Setsuda, D. J.; Williams, R. S. In *Carbon materials for advanced technologies;* Burchell, T. D.; Ed.; Pergamon: Amsterdam, 1999; pp 235-268.

[67] Romero-Anaya, A. J.; Lillo-Ródenas, M. A.; Salinas-Martínez de Lecea, C.; Linares-Solano, A. *Carbon.* 2011, doi:10.1016/j.carbon.2011.10.031.

[68] Lillo-Ródenas, M.A.; Cazorla-Amorós, D.; Linares-Solano, A. *Adsorption,* 2011, 17 (3), 473-481.

[69] Lillo-Ródenas, M.A. Cazorla-Amorós D.; Linares-Solano A. *Carbon.,* 2005, 43(8), 1758-1767.

[70]   Conway, B. E. *Electrochemical Supercapacitors: Scientific Fundamentals and Technological Applications;* Kluwer Academic: New York, NY; 1999.

[71]   Barranco, V.; Lillo-Rodenas, M. A.; Linares-Solano, A.; Oya, A.; Pico, F.; Ibañfez, J.; Agullo-Rueda, F.; Amarilla, J. M.; Rojo, J. M. *J. Phys. Chem., C* 2010, 114(22), 10302-10307.

[72]   Béguin, F.; Frackowiak, E. *Carbons for Electrochemical Energy Storage and Conversion Systems;* CRC Press: Boca Raton, FL, 2010.

[73]   Shiraishi, S.; Miyauchi, T.; Sasaki, R.; Nishina, N.; Oya, A.; Hagiwara, R. *Electrochemistry,* 2007, 75(8), 619-621.

[74]   Schlapbach, L.; Züttel, A. *Nature,* 2001, 414(6861), 353-358.

[75]   Von Helmolt, R.; Eberle, U. *J. Power Sources,* 2007, 165(2), 833-843.

[76]   Van Den Berg, A. W. C.; Areán, C. O. *Chem. Commun.,* 2008, 6, 668-681.

[77]   Morris, R. E.; Wheatley, P. S. *Angew. Chem. Int. Edit.,* 2008, 47(27), 4966-4981.

[78]   Linares-Solano, A.; Jordá-Beneyto, M.; Kunowsky, M.; Lozano-Castelló, D.; Suárez-García, F.; Cazorla-Amorós, D. In *Carbon materials-theory and practice;* Editors, Terzyk, A. P.; Gauden, P. A.; Kowalczyk, P.; Research Signpost: Kerala, 2008; pp 245-281.

[79]   Jordá-Beneyto, M.; Suárez-García, F.; Lozano-Castelló, D.; Cazorla-Amorós, D.; Linares-Solano, A. *Carbon.,* 2007, 45(2), 293-303.

[80]   Texier-Mandoki, N.; Dentzer, J.; Piquero, T.; Saadallah, S.; David, P.; Vix-Guterl, C. *Carbon,* 2004, 42(12-13), 2735-2747.

[81]   Thomas, K. M. *Catal. Today,* 2007, 120(3-4), 389-398.

[82]   Panella, B.; Hirscher, M.; Roth, S. *Carbon.,* 2005, 43(10), 2209-2214.

[83]   Gogotsi, Y.; Portet, C.; Osswald, S.; Simmons, J.M.; Yildirim, T.; Laudisio, G.; Fischer, J.E. *Int. J. Hydrogen Energy,* 2009, 34(15), 6314-6319.

[84]   Nijkamp, M. G.; Raaymakers, J. E. M. J.; Van Dillen, A. J.; De Jong, K. P. *Appl. Phys. A - Mater.* 2001, 72(5), 619-623.

[85]   Züttel, A.; Sudan, P.; Mauron, Ph.; Kiyobayashi, T.; Emmenegger, Ch.; Schlapbach, L. *Int. J. Hydrogen Energy,* 2002, 27(2), 203-212.

[86]   Zubizarreta, L.; Arenillas, A.; Pis, J. J. *Int. J. Hydrogen Energy,* 2009, 34(10), 4575-4581.

[87]   De La Casa-Lillo, M. A.; Lamari-Darkrim, F.; Cazorla-Amorós, D.; Linares-Solano, A. *J. Phys. Chem., B* 2002, 106(42), 10930-10934.

[88]   Cabria, I.; López, M. J.; Alonso, J. A. *Phys. Rev., B* 2008, 78(7), 075415.

[89]   Kunowsky, M.; Weinberger, B.; Lamari Darkrim, F.; Suárez-García, F; Cazorla-Amorós, D.; Linares-Solano, A. *Int. J. Hydrogen Energy,* 2008, 33(12), 3091-3095.

[90]   Zhou, L.; Zhou Y.; Sun Y. *Int. J. Hydrogen Energy,* 2004, 29(3), 319-322.

[91]   IPCC, Intergovernmental Panel on Climate Change (2005). *Carbon dioxide Capture and Storage.* http://www.ipcc.ch/publications _and_data/publications_and_data_ reports.shtml

[92]   Martin, C. F.; Plaza, M. G.; Rubiera, F.; Pevida, C.; Centeno, T. A. *Sep. Purif. Technol.,* 2010, 74, 225-229.

[93]   Plaza, M. G.; García, S.; Rubiera, F.; Pis, J. J.; Pevida, C. *Chem. Eng. J.,* 2010, 163, 41-47.

[94]   Plaza, M. G.; Pevida, C.; Martín, C. F.; Fermoso, J.; Pis, J. J.; Rubiera, F. *Sep. Purif. Technol.,* 2010, 71, 102-106.

[95] Thiruvenkatacharia, R.; Su, S.; Ana, H.; Xiang Yua, X. *Prog. Energ. Combust.,* 2009, 35, 438-455.

[96] Ana, H.; Feng, B.; Su, S. *Carbon,* 2009, 47, 2396-2405.

[97] Mercedes Maroto-Valer, M.; Lu, Z.; Zhang, Y.; Tang, Z. *Waste Manage.,* 2008, 28, 2320-2328.

[98] Arenillas, A.; Smith, K. M.; Drage, T. C.; Snape, C. E. *Fuel,* 2005, 84, 2204-2210.

[99] Linares-Solano, A.; Cazorla-Amorós, D.; Marco-Lozar, J. P.; Suárez-García, F. In *Coordination Polymers and Metal Organic Frameworks.* Eds. Ortiz, O. L.; Ramirez, L. D. Nova Science Publishers, Inc. 2011 (In press).

In: Research and Applications for Energy …
Editor: Riad Benelmir

ISBN: 978-1-62948-892-9
© 2014 Nova Science Publishers, Inc.

Chapter 6

ENERGY CONSUMPTION IN RELATION TO GOVERNMENT DEBT, INFLATION AND INVESTMENT IN SELECTED EUROPEAN COUNTRIES

Sayyed Mahdi Ziaei[*]

Universiti Teknologi Malaysia (UTM),
Faculty of Management and Human Resource Development,
Johor Bahru, Malaysia

ABSTRACT

Several European countries are at high risk relating to government debt, thus economic consequences of soaring public debt have developed into a crucial topic not only across Europe but also worldwide. This paper is the first to investigate the way in which energy consumption is correlated to inflation, investment and particularly government debt, for a panel of 15 European countries from1995 through to 2011. Given the relatively short span of time series data, a GMM model was employed to evaluate the correlation. The study forms the conclusion that energy consumption has a positive correlation with these three variables, whereas only the degree of effect differs. Investment has the most intense influence of these independent variables on energy consumption. According to the results as well, fiscal tightening would moderately decrease energy consumption.

Keywords: Energy consumption, government debt, inflation, investment, GMM

[*] Senior Lecturer, Universiti Teknologi Malaysia (UTM), Faculty of Management and Human Resource Development, Johor Bahru, Email:ziaei.mahdi@gmail.com.

INTRODUCTION

Economic recession and its effects on human existence have encouraged researchers to focus extremely on variables of macroeconomics. Austerity measures in European countries are causing government debt variables and their effects to become an agenda, especially in the Euro zone. Moreover, the worldwide economic crisis is tremendously constraining government debt in European countries, such that a debt of 66.3GDP in 2007 increased to 83.3 GDP in 2012, and particularly in Greece it reached 105.4 GDP[1]. Government debt deteriorates the financial balance of the European zone, and its immense influence appears to be extending both short-term and in the long run.

It is the aim of this research to investigate for the first time the relationship between government debt, inflation and investment in energy consumption for 15 European countries.

This paper is mainly responsible for contributing as a pioneer research work in evaluating the effects of government debt on countries with the highest debt problem in the Euro zone and secondly, it examines related empirical literature of studies on energy consumption focusing mostly on the rapport between variable and economic growth. The results obtained from this research indicate positive influence of all three independent variables on energy consumption, especially government debt.

Basically, for EU countries with debt, fiscal expansion/tightening would moderately increase/decrease energy consumption and may be effective in stabilizing energy utilization.

LITERATURE

Within the literature, the majority of papers on energy consumption have recently investigated the interrelationship between energy consumption and economic growth (Eggoh et al., 2011; Belekeet al., 2011; Wang S., 2011; Wang. Y, 2011; Chu and Chang 2012; Shahiduzzaman and Alam 2012; Mulugeta, et al., 2012). In fact, these works interpret the relative impotence of energy consumption in comparison with capital and labor on economic growth. Meanwhile, some studies focus on stationary and non-stationary conditions of energy consumption. Hendry and Juselius (2000) consider that were energy consumption a stationary variable, the effects of macroeconomic shocks on it would be permanent; otherwise, they would only temporarily influence energy consumption.

Carrion-i-Silvestre et al. (2005) tackled the issue by evaluating the stationary condition of energy consumption in different groups of countries, and found that in the majority of cases, this is one stationary variable.

Moreover, in pursuing research on the relation among energy consumption and economic growth, the latest studies investigate the impact of financial development on energy consumption demand. In a recent contribution, Sadorsky(2010) found that financial development variables such as capitalization, stock market value and turnover are directly connected with consumption demand.

In addition, several studies have also been carried out on government debt aspects. Various researchers believe that increasing government debt can lead to improvements in the

---

[1] According to European Commission, Public finances in EMU3|2011.

economic condition, whereas others maintain that higher debt is accompanied by extra risk, real volatility and economic uncertainties. Eggertson and Krugman (2011) advanced the discussion by demonstrating that the amount of debt determines economic calamity, with an atmosphere of higher economical debt encountering limited government function.

Although the Ricarsian equivalent theory and Barro theory emphasized the neutral effects of government debt on consumption, recent studies highlight both negative and positive influence of government debt on consumption. One of main variables where debt indirectly affects consumption is interest rate.

Elmendorf and Mankiw (1999) believe that debt accumulation leads to increasing long-term interest rates, and consequently a decrease in investment and consumption. Moreover, rising debt levels reduce the willingness of foreigners to invest (Patillo et al., 2002). In addition to government debt being considered a future tax liability for people, debt accumulation increases risk default and can potentially lead to a decrease in bank loans and consumption (Ricciuti (2003)).

Interestingly, while some studies emphasize the negative effects of government debt on consumption, various empirical works prove that a positive relationship exists between these two variables. Peersman and Pozzi (2004) speaking for the US, Pozzi et al. (2004) in the case of OECD countries, Heppke-Falk et al. (2006) on Germany, De Castro and Hernández de Cos (2006) in case of Spain, and Giordano et al. (2007) for Italy, demonstrate a positive relationship between government debt and consumption.

While several studies focus on the impact of macroeconomic variables on energy consumption, empirical evidence of the relationship between government debt and energy consumption is in contrast, scarce.

METHODOLOGY AND DATA

This study used a panel GMM model data set consisting of annual data for 15 European countries (Austria, Belgium, Czech Republic, Denmark, Finland, France, Greece, Hungary, Iceland, Italy, Netherlands, Portugal, Spain, Sweden, and Switzerland). The samples comprise annual data covering the period 1995-2012, obtained from the World Development Indicators.

Energy consumption was measured by total energy consumption per capita, fixed capital formation represented investment, and CPI was an inflation indicator. Panel modeling, especially GMM with respect to the 15 European countries, enhances evaluation power and efficiency. The estimated dynamic model for the European countries is:

$$\Delta \ln EC_{i,t} = \beta_1 \Delta \ln GD_{i,t\text{-}1} + \beta_2 \Delta \ln CPI_{i,t} + \beta_3 \Delta \ln INV_{i,t} + +\beta_4 \Delta D_{2008} + \Delta \varepsilon_{i,t} \tag{1}$$

where $i = 1,...N; t = 1...,T; \Delta \ln GD_{i,t} = \ln GD_{i,t} - \ln GD_{i,t\text{-}1}$, and analogously for the other variables; $\ln EC_{i,t}$ is energy consumption price; $\ln GD_{i,t}$ represents government debt; $\ln CPI_{i,t}$ denotes consumer price index; and $\ln INV_{i,t}$ stands for investment in each European country.

D_{2008} is a dummy variable for measuring the consequences of the 2008 economic crisis and $\varepsilon_{i,t}$ is the error term. All data is expressed in natural logs.

Table 1 provides GMM of Arellano and Bond estimation for the dynamic government debt, consumer price index and investment model. The estimation was performed via instruments lagged up to one period.

The Sargen test (used for the over-identification restriction test) demonstrates there is no correlation between the instruments and the first differenced equation's error term. WJS is the Wald statistic of joint significance of independent variables.

Table 1. Estimation for the dynamic model for Domestic Credit-Arellano-Bond two steps

Variable	Coefficient
EC_{t-1}	0.858*
	(0.031)
GD	0.056*
	(0.020)
CPI	0.002*
	(0.001)
INV	0.911*
	(0.0251)
D2008	-0.128*
	(0.073)
WJS	1039*
Sargen	33.2*

*Reject null hypothesis at 1 percent level; ** reject null hypothesis at 5 percent level; *** Reject null hypothesis at 10 percent level.

RESULTS AND DISCUSSION

This paper explored for the first time the relationship between energy consumption and inflation, investment and especially government debt, for a panel of 15 European countries. Results indicate that lagged energy consumption has a significant effect on the dependent variable. Government debt, inflation and investment prove to have substantial impact on energy consumption, whereas the degree of influence varies. In fact, according to the estimated value, a 1% increase in investment would lead to a 0.911% growth in energy consumption.

Similarly, a 1% rise in government debt would positively impact energy consumption by 0.031%. In high debt nations such as the European countries selected for this study, the level of government debt has a significant, positive impact on private consumption.

Essentially, in these countries, fiscal expansion would moderately increase energy consumption and is potentially effective in stabilizing energy consumption. Moreover, results demonstrate that the financial crisis of 2008 negatively influenced energy consumption of the countries selected for the present study.

REFERENCES

Barro, R. J. (1981). Output effects of government purchases. *Journal of Political Economy*, 84, 343-350.

Belke, A., Dobnik, F. and Dreger, C. (2011) Energy consumption and economic growth: New insights into the cointegration relationship. *Energy Economics*, 33(5), 782-789.

Carrion-i-Silvestre, J.L., Barrio-Castro, T.D., and Lopez-Bazo, E.. (2005). Breaking the panels: an application to GDP per capita. *Econometrics Journal*, 8, 159–175.

Chu, H. P., and Chang, T. (2012). Nuclear energy consumption, oil consumption and economic growth in G-6 countries: Bootstrap panel causality test, *Energy Policy*, Available 30 June 2012.

De Castro Fernández, F., and Hernández De Cos, P. (2006). *The economic effects of exogenousfiscal shocks in Spain: a SVAR approach*. European Central Bank, Working Paper no. 647.

Eggoh, J. C., Bangake, C., and Rault, C. (2011). Energy consumption and economic growth revisited in African countries. *Energy Policy*, 39(11), 7408–7421.

Eggertson, G., and Krugman, P. (2011). *Debt, deleveraging, and the liquidity trap: a Fisher-Minsky-Koo approach*. Federal Reserve Bank of New York, February.

Elmendorf, D.W., and Mankiw, N.G., (1999), Government debt. In J.B Taylor and M. Woodford (eds.) Handbook of Macroeconomics, North-Holland.

European Commission , Public finances in EMU − , *European Economy* 3|2011.

Giordano, R., Momigliano, S., Neri, S., and Perotti, R.(2007). The effects of fiscal policy in Italy: Evidence from a VAR model. European Journal of Political Economy, 23, 707-733.

Hendry, D.F., and Juselius, K.(2000). Explaining cointegration analysis, <u>Energy Journal</u>, 21, 1–42.

Heppke-Falk, K.H., Tenhofen, J., and Wolff, G. B. (2006). The macroeconomic effects of exogenous fiscal policy shocks in Germany: a disaggregated SVAR analysis. *Deutsche Bundesbank, Discussion Paper no. 41*.

Kahsai, M. S., Nondo, C., Tesfa, P.V. and Gebremedhin, G. (2012). Income level and the energy consumption–GDP nexus: Evidence from Sub-Saharan Africa. *Energy Economics*, 34(3), 739–746.

Pattillo, C., Poirson, H., and Ricci, L. (2002). *External Debt and Growth*, IMF Working Paper 02/69.

Peersman, G., and Pozzi, L. (2004). *Determinants of consumption smoothing*, working paper University of Ghent.

Pozzi, L., Heylen, F., and Dossche, M. (2004). Government debt and excess sensitivity of private consumption: estimates from OECD countries. *Economic Inquiry*, 42, 618-633.

Ricciuti, R., (2003) Assessing Ricardian equivalence. *Journal of Economic Surveys*, 17, 55-78.

Sadorsky, P. (2010). The impact of financial development on energy consumption in emerging economies. *Energy Policy*, 38 (2010), 2528–2535.

Shahiduzzaman, Md., and Alam, K. (2012). Cointegration and causal relationships between energy consumption and output: Assessing the evidence from Australia Energy Economics. *Energy Economics*. Available online 21 March 2012.

Wang, S.S., Zhoub, D.Q., Zhou, P., and Wang, Q.W. (2011). CO2 emissions, energy consumption and economic growth in China: A panel data analysis. *Energy Policy* ,39(9), 4870–4875.

Wang, Y., Wang, Y., Zhou, J., Zhu, X., and Lu, G. (2011). Energy consumption and economic growth in China: A multivariate causality test. *Energy Policy*, 39(7), 4399–4406.

In: Research and Applications for Energy …
Editor: Riad Benelmir

ISBN: 978-1-62948-892-9
© 2014 Nova Science Publishers, Inc.

Chapter 7

ASSESSMENT OF THE UTILIZATION OF THERMAL ENERGY STORAGE IN DISTRICT ENERGY SYSTEMS

Behnaz Rezaie*, Bale V. Reddy and Marc A. Rosen
Faculty of Engineering and Applied Science,
University of Ontario Institute of Technology, Oshawa, Ontario, Canada

ABSTRACT

District energy systems are a technology for using energy effectively and efficiently, at local or municipal scales, especially for thermal energy. Combining other beneficial energy technologies with a district energy system can significantly improve the efficiency of the combined system. The use is invesgtigated here of thermal energy storage (TES) in the Friedrichshafen district energy (DE) system, which uses solar energy and natural gas. The use of TES is observed to enhance the performance of the DE component of the Friedrichshafen system. In particular, TES improves the performance of the solar energy system, reducing annual natural gas consumption and annual fuel cost by 30% and harmful environmental emissions by 46%.

NOMENCLATURE

C_v Specific heat at constant volume, kJ/kg °C
m   Mass, kg
Q_g Energy input to boilers, kJ
$Q_{loss-TES}$ Heat loss from TES, kJ
Q_s Solar energy, kJ
Q_{TN} Energy demand of thermal networks, kJ
$T_{ave-TES}$ Average temperature of TES, °C
T_{max} Maximum temperature of TES, °C

*E-mail: Behnaz.Rezaie@uoit.ca.

T_{min} Minimum temperature of TES, °C
T_{return} Temperature of returningcirculating waterfrom thermal network, °C
U Internal energy of storage, kJ
U_c Internal energy of storageduring charging, kJ
U_d Internal energy of storageduring discharging, kJ
V Volume of natural gas, m^3
ρ Density, kg/m^3

1. INTRODUCTION

The environment is presently threatened by such phenomena as acid precipitation, stratospheric ozone depletion and greenhouse gas (GHG) emissions (Arroyo, 2006), prompting efforts to mitigate these impacts.

An important action in addressing environmental challenges is the intelligent and efficient use of energy, including reducing and/or reusing waste energy and using low carbon fuels to reduce GHG emissions.

Significant quantities of waste heat exit power production and industrial processes (TEAM, 2001; Sotoudeh, 2003), and research has been reported on technologies and techniques for utilizing this waste energy (Bonilla et al., 1997; Lunghi et al., 2004; Chinese et al., 2005). Low temperature heat from renewable energy such as solar and geothermal as well as industrial waste heat can be used advantageously in district energy (DE) systems (Bloomquist et al., 2003; Ozgener et al., 2005; Faninger et al., 2000; Lottner et al., 2000; Hepbasli and Canakci, 2003).

Increasing energy efficiency can be achieved using energy saving equipment (Patil et al., 2009) and recovering industrial waste heat (Casten and Ayres, 2005), and such measures can reduce GHG emissions (Patil et al., 2009). A district heating system can significantly reduce GHG emissions and air pollution according to the U.S. Department of Energy (DOE, 2003). Lund et al. (2010) state that DE not only reduces carbon dioxide (CO_2) emissions, but also results in significant reductions in overall costs of energy systems. DE can be integrated with renewable energy forms. For instance, using solar-vacuumed tubes to generate heat in a DE is popular technology in Europe in reducing GHG emissions.

District heating and/or cooling systems can be augmented through incorporation of TES. For instance, Anderpont (2006) determined that chilled water TES, used in large-scale DE systems, significantly lowers installation costs per ton compared with equivalent conventional non-TES chiller plants.

In some DE designs, TES is incorporated to store solar energy during periods when heating is not required. The Friedrichshafen district heating system in Germany, for example, uses TES with DE to enhance performance and efficiency (Mangold et al., 2003). In this article, we investigate the role and benefits of TES in DE using energy analysis, via a case study based on the TES in the Friedrichshafen DE system. The objective is to assess the utilization of thermal energy storage in district energy systems, in terms of characteristics and advantages.

2. BACKGROUND

2.1. District Energy

District energy systems allow the transport of thermal energy (heat or cold) via grids of pipes over a region, utilizing such transport media as liquid water, brine and steam. Anderpont (2006) points out that DE systems allow energy systems to operate more efficiently when used in conjunction with other energy technologies. These technologies include:

- Combined heat and power
- On-site or distributed generation
- Renewable energy technologies
- Energy recycling
- Thermal energy storage (TES)
- Multi-fuel heating systems
- Electric and non-electric chiller plants
- "Free" cooling (e.g., deep lake water cooling)

The Canadian District Energy Association (CDEA) surveyed 118 owners and operators of DE systems in Canada in 2008 (CDEA, 2009). The results illustrate the scope and growth of the technology. The survey results indicate that DE systems are distributed in Canada as shown in Table 1.

Table 1. Distribution of district energy systems in Canada

Region	Province	Number of DE systems	% of DE systems	Floor space served by DE (m^2)	% of floor space
North	Nunavut	9	8	n/a	n/a
	Yukon	3	3	n/a	n/a
	Northwest Territories	8	7	6,500	0
West	Manitoba	4	4	540,231	4
	Saskatchewan	2	2	725,573	5
	Alberta	14	12	2,311,608	17
	British Colombia	11	9	1,272,756	9
East	Newfoundland	0	0	n/a	n/a
	Prince Edward Island	3	2	n/a	n/a
	New Brunswick	1	1	371,612	3
	Nova Scotia	5	4	201,685	1
Central	Quebec	7	6	2,272,255	17
	Ontario	51	43	5,955,298	44
Country	All	118	100	13,657,518	100

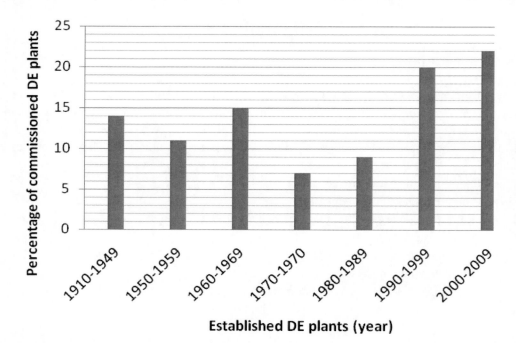

Figure 1. Hisorical development of DE plants in Canada, based on a survey in which 54 plants were reported. Adapted from CDEA (2009).

The highest shares of DE in Canada exist in Ontario (43%), Alberta (12%) and British Colombia (10%). Table 1 also shows that 27 million square meters of floor space is heated by DE in Canada. The largest percentages of DE-heated floor space in Canada are located in Ontario (44%), Alberta (17%) and Quebec (17%). The historical development of DE in Canada is illustrated in Figure 1, which shows two major periods of growth (CDEA, 2009): in the 1970s when energy prices drastically increased and in the late 1990s when the Canadian government encouraged the application of DE to foster sustainable energy and community planning.

2.2. Thermal Energy Storage

TES can be classified by various characteristics and applications. One TES categorization is based on type of storage (Dincer and Rosen, 2011):

- Sensible heat storage, where transferred heat changes the storage medium's temperature without changing its phase. Sensible storage media include water, air, oil, rocks, bricks, sand and soil. Underground TES is becoming an increasingly common type of sensible TES, for such applications as storing solar and waste thermal energy and for cooling purposes. Underground TES includes aquifer TES and borehole TES (Sanner et al., 2003). Underground TES systems based on tanks, pits, rock caverns, aquifer TES and ducts have been developed and implemented since the 1970s in various countries, including Belgium, Canada, Germany, Poland, Sweden, The Netherlands, Turkey and the US (Paksoy et al., 2000).

- Latent heat storage, where heat transfer to or from the storage medium changes its phase at constant temperature. Since phase change involves large energy interactions, the thermal storage capacity of such a TES is markedly higher than for a sensible TES of the same volume, making latent TES particularly useful where space is limited. Latent storage media include water/ice and salt hydrates.

Some TES systems combine sensible and latent storage, so as to achieve the benefits of each. In some cases combinations of storage media can be used, some of which utilize sensible and/or latent storage and others of which use thermochemical storage. Such systems can be classified as thermal or thermochemical.

Another TES categorization is based on storage duration (Dincer and Rosen, 2002). Long term storage has storage durations usually ranging from weeks to seasons. Common long term storage media are water, ground and rock, and some chemicals. Long term TESs are further classified by technology, e.g., rock cavern, borehole, aquifer and pit storage (Tveit et al., 2009). The storage duration for short term storage varies from hours to days. Short term storage media include salt hydrates, concrete, rocks and water. Short term thermal storage is common with cold storage to shift peak electrical demands for cooling to off-peak periods, while seasonal thermal storage is normally suitable for heating applications, often in conjunction with district heating systems (Dincer and Rosen, 2011).

TES can also be categorized based on other parameters, e.g., application, temperature (high, low, medium), efficiency and cost. TES applications, which can allow classification, include storage of excess energy from power plants, storage of waste heat from air conditioning for subsequent heating and storage of industrial/process waste heat.

3. INTEGRATING TES WITH DISTRICT ENERGY

3.1. Applications of TES and DE

TES can assist the operation of a DE system by allowing the accumulation of thermal energy from off-peak periods for use when demands are high, more effective use of renewable thermal energy sources like solar than is otherwise possible due to the intermittent nature of the resource supply, and the storage of excess thermal energy when it is available, for subsequent release to the DE distribution system when thermal demands increase. TES consequently avoids thermal energy losses that would otherwise occur.

Regardless of the source of energy in a DE system, reducing energy losses is usually a main advantage of using TES in DE systems. Incorporating TES in DE systems allows the reduction of thermal losses, increasing the efficiency for the overall thermal system. Large seasonal TES systems have been built in conjunction with DE technology (Dincer and Rosen, 2002). Besides improved efficiency and economics, environmental benefits are another reason for the expansion of TES technology in general and with DE.

Many beneficial applications of TES with DE exist or can be developed. For example, Andersson (1997) reports that the application of aquifer TES in one DE system reduced energy use by 90-95% compared to conventional systems not incorporating TES. Also, Rosen et al. (2005) state DE with hybrid systems can advantageously combine sources of energy like natural gas, waste heat, wood wastes and municipal solid waste.

TES can increase the benefits provided by such systems. Also, Lund et al. (2010) point out that "low energy" buildings can be operated with industrial waste heat, waste incineration, power plant waste heat and geothermal energy in conjunction with a DE network. Incorporating TES can improve designs of such systems. The types of energy sources that can be used with DE and TES systems vary, and systems designs are often tailored to best adapt to the energy source.

3.2. Energy Sources for TES and DE Systems

Various energy sources can be used in DE systems incorporating TES.

3.2.1. Renewable Energy

Lund et al. (2010) indicate that renewable energy is the focus of many countries, for such reasons as improving energy security and mitigating climate change. The types of renewable energy most applicable to DE are solar and geothermal.

The advantages of using solar energy for such applications as solar space and water heating are significantly enhanced by including TES in the thermal system, while the key benefit of TES is its ability to integrate the solar thermal application (Dincer and Rosen, 2002; Dincer, 1999). That is, the energy stored by TES can be made available when thermal energy is in demand and solar availability is uncertain.

TES increases the impact of solar collectors by avoiding the loss of solar energy which exceeds demand. Annual TES is desirable if the excess solar energy is stored for a season or longer, while short-term storage is more appropriate if the solar energy is stored for hours or days.

In both cases, however, TES provides a beneficial alternative to the use of conventional fuels. Short term TES applications in conjunction with solar energy in district heating systems have been tested in pilot projects and used in several countries (Dincer, 1999).

Geothermal energy can be exploited using a ground source heat pump, which is an efficient device that can be used advantageously with DE for heating, ventilating and air conditioning (HVAC) systems. When a ground source heat pump is the source of energy in DE system, TES can help the energy system store extracted heat from the earth for use when in demand (Lund et al., 2010).

3.2.2. Recovered Waste Heat

Industry can be a supplier of waste heat for a DE system and/or a heat consumer from the DE system. When industry has excess heat or waste heat, it can supply a DE system, while it becomes a consumer and when it requires heat. Holmgren and Gebremedhin (2004) point out that cooperation between industry and DE can allow technical and economical factors to be appropriately addressed for both parties in terms of the thermal energy quality and quantity as well as profitability.

When the supplied energy for a DE system is supplied by waste heat, the key parameters to be considered in designing DE and TES include the temperature, rate and duration of heat supply and of heat consumption. Rosen and Dincer (2002) suggest underground thermal storage such as aquifer TES as an appropriate storage for waste heat. This type of system allows stored thermal energy to be made available for consumers and also permits load levelling in the DE system.

Rosen et al. (2005) point out that a DE system can supply waste heat from an existing boiler which has waste heat or from other industrial processes. DE systems using such energy sources are generally more clean, economic and efficient than DEs using conventional fuels. Holmgren and Gebremedhin (2004) also note that the integration of DE with industry reduces not only the cost of heat production but also CO_2 emissions.

3.2.3. Fuel

When a DE system directly operates using fuel, there is not always a need for TES. Nonetheless, TES provides the possibility of using smaller equipment in designs, by reducing energy use from external energy sources. The reduced fuel consumption is relative to a reference case.

3.2.4. Electricity

Electricity is significant energy source in a DE system. TES helps reduce electricity costs during peak demand periods and allows the system to operate during off-peak periods, e.g., running chillers during the night and storing the cold medium for use in cooling the next day. Short term cold TES is used in such applications.

3.2.5. Waste

According to Holmgren and Gebremedhin (2004), waste incineration is a useful technology for recovering the energy content of waste. Alternatively, waste can be disposed of in landfill sites and accelerated processes (e.g., gasification, pyrolysis) can be used that produce a combustible fuel gas Sahlin (2003). Holmgren and Gebremedhin (2004) believe waste incineration to be a beneficial investment for producing heat for district heating economically and environmentally, to be a preferred option among other waste treatment methods. Parameters that need to be considered in DE and TES systems where waste incineration supplies the thermal energy including the capacity of the waste incineration process, the availability of the waste and the time profile of the heat demand.

3.3. Advantages and Disadvantages of Using TES in DE

Tanaka et al. (2000) state the use of TES in conjunction with DE decreases energy consumption compared to a reference system, and that seasonal TES is more effective than short-term TES. Andrepont (2006) assessed the economic benefits of using TES technologies in DE systems, and notes that cool TES is applied widely in heating, ventilation and air-conditioning systems by shifting the cooling load from peak periods during the day to the off-peak periods at night.

This time shift significantly reduces operating costs, and this benefit is particularly noteworthy in large scale DE systems. Andrepont also notes that using TES with DE prevents inefficient operation of chillers and auxiliary equipment during low-level operation, enhances system reliability and flexibility, balances electrical and thermal loads in combined heat and power for better economics, and reduces accident risks and insurance by enhancing fire protection (since the stored chilled water or other storage fluid in the TES is in the vicinity of the DE and may be utilizable as a reserve firefighting fluid in the event of a fire).

The benefits of TES in facilitating the use of renewable energy, especially solar thermal energy for use in heating and cooling buildings, have been pointed out (Dincer and Rosen, 2007). Demand is growing for facilities that utilize TES, as they are more efficient and environmentally friendly, exhibiting reductions in consumption of fossil fuels and emissions of CO2 and other pollutants and chlorofluorocarbons.

Griffin (2010) reports that buildings with TES systems in DE applications consume more energy than buildings without TES in many cases, and that all systems are beneficial environmentally. The U.S. Green Building Council (USGBC) did not discourage the use of TES in the first version of the Leadership in Energy and Environmental Design (LEED) criteria, but also did not deal with the use of TES in district heating systems; however a building with TES is eligible to earn more point for its lower electrical power use.

Building a TES requires initial capital for land, construction, insulation and other items. Determining the appropriate location, designing the proper structure and insulation, and executing the design are important steps in installing a TES, which involve significant costs. The high initial cost is a disadvantage of TES.

4. CASE STUDY: FRIEDRICHSHAFEN DE SYSTEM

The Friedrichshafen DE system (see Figure 3) in Germany contains two boilers which run with natural gas, a set of solar thermal collectors mostly on roofs of buildings, a central solar heating plant with seasonal heat storage, heat exchangers to exchange heat with thermal networks and solar collectors and thermal networks which distribute heat to consumers, as well as ancillary equipment like pipes, pumps and valves.

Water is the working media circulating in the Friedrichshafen thermal cycle for heat transport, water also is the heat storage media. The boilers and solar thermal collectors are the heat suppliers in Friedrichshafen DE system, and the thermal network is the main heat consumer.

The Friedrichshafen DE system is noteworthy since the first district heating plants assisted with solar energy and seasonal thermal storage were established under the "Solarthermie2000" program in the Friedrichshafen DE and Hamburg DE systems (Mangold et al., 2003). The success of the Solarthermie2000 program led to the realization of three more DE plants in Germany between 2007 and 2008 (Schmidt and Mangold, 2008).

Schmidt et al. (2005) note that the Friedrichshafen DE has a hot water thermal energy storage made of reinforced concrete with a volume of 12,000 m^3. The first phase of the Friedrichshafen DE system served 280 apartments in multi-family houses and a daycare. The area of the solar thermal flat plate collectors was 2700 m^2 and 24% of the total heat demand of the district heating system is met by solar heat (Bauer et al. 2010).

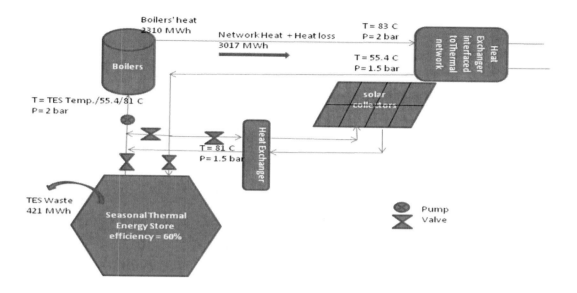

DE system. Figure 2. A simplified diagram of the Friedrichshafen.

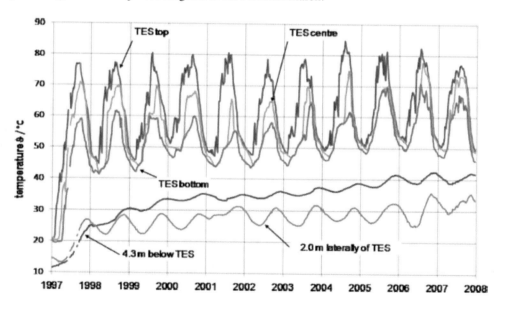

Figure 3. History of temperature variations in and around the Friedrichshafen DE system. Reprinted from Schmidt et al. (2005) by permission.

The second phase, implemented in 2004, expanded the district heating to serve a second set of buildings containing 110 apartments which necessitated the addition to the system of solar collectors with an area of 1350 m^2. Also, two gas condensing boilers, with capacities of 750 kW and 900 kW, were installed to allow energy demands on the district heating system to be met when they could not be provided by the solar collectors and/or thermal storage.

Schmidt et al. (2005) report the following data for the Friedrichshafen DE system:

- Return temperature: 55.4°C
- Measured TES heat losses: 421 MWh
- Storage efficiency: 60%
- Solar yield of collectors: 1200 MWh
- Solar heat input to district heating network: 803 MWh
- Overall heat input to the district heating network: 3017 MWh
- Heat delivered by gas bolilers to the district heating network: 2310 MWh
- Solar fraction: 26%
- Heat losses for the district heating network of the second residential area: 7.3%
- Maximum temperature inside the TES (at the top): 81°C

Also, Lottner and Mangold (2000) and Fisch and Kubler (1997) report that the temperature of the thermal network (T) is 70°C during building heating. Gas-fired condensing boilers are used in the Friedrichshafen DE system, and circulate hot water to users. SAP (2010) reports that the efficiency of gas-fired condensing boilers is about 90%.

Several assumptions are made here either to complete the data or to simplify the analysis. Most of the assumptions were based on those for a similar system reported by Zhai et al. (2009), who indicate that the thermodynamic effects of valves on the circulating fluid and heat losses from heat exchangers and pipelines can be neglected.

Table 2. TES and ambient temperature during the year 2006

Season	Month	TES temp. (°C)	Ambient temp. (°C)
Spring	March	56	3.4
	April	61	9.9
	May	69	13.7
Summer	June	74	19.8
	July	76	19.7
	August	74	16.1
Fall	September	65	17.9
	October	59	13
	November	52	6.6
Winter	December	51	2.7
	January	52	−2.6
	February	54	0.3

The operation of the Friedrichshafen DE system is evident in Figure 3. Boilers and solar collectors are the heat suppliers. Solar energy flows directly through the thermal cycle when solar energy availability exceeds DE demand, as is typical in summer, while surplus solar heat is stored in the TES. When demand is greater than the heat generated by the solar collectors, the TES releases stored energy to the DE network. Also, natural gas heats the Friedrichshafen DE system when there is inadequate solar heat. Boilers heat the circulating water to ensure it reaches a temperature of 83 °C. A heat exchanger is located between the thermal network (consumers) and the thermal cycle in which water circulates, and another heat exchanger sits between the solar collectors and the thermal cycle of circulating water. Solar heat passes through the latter heat exchanger to the thermal cycle of the Friedrichshafen DE system.

Schmidt et al. (2005) report the temperature history of the TES since it was built in 2005 (see Figure 3). There, temperature variations with time are shown in and around the TES in the Friedrichshafen DE system. Monthly temperatures in the TES over the year 2006, based on Figure 2, are listed in Table 2.

4.1. Energy Balance

An energy balance for a thermal system can be written as follows:

Energy input − Energy output = Energy accumulation　　　　　　　　　(1)

The energy output can be broken down as follows:
Energy output = Product energy output + Waste energy output　　　　　(2)

Equations (1) and (2) can be combined as follows:

Energy input − (Product energy output + Waste energy output) =
= Energy accumulation　　　　　　　　　　　　　　　　　　　　　(3)

Equation (3) can be expressed as follows for the Friedrichshafen DE:

$$Q_g + Q_s - (Q_{TN} - Q_{loss\text{-}TES}) = \Delta U \qquad\qquad (4)$$

Here, Q_g is the energy input to the boilers (in the form of natural gas), Q_s is the solar energy input to the Friedrichshafen DE system, Q_{TN} is the energy demand of the user thermal networks, $Q_{loss\text{-}TES}$ is the heat loss from the TES, and ΔU is energy accumulation for the Friedrichshafen DE system. The boilers and solar collectors supply energy to the Friedrichshafen DE, and the user thermal network utilizes the product energy output. Losses in the DE system are accounted for in the energy demand of the user thermal network. The TES loss is reported separately and is considered as energy output according to equation (2). The TES is the only component that can accumulate energy during the year. Energy accumulation of the TES is positive during the charging stage of TES operation and negative during the discharge stage. The difference between the energy accumulation during charging and discharging over one year represents the energy accumulation of the Friedrichshafen DE over that year, excluding thermal losses. Therefore,

$$\Delta U = \Delta U_c - \Delta U_d \qquad\qquad (5)$$

where ΔU_c denotes the TES energy accumulation during the charging stage and ΔU_d is the TES energy accumulation during charging. During the storage stage no energy is accumulated in the TES, so only the charging and discharging stages are considered in calculating ΔU. Specifically,

$$\Delta U_c = m \, C_v \, (T_{max} - T_{min}) \tag{6}$$

where m is the mass of the water in the TES, C_v is the specific heat at constant volume, T_{max} is the maximum temperature of the TES, and T_{min} is the minimum temperature of the TES over the year. During the charging stage, the temperature of the water in the TES increases from T_{min} to T_{max}; hence ΔU_c is determined based on these two temperatures differences. Also,

$$\Delta U_d = m \, C_v (T_{max} - T_{return}) \tag{7}$$

Here, T_{return} represents the temperature of returning circulating waterfrom the thermal network, which is 55.4 °C in Friedrichshafen DE system, while other terms are as already defined. Throughout the discharging stage, the temperature of water in the TES decreases from T_{max} to T_{return}, and ΔU_d is evaluated according to the temperature difference between T_{max} and T_{return}. When the temperature of the TES is lower than T_{return}, there is no benefit to using the water in the TES.

By substituting equations (6) and (7) into equation (5), it can be shown that:

$$\Delta U = m \, C_v(T_{max} - T_{min}) - m \, C_v(T_{max} - T_{return})$$

or

$$\Delta U = m \, C_v(T_{return} - T_{m \, in}) \tag{8}$$

To determine the mass of the water in the TES, the density and specific heat of water at the average temperature of water ($T_{ave\text{-}TES} = 61.5$ °C) are used, that is, $\rho = 982.15$ kg/m^3 and $C_v = 4.19$ kJ/kg/°C.

Substitution of numerical values into equation (8), which is the right side of equation (4), yields

$$\Delta U = (12{,}000 \text{ m}^3)(982.15 \text{ kg/m}^3)(4.19 \text{ kJ/kg/°C})(55.4 - 51)\text{°C}/(3{,}600{,}000 \text{ kJ/MWh}) = 60.4 \text{ MWh}$$

The left side of equation (4) can also be evaluated numerically:

$$Q_g + Q_s - (Q_{TN} + Q_{loss\text{-}TES}) = 2{,}310 \text{ MWh} + 1200 \text{ MWh} - (3{,}017 + 421) \text{ MWh} = 72 \text{ MWh}$$

A comparison of the above two expressions shows an imbalance in evaluating equation (4) of about 20%, which is due to the simplifying assumptions invoked in this study but adequate for the purposes of the study.

4.2. Fuel Consumption

The Friedrichshafen DE system needed 3017 MWh of energy to operate the thermal network in the year 2006. This energy can be supplied by the natural gas boiler and/or solar energy. Hence, three cases are considered:

- Case 1: Supply energy = Solar energy with the TES + Natural gas
- Case 2: Supply energy = Solar energy + Natural gas
- Case 3: Supply energy = Natural gas

Case 1: The boiler provides 2,310 MWh for the year 2006 to the Friedrichshafen DE system, as reported in section 5.1, to the thermal network. Assuming a 100% heating efficiency, the volume V_1 of natural gas for replacing of 2,310 MWh is estimated using the energy content for natural gas. The energy density based on higher heating value for natural gas is 38 MJ/m^3 (Elert, 2010); by applying this heating value for natural gas, V_1 can be computed as:

$$V_1 = 2,310 \text{ MWh/yr x } 3600 \text{ s/h } / 38 \text{ MJ/m}^3 = 218,800 \text{ m}^3/\text{yr}$$

From the data reported in section 5.1, the solar collectors generate 1200 MWh/yr of heat and deliver 800 MWh to the DE system; the energy difference of 400 MWh represents heat loss from solar equipment. The efficiency of solar collection subsystem is thus (800 MWh)/(1200 MWh) = 0.67 (or 67%).

Case 2: In winter, spring, summer and fall respectively there are 1.8, 5.8, 7.3 and 3.6 effective sunny hours per day for Zurich, based on the NASA database in the RETScreen software (*www.retscreen.net*), which is assumed representative of Friedrichshafen since it is located nearby. For roughly half of the spring and the fall there is a demand for space heating. For simplicity, we consider there to be six months of space and domestic hot water heating with 2.8 effective sunny hours per day, and six months of only domestic hot water heating with 6.5 effective sunny hours per day. Effective sunny hours per day are defined here for the summer and winter seasons as the average sunny hours per day over each six-month time frame. Figure 4 depicts the approximate distribution of sunny hours over a typical year in Friedrichshafen.

By considering the temporal availability of the sun, the distribution of 1,200 MWh, the solar energy provided by the solar collectors, over the year is as shown in Figure 5. That figure also shows the energy demand of the district heating system in the two different seasons (winter and summer).

Based on data for residential buildings, gas consumption constitutes almost 85% of energy use in the winter period and about 15% in the summer period. Given that the total heat demand of the Friedrishchafen DE system is 3,017 MWh, the energy demand for the district heating system during the winter period is 3,017 MWh x 85% = 2,564 MWh and during the summer period is 3,017 MWh x 15% = 453 MWh.

Since the energy generated by solar collectors in the summer is 839 MWh, the surplus solar energy which goes to waste is 839 MWh − 453 MWh = 386 MWh. Therefore, the useable solar energy throughout the year for the DE system for case 2 is the solar heat generated in winter, 361 MWh, plus the useable solar heat in the summer, 453 MWh, or 814 MWh. The actual solar heatproduced can then be determined with the efficiency of the solar collection system, 0.67, and the available solar energy, 814 MWh, as 545 MWh.

The energy produced from natural gas (in the boilers) can be estimated as 3,017 − 545 = 2,472 MWh, and the volume of natural gas required to provide this energy can be shown to be $V_2 = 225,359$ m^3/yr.

Case 3: The boilers provide 3017 MWh annually and solar energy is not utilized. So, the volume of natural gas consumption, following the procedure in case 1, can be shown to be V_3 = 234,164 m^3/year.

WINTER	SPRING	SUMMER	FALL
1.8 sun hr/day	5.8 sun hr/day	7.3 sun hr/day	3.6 sun hr/day

| **Winter** Domestic hot water + space heating, 2.8 sun hr/day | | **Summer** Just domestic hot water, 6.5 sun hr/day | |

Figure 4. Approximate distribution of sunny hours per day over a typical year in the Friedrichshafen DE system.

WINTER	SPRING	SUMMER	FALL
1.8 hr/day sun	5.8 hr/day sun	7.3 hr/day sun	3.6 hr/day sun
116.76 MWh	*376.07 MWh*	*473.33 MWh*	*233.42 MWh*

| **Winter** Domestic hot water + space heating, 2.8 hr/day sun *Solar heat generation: 361 MWh* **Needed heat: 2564 MWh** | | **Summer** Domestic hot water heating, 6.5 hr/day sun *Solar heat generation: 839 MWh* **Needed heat: 453 MWh** | |

Figure 5. Rough distribution of generated solar energy during the year.

4.3. Fuel Costs

The fuel cost is dependent on the contribution of solar energy to the energy input for the district heating system. The greater the solar energy utilization for the district heating system the lower is the demand for natural gas and the lower fuel cost for the district heating system. The natural gas consumption is evaluated here for the three cases considered. The average price of natural gas in U.S. currency was $7.87 per 1000 ft^3 for industrial usage for the year 2006 according to the U.S. Energy Information Administration (EIA, 2010), and the price for residential use was slightly more than half that value.

Note that U.S. dollar values are used in this chapter. Here, we treat the Friedrichshafen DE system as an industrial unit for costing purposes, and evaluate the fuel costs for the three cases.

Case 1: When the boilers provide 2,310 MWh, by burning 218,842 m^3 of natural gas, the solar collectors provide 1200 MWh and the TES stores solar energy, the fuel cost is

(218,842 m^3)(35.31 ft^3/m^3)($7.87/1000 ft^3) = $60,814

Case 2: When boilers provide 2,762 MWh through burning 234,164 m^3 of natural gas, the solar collectors provide 1200 MWh, but only 545 MWh is used by the district heating system, the fuel cost is

$(234{,}164 \text{ m}^3)(35.31 \text{ ft}^3/\text{m}^3)(\$7.87/1000 \text{ ft}^3) = \$65{,}072$

Case 3: When boilers provide 3,017 MWh and no solar energy is utilized, the fuel consumption is 285,821 m^3 of natural gas and the fuel cost is $(285{,}821.05 \text{ m}^3)(35.31 \text{ ft}^3/\text{m}^3)(\$7.87/1000 \text{ ft}^3) = \$79{,}427$

4.4. Fuel Cost Saving

Fuel cost savings are calculated here for the three cases considered relative to the fuel cost for case 3, which consumes the greatest amount of fuel. Then, the annual fuel cost savings can be shown to be as follows:

- *Case 1* (solar collectors and TES): $79,427 − $60,814 = $18,613
- *Case 2* (solar collectors): $79,427 − $65,072 = $14,355
- *Case 3* (reference case): $0

The above fuel cost savings are for the year 2006, and are highly dependent on the costs of fuel. To determine the precise economic advantages of the three cases, a more comprehensive financial analysis is required, which accounts for initial costs of the TES and solar collectors, maintenance costs and other economic factors. For the initial cost of the TES in the Friedrichshafen DE system, the federal government of Germany subsidized the total cost by 53% of the total costs, plus 24% of total cost of the connections between the solar collectors of the district heating system and the client facilities (Energie Cites, 2002). Note that a significant weighting was placed on sustainability rather than economics in designing the TES in the Friedrichshafen DE system. Clark (2010) states that the simple payback period based on energy cost saving is long. He suggests a return-on-investment analysis using a capital-recovery-factor-based cost-to-benefit ratio as the most appropriate measure of total cost saving.

4.5. Environmental Impact

The use in the case study of TES technology in conjunction with renewable energy reduces environmental emissions by avoiding the combustion of natural gas. The environmental benefits include mitigation of climate change through reduced CO_2 emissions and the avoidance of emissions of pollutants like carbon monoxide (CO), nitrogen oxides (NO_x) and others.

The quantity of environmental impact avoided can be estimated based on the properties of natural gas and its combustion characteristics. Table 2 lists typical emissions from natural gas combustion (Natural Gas Supply Association, 2010). Using these data, the reductions in emissions for the cases considered, relative to the reference case, are determined below and presented in Table 4. That table shows the environmental impact reductions for Cases 1 and 2 relative to Case 3, which is the reference case in which boilers are the sole energy provider for the Friedrichshafen DE system.

Table 3. Typical emissions associated with combustion of one billion kJ of natural gas

Pollutant emission	Mass (kg)
Carbon dioxide	50,301
Carbon monoxide	19
Nitrogen oxides (NO_x)*	39.5
Sulfur dioxide	0.427
Particulates (ash)	3
Mercury	0.000
* NO_x represents nitrogen monoxide (NO) and nitrogen dioxide (NO_2) in emissions, and in many publications NO and NO_2 are addressed as NO_x. There is a tendency for NO to convert to NO_2 in the presence of oxygen. NO_x forms a small portion (approximately 0.08%) of natural gas emissions.	

Source: Natural Gas Supply Association (2010).

Table 4. Reductions in environmental emissions (in kg) for Cases 1 and 2 relative to the reference case (Case 3)

Pollutant	Case 1	Case 2
Carbon dioxide	191,100	130,800
Carbon monoxide	72.2	49.4
Nitrogen oxides	150	103
Sulfur dioxide	1.62	1.11
Particulates	11.4	7.80

Case 1: Solar collectors provide 800 MWh (3.8 billion kJ) annually to the Friedrichshafen DE system, avoiding the boilers from burning natural gas to generate this energy. The environmental avoided emissions for case 1 are given in Table 4.

Case 2: Solar energy provides 547 MWh (2.6 billion kJ) annually to the Friedrichshafen DE system, again reducing natural gas consumption in the boilers. The resulting reductions in environmental emissions for case 2 are given in Table 4.

Case 3: When the boilers provide 3017 MWh and solar energy is not utilized, all energy is provided to the DE system by burning natural gas. This is the reference case against which reductions in environmental emissions are evaluated for cases 1 and 2 (see Table 4).

4.6. Further Discussion

The results of the case study are summarized in Table 5, which shows that the use of TES increases fuel cost savings and decreases fuel consumption during operation. It is also observed that solar collectors plus TES are more effective than solar collectors alone, in terms of increasing solar fraction and reducing emissions. TES enhances the reduction in fossil fuel consumption manner associated with solar collector use. Relative to Case 3, the reference case in which natural gas boilers supply all energy required by the Friedrichshafen DE system, Case 2, which utilizes boilers and solar collectors but no TES, achieves a 18%

reduction in fuel consumption for 2006, while Case 1, which adds a TES to Case 2, achieves an annual fuel consumption reduction of 23%. The annual operating cost reductions follow similar patterns: 18% for Case 2 and 23% for Case 1.

Table 5. Summary of fuel and fuel cost savings for Cases 1 and 2 relative to the reference case (Case 3)

	Case 1 (boilers + solar energy + TES)	Case 2 (boilers + solar energy)
Annual fuel saving (m^3)	66,979	51,357
Annual fuel saving (%)	23	18
Annual fuel cost saving ($)	18,613	14,355
Annual fuel cost saving (%)	23	18

Comparing Cases 1 and 2 highlights the role of TES in achieving the annual fuel and fuel cost savings. The relative improvement in the reduction in annual fuel use for Case 1 compared to Case 2 can be evaluated as

$(66,979 - 51,357)/51,357 = 0.30$ (or 30%)

while the improvement in the reduction in annual fuel cost is

$(18,613 - 14,355)/14,355 = 0.30$ (or 30%)

That is, a 30% greater reduction in natural gas consumption is achieved with Case 1 compared to Case 2. Similarly, a 30% greater reduction in natural gas costs is achieved with Case 1 compared to Case 2. The three cases differ in terms of environmental impact during operation depending on fuel consumption in the boilers. Solar collectors produce heat for the Friedrichshafen DE, thereby reducing demand for natural gas. The environmental impacts for Cases 1 and 2, relative to Case 3 (the reference case), are summarized in Table 4. It can be seen that the use of solar collectors in Case 2 avoids an annual release of 130 tons of CO_2 into the atmosphere, while the use of solar collectors with TES in Case 1 avoids the release of 191 tons. The difference between Cases 1 and 2 is the incorporation of TES in the design of Case 1. The reduction in environmental emissions of carbon dioxide is improved in Case 1 relative to Case 2 by

$(191,100 - 130,800)/130,800 = 0.46$ (or 46%)

This percentage reduction attributable to utilization of TES is also obtained for other pollutants.

CONCLUSION

Thermal energy storage can improve the performance of a district energy system. The use of TES complements the use of solar energy in the Friedrichshafen DE system, allowing surplus solar heat in the spring and summer to be stored for subsequent use in the fall. TES thereby enhances the benefits of using solar energy in the DE system.

It is observed that TES reduces annual fuel use and fuel costs by 30% in the Friedrichshafen DE system, reducing the use of natural gas boilers. The use of TES is also advantageous environmentally, reducing emissions to the atmosphere like CO_2 by 46% in the DE system.

The advantages of incorporating TES in the Friedrichshafen DE system, in terms of enhancing the use of solar thermal energy, suggests TES is likely going to become increasingly important and utilized in industry, power generation and DE as use of renewable energy expands.

ACKNOWLEDGMENTS

Financial support was provided by the Natural Sciences and Engineering Research Council of Canada, and is gratefully acknowledged.

REFERENCES

Andersson, O., 1997, "ATES utilization in Sweden: An overview", Proceeding of 7th International Conference on Thermal Energy Storage (MEGASTOCK'97), Sapporo, Japan, 2: 925-930.

Andrepont, J., 2006, "Maximize DE value by leveraging technology options", *District Energy*, Fourth quarter, 40-41.

Arroyo, V., 2006, *Agenda for Climate Action*, Pew Centre on Global Climate Change, Arlington, VA.

Bauer, D., Marx, R., Nubicker-Lux, J., Ochs, F., Heidemann, W., Muller-Steinhagen, H., 2010, "German central solar heating plants with seasonal heat storage", *Solar Energy* 84:612- 623.

Bloomquist, R. G., 2003, "Geothermal space heating", *Geothermics*, 32 (4-6): 513-526.

Bonilla, J. J., Blanco, J. M., Lpezt, L., Salat, J. M., 1997, "Technological recovery potential of waste heat in the industry of the Basque Country", *Applied Thermal Engineering*, 17: 283-288.

Canadian District Energy Association (CDEA), *2009, District Energy: A National Survey Report,* Report, Natural Resources Canada.

Casten, T. R., Ayers, R. U. 2005, *Recycling Energy: Growing Income while Mitigating Climate Change, Report*, Recycled Energy Development, Westmont, IL, Oct. 18. Accessed 27 January 2010, http://www.recycled-energy.com/_documents/articles/tc_ energy_climate_ change.doc.

Chinese, D., Meneghetti, A., Nardin, G., 2005, "Waste-to-energy based greenhouse heating: Exploring viability conditions through optimization models", *Renewable Energy*, 30: 573-1586.

Clark, L., 2010, "The benefit of ice-based thermal energy storage", *HPAC Engineering*, May: 34-36.

Dincer, I., Rosen, M., 2011, *Thermal Energy Storage: Systems and Applications*, 2nd edition, Wiley.

Dincer, I., Rosen, M., 2007, *Exergy: Energy, Environment and Sustainable Development*, Elsevier.

Dincer, I., 1999, "Evaluation and selection of energy storage systems for solar thermal applications", *International Journal of Energy Research*, 23: 1017-1028.

DOE, 2003, *Cogeneration or Combined Heat and Power*, Office of Energy Efficiency and Renewable Energy, U.S. Department of Energy, Washington, DC.

Energie Cites, 2002, Friedrichshafen (Germany): *Report on Solar District Heating*. Accessed 20 November 2010, *http://www.energy-cities.eu/db/friedrichshafen_139_en.pdf*.

Faninger, G., 2000, "Combined solar biomass district heating in Austria", *Solar Energy*, 69: 425-435.

Fisch, N., Kubler, R., 1997, "Solar assisted district heating: status of the projects in Germany", *International Journal of Sustainable Energy*, 18, 259-270.

Griffin, T., 2010, "District energy guidance documents: A look at what's new", *District Energy*, first quarter, 62-64.

Hepbasli, A., Canakci, C., 2003, "Geothermal district heating applications in Turkey: A case study of Izmir-Balcova", *Energy Conversion and Management*, 44: 1285-1301.

Holmgren, H., Geremedhin, A., 2004, "Modeling a district heating system: Introduction of waste incineration, policy instruments and co-operation with an industry", *Energy Policy*, 32: 1807-1817.

Elert, G., Ed., "Energy in cubic meter of gas", *The Physics Factbook*. Accessed 27 April 2010, *http://hypertextbook.com/facts/2002/JanyTran.shtml*.

Lottner, V., Mangold, D., 2000, "Status of seasonal thermal energy storage in Germany" Proc. TERRASTOCK 2000: 8th International Conference on Thermal Energy Storage, Stuttgart, Germany, August 20–September 1, Vol.1, pp. 53-60.

Lottner, V., Schulz, M. E., Hahne, E., 2000, "Solar assisted district heating plants: Status of the German programme Solarthermie-2000", *Solar Energy*, 69: 449-459.

Lund, H., Moller, B., Mathiesen, B.V., Dyrelund, A., 2010, "The role of district heating in future renewable energy systems", *Energy*, 32: 1381-1390.

Lunghi, P., Bove, R., Desideri, U., 2004, "Life-cycle-assessment of fuel-cells-based landfill-gas energy conversion technologies", *Journal of Power Sources*, 131: 120-126.

Mangold, D., Schmidt, T., Lottner, V., 2003, "*Seasonal thermal energy storage in Germany*" Presented at Futurestock, Warschau, September 1-4, Accessed 30 April 2010 *http://www.solites.de/download/03-06.pdf*.

Natural Gas Supply Association, 2010, "*Natural Gas and Environment*". Accessed 10 June 2010, *http://www.naturalgas.org/environment/naturalgas.asp*.

Ozenger, L., Hepbasli, A., Dincer, I., 2005, "Energy and exergy analysis of geothermal district heating system: An application*", Building and Environment*, 40: 1309-1322.

Paksoy, H. O., Andersson, O., Abaci, S., Evliya, H., Turgut, B., 2000, "Heating and cooling of a hospital using solar energy coupled with seasonal thermal energy coupled with seasonal thermal energy storage in an aquifer", *Renewable Energy*, 19: 117-122.

Patil, A., Ajah, A., Herder, P., 2009, "Recycling industrial waste heat for sustainable district heating: A multi-actor perspective", *Int. J. Environmental Technology and Management*, 10: 412-426.

Rosen, M. A., Le, M. N., Dincer, I., 2005, "Efficiency analysis of a cogeneration and district energy system", *Applied Thermal Engineering* 25: 147-159.

Sahlin, J., 2003, *Waste incineration-future role in the Swedish District heating system*, Report, ISRN CTH-EST-R-03/06, Chalmers University of Technology, Goteborg, Sweden.

Sanner, B., Karytsas, C., Mendrinos, D., Rybach, L., 2003, "Current status of ground source heat pumps and underground thermal energy storage in Europe", *Geothermics*, 32: 576-588.

SAP, 2010, "*Boiler Efficiency Database: Seasonal Efficiency of Domestic Boilers in the UK (SEDBUK)*". Accessed July 10, 2010 (*http://www.sedbuk.com*).

Schmidt, T., Mangold, D., 2008, "*Seasonal thermal energy storage in Germany*", Proc. EUROSUN 2008: 1st International Congress on Heating, Cooling, and Building, Lisbon, Portugal, October 7-10, paper 225.

Schmidt, T., Nußbicker, J., Raab, S., 2005, "Monitoring results from German central solar heating plants with seasonal storage", *Proc. International Solar Energy Society* (ISES) 2005 Solar World Congress, Orlando, Florida, August 6-12.

Sotoudeh, M., 2003, "Participatory methods: A tool for improvement of innovative environmental technology", *Int. J. Environmental Technology and Management*, 3: 336-348.

Tanaka, H., Tomita, T., Okumiya, M., 2000, "Feasibility study of a district energy system with seasonal water thermal storage", *Solar Energy*, 69: 535-547.

Technology Early Action Measurement (TEAM), 2001, "District heating and cooling to save energy". Section in "Innovation for sustainability: TEAM progress report on climate change solutions 1998-2001", report (Available online: *www.team.gc.ca/english/ publications/team_199801/nation.asp#districts*).

Tveit, T., Savola, T., Gbremedhin, T., Fogelholm, C. J., 2009, "Multi-period MINLP model for optimizing operation and structural changes to CHP plants in district heating networks with long-term thermal storage", *Energy Conversion and Management*, 50: 639-647.

U.S. Energy Information Administration (EIA), "Natural gas prices", report. Accessed August 28, 2010, *http://www.eia.doe.gov/dnav/ng/ng_pri_sum_dcu_nus_a.htm*.

Zhai, H., Dai, Y.J., Wu, J.Y., Wang, R. Z., 2009, "Energy and exergy analyses on a novel hybrid solar heating, cooling and power generation system for remote areas", *Applied Energy*, 86: 1395-1404.

In: Research and Applications for Energy …
Editor: Riad Benelmir

ISBN: 978-1-62948-892-9
© 2014 Nova Science Publishers, Inc.

Chapter 8

THE CURRENT AND FUTURE ROLE OF RENEWABLE ENERGY SOURCES FOR THE PRODUCTION OF ELECTRICITY IN LATIN AMERICA AND THE CARIBBEAN

Jorge Morales Pedraza[*]

ABSTRACT

It is certain that energy production and, particularly, the generation and sustained growth of electricity, constitute indispensable elements for the economic and social progress of any country. Energy, undoubtedly, constitutes the motive force of civilization and it determines, to a high degree, the level of the future economic and social development of a country. To ensure adequate economic and social growth of a country it is vital that all available energy sources are used in the most efficient and economical manner for the generation of electricity.

In the Latin American and the Caribbean region, all types of renewable energy sources[1] can be found, most of them already used for the generation of electricity. In some countries, some renewable energy sources can be used more effectively for the production of electricity than in others. For example, in some countries, the use of specific renewable energy sources such as geothermal energy cannot be used for the electricity generation due to the nonexistence of volcanic zones. In some others, the use of hydro power for the generation of electricity is very limited, due to the lack of big rivers or due to large period of dry seasons or because the possible new sites to be exploited are located very far from populated areas.

The generation of electricity using fossil fuels is a major and growing contributor to the emission of carbon dioxide, a greenhouse gas that contributes significantly to global warming that is producing a significant change in the Latin American and the Caribbean

---

[*] E-mail: jmorales47@hotmail.com

[1] The term renewable energy is used in the present paper to identify a type of energy that is derived from natural processes that are replenished constantly. There are various forms of renewable energy sources included in the present paper.

climate. These changes are affecting, in one way or another, almost all countries of the region.

One of the main problems that the region is now facing is how to satisfy the foreseen increase in electricity demand using all available energy sources in the most efficient manner, and without increasing the emission of CO_2. The paper will talk about the possible future role of the different renewable energy sources available in the region for the generation of electricity.

Keywords: Renewable energies; hydro power; wind energy; solar energy; geothermal energy; hydrogen; biomass; production of electricity; Latin America; Central America; the Caribbean

GENERAL OVERVIEW

Renewable energy sources as a whole is the third world's largest contributor to global electricity production. They accounted, in 2004, for almost 18% of the world's electricity production after coal (40%), and natural gas (19%) but ahead of nuclear (16%), oil (7%), and non-renewable waste (7%). In 2009, the use of renewable energy sources for the generation of electricity reached 19.1%; this represents an increase of 1.1% respect to 2004.

It is foreseen, in the IEO (2010) reference case that electricity generation in Central and South America will increase by 2.1% per year increasing from 1 million GWh in 2007 to 1.8 million GWh in 2035, despite that recent economic crisis lowered demand for electricity in almost of countries of the region, especially in the industrial sector. In the long-term, however, the region's electricity markets are expected to return to trend growth as economic difficulties recede.

There are five different types of renewable energy sources used for the generation of electricity in the Latin American and the Caribbean region: hydro power, wind power, solar energy, geothermal energy, biomass, and hydrogen. Hydro was the world's main renewable energy source used for the generation of electricity in 2009, with an 84.3% share of the total renewable output (3 810.3 TWh), followed by wind power, with 7% of the total electricity produced in the world (268.2 TWh), biomass with a share of 6.3% of the world's total electricity produced (241.2 TWh), geothermal energy with a share of 1.7% of the total electricity produced (65 TWh), solar energy with a share of 0.6% of the world's total electricity produced (21.4 TWh) and other types of renewable energy sources with a share of 0.01% of the world's total electricity produced (0.524 TWh).

The world's generation of electricity using renewable energy sources as fuel increased by 1 000 TWh during the period 1999-2009; the annual growth was 3.1%. The major contributor in this increase was hydro power, with a total generation of 528.7 TWh (52.8% of the total).

Analyzing the contribution of all renewable energy sources to the generation of electricity during the period 1999-2009, the following conclusion can be stated: The best performance over the period considered were put in by solar and wind power, with an annual rises of 36% and 28.9%, respectively.

Renewable energy is the fastest-growing source of electricity in the IEO (2010) reference case. According to this report, total generation of electricity from renewable energy sources will increase 3% per year during the coming years, percentage that is almost the same that the one reached during the period 1999-2009.

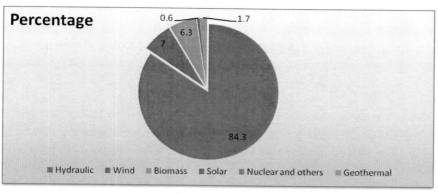

Source: SENER.

Figure 1. Structure of electricity generation by renewable energy sources in 2009.

The renewable share of world's electricity generation is expected to grow from 18% in 2004 to 23% in 2035; this represents an increase of 5% in the next thirty years, an increase of 1.9% respect to the period 1999-2009. Hydroelectricity leads the field. Of the 4.5 million GWh of new renewables added over the projection period, 2.4 million GWh are attributed to hydroelectric power. Aside from hydro, most renewable energy technologies will not be able to compete economically with fossil fuels during the projection period.

On the other hand, it is important to know that government policies or incentives often provide the primary economic motivation for the use of renewable energy sources for the generation of electricity in any given country. For this reason, governments should continue adopting specific policies or incentives with the purpose of increasing, in the coming years, the participation of different renewable energy sources in their mix balance.

From Figure 2, the following can be stated: Latin America was the second region with the highest share of renewable energy sources in the world's production of electricity (30.5%) in 2009. At first, this figure looks relatively high and somewhat impressive, especially if compare it to the 6.5% share of renewable energy sources of OECD countries, and with the 0.7% share in the Middle East.

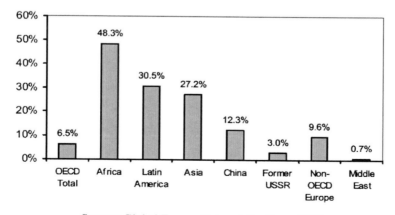

Source: Global Energy Network Institute, 2009.

Figure 2. Renewable energy sources supply shares.

These numbers, however, can be very misleading. In reality, the situation of the use of renewable energy sources for the production of electricity in Latin America and the Caribbean is not as positive or optimistic as certain statistical data lead to believe.

There are many problems associated to the use of renewable energy sources for the generation of electricity in several countries of the region, particularly, if the impact on the environment and society is included. The main problem to increase the use of renewable energy sources for the generation of electricity in the Latin American and the Caribbean region in the future is to understand how energy and development policies have been elaborated by the different governments. In most cases, energy policies and strategies consider some renewable energy sources as too costly and technologically unfeasible, arguing in top of this that the country does not have the capabilities and the resources to use some of them in the most effective manner for the generation of electricity. The easiest explanation for this, and one which is usually mentioned, is the lack of incentive and foresight of the governments and energy industry to increase the use of this type of energy for the generation of electricity. Since the region has an abundance of conventional energy resources such as oil and natural gas, it is in general easier, cheaper, and more technically feasible to keep exploiting these type of energy sources than to invest in the use of renewable energy sources or to establish appropriate renewable energy policies to promote them. Another common explanation is that the development of renewable energy sources clash with the interest of powerful players, particularly large oil and gas companies most of them located in developed countries and, therefore, there are few incentives that some governments are ready to adopt with the purpose of promoting the use of these type of energy resources for the generation of electricity in the near future.

The renewable energy sector in the region is almost entirely dominated by one type of renewable energy source: hydro. Around 62% of the total production of electricity in the region is produced using this type of energy source. Other forms of renewable energy sources used in the region for the generation of electricity, except biomass, represent only an insignificant fraction of the total electricity produced in the region (1.4%). However, hydro is not, in all cases, the most effective energy source for the generation of electricity. In fact, the use of hydro for this specific purpose has been rejected by several experts because in their opinion this type of energy source cannot be considered as renewable and sustainable. During many years, large hydro power plants have been used for the production of electricity in several Latin American and the Caribbean countries. In countries, like Uruguay and Paraguay, for example, the share of hydro power within their energy mix rises to more than 95% of the total electricity produced (see Figure 9). Several other countries such as Costa Rica, Ecuador, Brazil and Venezuela, depends in a high proportion on the hydro power sector for the generation of electricity. This strong dependency has created several problems to these countries on several occasions, particularly in large dry periods when water levels fall down significantly, as happened in 2001 in Brazil and in 2010 in Venezuela and Ecuador, just to mention two examples.

Moreover, apart from creating energy security concerns, the construction and operation of large hydro power plants have caused serious environmental and social problems, particularly, in sensitive areas of the region like the Amazon rainforest. The construction, for example, of the Tucurui hydro power plant in the Brazilian rainforest flooded around 2 400 square kilometers of rainforest, and displaced around 30 000 indigenous people from their traditional territories.

It is important to stress that almost all countries in the region are endowed with abundant renewable energy sources. Solar, wind, biomass, geothermal, and hydro are available in the region in larger or smaller quantities, depending on the geographical location and morphology of individual countries. The renewable energy reserves in the region are estimate between 22.7% and 24.8% of the world's renewable energy reserves. It is expected, according to some expert's studies, that the use of renewable energy sources for the generation of electricity could reach 47% of the energy balance in the Latin America and the Caribbean region in 2030.

The use of renewable energy sources for the generation of electricity is being promoted by the most advanced countries in the region, with the purpose of cleaning up the negative impact in the environment due to the massive use of fossil fuels for the generation of electricity for so many years, particularly the use of oil.

From Figure 3, the following can be stated: With over one-third of the share of total production, Brazil can greatly affect regional generation mix statistics. Specifically, Brazil's reliance on hydroelectricity directly contributes to the high proportion of hydroelectricity in the region, which in turn has made Latin America and the Caribbean the region with one of the highest share of renewable energy for the generation of electricity in the world (see Figure 2). Conversely, as the share of electricity contributed by hydroelectricity has fallen in Brazil in recent years, this has raised the carbon-intensity of Latin American and the Caribbean's electricity production.

Following Brazil, Mexico is the second largest electricity producer in the region, with almost 21% of total production in 2005. If Bolivia, Colombia, Ecuador, Peru, and Venezuela are treated as part as the Andean Community, although Venezuela is formally not a member of this group of countries, their combined electricity production closely follows the pattern displayed by Mexico and the Southern Cone.

On the other hand, the use of renewable energy sources for the production of electricity by the Caribbean and Central American countries during the period 1985-2005 (see Figure 3), is very far from the level reached by the Southern Cone and the Andean Community in the same period (see Figure 3).

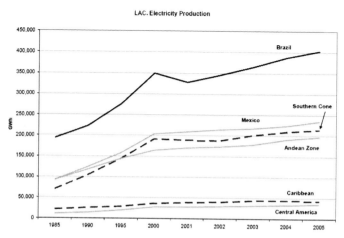

Source: Yepez-Garcia et al, 2010) and World Development Indicators (2009).

Figure 3. Electricity production over time by sub-region.

It is interesting to know the following: The goal of reducing dependency on high-price imported oil for the generation of electricity, the goal of reducing environmental impact and, at the same time, promoting the integration of the region, turned out to be complementary. The most direct benefit of the integration process by promoting the interconnection of electrical grids comes when one country has a source of low cost power and its neighbor does not.

The three lowest cost resources for operation at capacity factors above 30% are geothermal, wind (including the cost of backup generation), and small hydro power plants. This assumes that high-quality sites can be identified and acquired for their exploitation in benefit of a group of countries. Geothermal, on a local and sub-regional basis, and wind energy on a local basis, provides a path toward a less oil-dependent, lower cost, lower environmental impact, and more sustainable future in the field of electricity generation using renewable energy sources.

Table 1 show the electricity interconnections between countries in the Central American region, and Figure 4 the electricity interconnections currently in operation, under construction, and planned in South America.

Renewable energy sources currently in use for the generation of electricity in the region, reveal considerable growth in infrastructure, power generation and their related industries, particularly, in the electrical sector but this growth if not enough to significantly increase the participation of this type of energy in the energy mix-balance of several countries of the region in the near future.

At regional level, other more pressing and shorter term needs could be also addressed by using renewable energy sources for the generation of electricity. For instance, substituting imported oil by locally available renewable energy sources for the generation of electricity could save scarce foreign currency or favor the use of site-specific energy resources to cope with old and critical needs such as rural electrification. Solar and wind energies have shown that they could reduce the dependency of oil for the production of electricity in remote areas in several countries of the region.

Table 1. Central America electricity interconnections

To-From	Capacity (MW)
Guatemala- El Salvador	100
El Salvador- Guatemala	95
El Salvador- Honduras	100
Honduras- El Salvador	100
Honduras- Nicaragua	80
Nicaragua- Honduras	80
Nicaragua- Costa Rica	60
Costa Rica- Nicaragua	60
Costa Rica- Panama	70
Panama- Costa Rica	110

Source: CRIE.

Source: Yepez-Garcia et al (2010) using CIER (2008) and potential interconnections included by Manuel Brugman (South America) and Power of America (Central America).

Figure 4. Electricity interconnections in operation, under construction, and planned in South America.

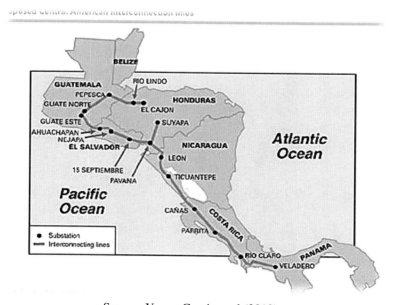

Source: Yepez-Garcia et al (2010).

Figure 5. Electricity interconnections in operation, under construction, and planned in Central America.

But the adoption of renewable energy sources for the generation of electricity could also mean additional benefits for several countries in the region such as the creation of new jobs, revitalization of small and medium size industries, and solution of local environmental problems, among others. The use of renewable energy sources for the production of electricity in the region offers also the opportunity of using available human resources more effectively, putting the local research and development establishment to work after a common goal, and attracting new investments to expand the energy infrastructure of individual countries. In the event of project development, however, it is important to stress that available information on the local renewable energy sources is, in some countries at best limited, if not unreliable. In most cases, information is non-existing, which represents a major barrier to the incorporation of this type of energy as part of the national energy inventories and planning exercises (Huacuz, 2003).

In Latin America and the Caribbean, despite its potential rich renewable energy sources, only a limited number of countries are actively working to develop policies, strategies, institutional settings, financing schemes, industrial infrastructure, human resources, and other necessary elements, with the purpose of facilitating the introduction or the expansion of the use of different renewable energy sources for the generation of electricity as part of their energy supply options for the coming years (Huacuz, 2003).

With the purpose of increasing the participation of renewable energy sources in the regional energy mix, decision makers should identify the specific impediments to grid-tied renewable energy development or the adoption of energy efficiency technologies in their respective countries, with the aim of adopting specific measures to overcome these impediments. An obvious first step involves the reduction or removal of incentives for the use of fossil fuelled systems for the generation of electricity. Further, regulatory reforms should be considered to ensure that renewable energy projects could feed into the power grids in a competitive manner with fossil fuel sources.

How to achieve this goal? The following are some proposals that could be considered:

1. Creation of a renewable energy portfolio. To implement this proposal a minimum percentage of renewable energy sources to be part of the overall energy supply portfolio of the country is required. It can be applied to all large suppliers with diverse portfolios or can be set for the nation (or State) as a whole, in addition to some type of tradable credit system or systems benefit charge, which ensures that all power providers share the cost of supporting the renewable energy portfolio;

2. Establishment of a system of benefit charges. This system is basically a tax collected from all power services, which goes into a fund to be established by the government, with the aim of supporting the use of renewable energy sources and energy efficiency developments for the generation of electricity. The government should imposes a tax on all retail electricity sales in order to help finance the implementation of renewable energy projects;

3. Adoption of exemptions from taxes. In an effort to stimulate investments in renewable energy projects, governments may elect to reduce or eliminate certain taxes associated with the development and use of renewable energy sources for the generation of electricity. Tax exemptions may include income taxes, depreciations allowances, and import taxes, among others;

4. Adoption of exemptions from systems charges. This approach allows renewable energy providers to be exempt from some of the systems charges that conventional power

generators must pay. This can include considering renewable energy sources as load-reduction technologies, and exempting them from general kWh surcharges;

5. Adoption of renewable energy resource laws. This means the adoption of specific laws supporting the use of renewable energy sources to generate electricity, and the establishment of specific goals to be achieved in the use of this type of energy source for this specific purpose in the coming years.

The Initiative for Sustainable Development

The Latin American and the Caribbean countries adopted, in 2002, the so-called "Initiative for Sustainable Development (ILACDS)". This initiative was presented to and approved by the first special meeting of the Forum of Ministers of the Environment of Latin America and the Caribbean, held in Johannesburg, South Africa, in August 2002. One of its most ambitious goals adopted in the meeting was "to increase renewable energy sources' share of national and regional energy matrixes by 2010, bringing renewable share to 10% of Total Primary Energy Supply."

This goal has been already achieved but mostly through the construction of big hydroelectric dams, which many environmentalists argue are not sustainable and have a negative impact in the environment.

It is important to stress that the share of other renewable energy sources in the generation of electricity in several countries of the region is still very low. The situation in some countries is the following: Argentina, highly dependent on natural gas, is the only country in the region with a share below 10% in the use of renewable energy sources for the generation of electricity but there are others in the critical zone of 10% to 20%, such as Mexico, Ecuador and Chile.

On the other extreme is Costa Rica, with a share of 99.2%. In the case of Honduras, Haiti and El Salvador, the share of renewable energy sources in the generation of electricity is above 80%. But in that group, all is not positive. Paraguay and Uruguay are almost totally dependents on hydroelectric energy, while Honduras, Haiti and El Salvador, like its Central American neighbors Nicaragua and Guatemala, and rely heavily on firewood for the production of energy[2].

Without any doubt, the biggest challenge facing the use of renewable energy technologies for the generation of electricity is to advance the state-of-the-art to the point, where more renewable options can generate energy at costs that can be competitive with conventional energy sources, such as oil, coal and gas.

With worldwide adoption of stricter environmental standards and guidelines for greenhouse gas emissions, it is becoming clear that renewable energy systems will be credited for their inherent advantage in lowering emissions. Nevertheless, achieving substantial technology breakthroughs to improve cost-competitiveness remains a priority for many countries.

---

[2] Firewood is a renewable energy resource but only as long as it is accompanied by adequate reforestation, otherwise the impact to the environment for the use of this type of energy source for the generation of electricity could be very negative from the economic, environment and social point of view.

Main Off-Grid Renewable Energy Programmes

According to Huacuz (2006), there are four major off-grid renewable energy programmes[3] in the Latin American and the Caribbean region related to the promotion of the use of different renewable energy sources for the generation of electricity. These programmes are the following:

a) PAEPRA in Argentina;
b) PRONER in Bolivia;
c) PRODEEM in Brazil;
d) PRONASOL (and subsequently named programmes) in Mexico.

Programme for Electricity Supply to the Rural Population of Argentina (PAEPRA)

The Programme for Electricity Supply to the Rural Population of Argentina (PAEPRA) was launched in 1994 by the Ministry of Energy. The goal of this Programme is the supply of electricity to 1.4 million people and to around 6 000 public services in remote areas of low population density, where electricity supply from the grid is too costly. The objective of this Programme is to prevent rural migration to the cities, and to open opportunities for the private sector to provide electrical services through rural energy concessions in each province of the country. Additional benefits of the Programme include job creation, the use of renewable energy sources in a sustainable manner, the increase in the access of more Argentinean to electricity, and to ensure a good performance of the private supplier with a minimum amount of subsidy.

National Rural Electrification Programme (PRONER)

The National Rural Electrification Programme (PRONER) was approved by the Bolivian government, with the purpose of promoting and supporting economic development and to improve living conditions in rural areas. The Programme is expected to open ways for the use of renewable energy sources for the generation of electricity in a reliable, high-quality and long-term sustainable manner, while saving fuel and avoiding air pollution at the same time. The Programme seeks to develop integral sustainability schemes, including adequate institutional, financial, technological, and environmental frameworks.

The first phase of the Programme is carried out by the Bolivian government with financial support from the United Nations Development Programme/Global Environment Facility. Its main objective is to remove financial, institutional and technical barriers to ensure the successful application of renewable energy sources for the generation of electricity in rural areas. The original plan called for the implementation of twenty two projects in five municipalities, supporting the installation of 3 200 solar home systems.

---

[3] On-grid renewable energy programmes are at an earlier stage of development in the region than off-grid programmes.

Programme for Energy Development of States and Municipalities (PRODEEM)

In 1992/93, the government of Brazil adopted a rural electrification programme promoting the use of renewable energy sources, through the implementation of pilot projects in cooperation with the German and US governments. Around 1 500 solar home systems were installed with the participation of local electricity distribution companies in several States. Based on this experience, the Brazilian government established the Programme for Energy Development of States and Municipalities (PRODEEM). The Programme has been coordinated by the Ministry of Mines and Energy and its main purpose is of delivering electricity to rural communities not served by the grid, using locally available renewable energy sources.

PRODEEM seeks the social and economic development in rural areas, directly impacting job creation and reducing rural migration to the cities. Several States, including Minas Gerais, Sao Paulo y Paraná, followed suit and created their own photovoltaic rural electrification programmes, based on the experience of PRODEEM.

It is important to stress that Brazil is the only country in the region where commercial manufacturing of photovoltaic cells and modules is carried out with indigenous technology.

National Solidarity Programme (PRONASOL)

The National Solidarity Programme (PRONASOL), approved by the Mexican government, provides the framework for one of the largest rural renewable energy based electrification programmes that exist in the Latin American and the Caribbean region. It is characterized by the active involvement of the national electrical utility in order to maintain quality control standards during the project's implementation, and the existence of a technical normative agency to assure the quality of the installations. Since the beginning of the 1990s, between 60 000 and 90 000 solar home systems were installed in 2 500 communities, benefiting 3 500 schools and health and community centers; around 13 000 rural telephones and 12 mini-grids powered by the use of renewable energy sources were also installed. The communities benefiting contribute 10-15% to the PRONASOL Fund (US$10 million a year). Grid coverage reaches over 95% of the total Mexican population, leaving around 5 million Mexicans living in small and dispersed communities without access to the grid in very remote regions.

In addition to PRONASOL, Mexico is implementing the Energy Sector Programme (PROSENER) with the aim of increasing the use of renewable energy sources as a sector priority. The Programme defines a number of strategic actions, including:

- Develop programmes, projects, and actions to increase the use of renewable energy sources for the generation of electricity;
- Increase the capacity share of renewable energy sources in the electricity sector;
- Strengthen research and technology development activities on the use of renewable energy sources for the generation of electricity;
- Promote education, within the Mexican population, on the use of renewable energy sources for the generation of electricity.

Summing up, the following can be stated: The use of renewable energy technologies should no longer seen only as a solution to global warming but also as a means to cleaning up the messy politics that promoted in the past the massive use of fossil fuels for the generation of electricity. Renewable energy sources currently in use reveal considerable growth in infrastructure and power generation and their related industries, particularly in the electrical sector. However, it is important to single out that in Latin America, despite being rich in renewable energy resources, only a few countries are actively working with the purpose of increasing the use of this type of energy for the generation of electricity in the near future.

Without any doubt, large-scale renewable energy systems such as wind farms, biomass, hydro power, and the use of geothermal energy for the generation of electricity, offer considerable economic, environmental, and energy security benefits that may be considered by policymakers in their respective countries during the consideration of future energy reforms for the diversification of the electricity generation portfolio. These benefits include:

- Long-term competitive price stability;
- Reduced vulnerability to fuel supply disruptions;
- Flexibility to delivery distributed and household energy to outside urban areas and rural populations;
- Minimal emissions of greenhouse gases and minimum impact on the climate;
- Minimal local pollutants;
- Attracts investment for domestic infrastructure projects;
- High-tech job creation;
- Many systems are modular and can be expanded as demand grows.

Despite technological advancements in the field of sustainable energy technologies, the adoption of substantial energy efficiency measures by governments of the different Latin American and the Caribbean countries will depend on the changes in the current energy policies and strategies in force. Utility investment decisions regarding grid-tied power and off-grid energy services are largely driven by rate of return expectations for private power projects. Financial arrangements, encouraging the participation of the private sector in the construction of new electricity generation facilities should favor, in the long-term, high up-front costs and low fuel costs facilities, over low up-front costs and continued fuel costs using fossil fuel. The same reticence to invest in high up-front costs facilities is hindering the widespread deployment of and use of energy efficiency technologies.

In addition to the basic structure of the market, other factors may favor the use of conventional fossil fuel power systems for the generation of electricity, instead of using renewable energy sources for this specific purpose. These factors are:

- Fossil fuel subsidies offered by many governments;
- Fossil fuel storage and delivery infrastructure costs borne by the public;
- Petroleum exploration tax and other economic incentives;
- Availability of low cost project finance;
- The absence of charges for environmental impacts;
- Experience gained in the use of fossil fuels and facilities built;

- Widespread knowledge and general familiarity in the use of conventional technologies.

However, with minor changes in the electricity market through policy reform, the use of renewable energy sources for the production of electricity and the introduction of energy efficiency technologies can make renewable energy generation facilities competitive with conventional fossil-fuelled electricity generation plants, offering long-term price stability (given their independence from fossil fuel price fluctuations), along with other benefits as important contributors to well-diversified and far-reaching energy portfolios.

Policy Framework

According to Huacuz (2003), legal, regulatory, institutional, and financing schemes with the purpose of fostering and facilitating the use of renewable energy sources for electricity generation, are at different stages of development within the Latin American and the Caribbean region. Even though there are common denominators among different countries that could facilitate the energy integration process in the region, no integration process promoting the use of renewable energy sources for the generation of electricity at large scale has been adopted at regional level until today. However, several initiatives, with specific reference to the use of renewable energy sources for the generation of electricity, could be identified in the following countries:

1. The Electricity Law in Bolivia: Article 61 of the Electricity Law "charges the State with the responsibility of electrifying small townships and rural areas, which could not be served by private companies. According to this Law, "financial resources for this purpose must be delivered by the government through the National Development Fund". It is also stated that "the Executive should propose energy policies and strategies allowing the use of renewable energy sources for the generation of electricity, within the general framework of the development policy for the energy sector";

2. The Law 10.438 in Brazil: The mentioned Law deals with the supply of electric energy and extraordinary tariff schemes. By this Law, "the Incentives Programme for Alternative Sources of Electric Energy (PROINFA) is created, along with the budget for energy development, and mandates on the universality of the public served with electricity". The Law amends a number of similar laws previously issued at national and State levels;

3. The Law 143 in Colombia: Article 40 of Law 143 sets "a target for the next twenty years in which equal levels of energy coverage in the whole country must be achieved. The Colombian Institute for Electric Energy is charged with the responsibility of formulating an off-grid national energy plan. The Institute is also responsible for the execution of the corresponding alternative energy projects, explicitly small hydroelectric power plants in substitution of fossil-fuelled generating units;

4. The Law 7200 in Costa Rica: This Law deals with autonomous or parallel generation, defined as that produced by power plants of limited capacity, owned by private companies with more than 65% of Costa Rican capital or rural electrification cooperatives. Incentives of different kinds are awarded to these companies, plus the right of selling electricity to the Costa Rican Electricity Institute, as long as the power is produced from small hydroelectric and non-conventional energy sources;

5. The Regime Law for the Electrical Sector in Ecuador: Article 5 of the Law deals with rural electrification issues, preferential tariffs for low income sectors and incentives to the development and use of non-conventional energy resources. This Law has provisions on project financing (Articles 37 and 62) and priorities for rural electrification projects with renewable energy in the Amazon region and Galapagos Islands;

6. The Decree 93-96 in Guatemala: The Decree, also known as the "General Electricity Law", empowers the State "to provide resources to finance, fully or partially, rural electrification projects outside the concession territories. The Law does not specifically addresses the use of renewable energy sources for the generation of electricity but in practice projects of this kind are more suitable in rural areas not served by the grid. The evolution in the use of different renewable energy sources for the generation of electricity in Guatemala from 1990 to 2008 is shown in Table 2;

7. The Framework Law for the Electricity Sub-sector in Honduras: Article 42 of the Law "creates a fund for projects of social interest and gives facilities so that electricity distributors can generate electricity with isolated off-grid systems. As in the Guatemala case, the Law does not specifically addresses the use of renewable energy sources for the generation of electricity but implies its use;

8. The Electric Industry Law in Nicaragua: Article 6 of the Law "sets provisions for the financing of off-grid projects in rural areas. The government assigned to the National Energy Commission the responsibility for the elaboration of rural electrification plans, the administration and ruling of the National Fund for the Development of the National Electric Industry, mainly to finance rural electrification projects, and to implement policies and strategies that allow the use of renewable energy sources for electricity generation;

9. The Energy Sector Programme 2001-2006 in Mexico: The Programme sets targets for the implementation of grid connected renewable energy projects and outlines strategies to achieve these targets. The use of renewable energy sources are the preferred option for off-grid projects in remote rural areas, albeit they are not mandatory. Regional development plans by some State's governments also incorporate the use of renewable energy sources for the generation of electricity;

10. The Executive Decree Number 22 in Panama: Article 5 of the Decree creates the Office of Rural Electrification which, among other things, has the following responsibilities: a) Identification of priority rural areas not served by the grid and not included in concession areas; b) Evaluation of technological options to serve those areas; c) Evaluating options for application of new technologies for rural electrification; and d) Carrying out regional studies to identify possibilities for the use of renewable energy sources for the generation of electricity;

11. The Law of the National Electricity Service in Venezuela: No provisions are made for the use of renewable energy sources in the project for the Organic Law of the National Electricity Service in this country. However, specific off-grid project are good candidates for the use of renewable energy sources in the country in the coming years;

12. Environmental Law 81, Foreign Investment Law and the Law 85 on Forestry Resources in Cuba: No specific law governs the use of renewable energy sources in the Republic of Cuba. However, in May 1993, the Executive Committee of the Council of Ministers approved a "Programme for Developing Domestic Energy Sources," prepared by the then National Energy Commission. Later, in October 2002, the Executive Secretariat of the Council of Ministers ordered the creation of the Renewable Energies Front, a State agency

specializing in coordinating and supervising the different State bodies involved in the development of domestic energy sources. Environmental Law No. 81 was approved in 1997, and lists the instruments committed to applying Cuba's environmental policy, including: the National Environmental Strategy, the National Environmental and Development Programme, and the Economic and Social Development Plan. Moreover, it created the National Environmental Fund, to fully or partially finance projects and activities that aim to protect nature and ensure its rational use. For forestry resources, Law No. 85 was approved in August 1998, establishing general principles and regulations on protecting, increasing and sustainably developing the country's forestry heritage, and promoting the rational use of non-wood forestry products. It assigned the Ministries of Agriculture, Science, Technology and the Environment, and the Interior, with different forest-related functions. Meanwhile, the Foreign Investment Law, approved in September 1995, approves fiscal exemptions for all foreign investment, including energy;

13. Law 112-00 in the Dominican Republic: The Constitution of the Dominican Republic makes no specific references to natural resources or energy. Law 112-00, however, specifically refers to a tax on fossil fuel and oil derivative consumption, and creates a special fund to encourage the use of different renewable energy sources for the generation of electricity and an energy saving programme. According to this Law, "the fund will consist of 2% of income received as part of the application of this Law, rising annually by 1% to reach a total of 5% of these revenues."

Table 2. Gross generation evolution in Guatemala during the period 1990-2008 (GWh)

Year	Hydro	Geothermal	Vapor	Gas	Coal	Co-generation
1990	2 140.8	-	81.2	95.1	-	-
1995	1 903.8	-	192.4	491.7	-	114.6
2000	2 673.9	202.2	73.3	253.7	558.4	668.6
2005	2 927.9	145.0	79.8	19.2	978.5	723.7
2008	3 581.3	289.2	20.0	25.4	1 47.6	870.0

Source: CEPAL.

THE USE OF HYDRO POWER PLANTS FOR THE GENERATION OF ELECTRICITY

Hydro power plants convert the kinetic energy contained in falling water into electricity. The energy in flowing water is ultimately derived from the sun and, for this reason, is constantly being renewed. Energy contained in sunlight evaporates water from the oceans and deposits it on land in the form of rain.

Categories of Hydro Power Plants

With any doubt, hydroelectricity has certain advantages over other renewable energy sources for the production of electricity: it is continually renewable thanks to the recurring nature of the water cycle, and causes no pollution. Also, it is one of the cheapest sources of electrical energy available worldwide.

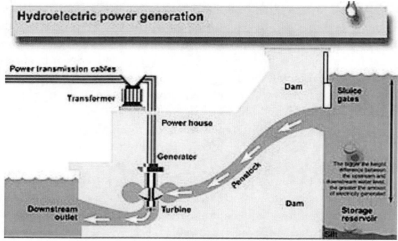

Source: Environment Canada.

Figure 6. Hydroelectric power generation scheme.

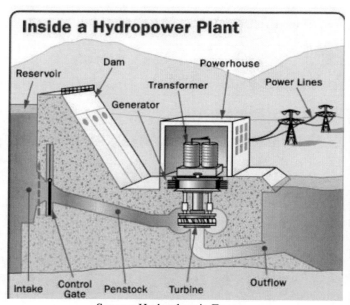

Source: Hydroelectric Energy.

Figure 7. Inside of a hydro power plant.

Generally, based on the head and storage capacity availability, hydro power plants are categorized as follows:

–   Low-head power plants (between 2 m and 20 m);
–   Medium head power plants (between 20 m and 150 m);

- High-head power plants (+150 m);
- Run-of-the-river hydro power plants[4];
- Pumped-storage hydro power plants.

High-head power plants are the most common and large hydroelectric power plants. This type of plants, generally utilize a dam to store water at an increased elevation. The use of a dam to impound water also provides the capability of storing water during rainy periods, and releasing it during dry periods. This results in the consistent and reliable production of electricity able to meet demand. High-head power plants with storage are very valuable to electric utilities because they can be quickly adjusted to meet the electrical demand.

Source: Photo courtesy of Caio Coronel/Itaipu Binacional.

Figure 8. The largest hydro power plant in the region: Itaipu (14 000 MW in 2007).

Low-head power plants are those that utilize either a low dam or weir to channel water or simply use the "run of the river". However, it is important to know that run of the river generating power plants cannot store water, thus their electric output vary with seasonal flows of water in a river.

Pumped storage is another form of hydroelectric power. Pumped storage facilities use excess electrical system capacity, generally available at night, to pump water from one reservoir to another reservoir at a higher elevation. During periods of peak electrical demand, water from the higher reservoir is released through turbines to the lower reservoir producing electricity. Although pumped storage sites are not net producers of electricity— it actually takes more electricity to pump the water up than is recovered when it is released — they are a valuable addition to electricity supply systems. Their value is in their ability to store electricity for use later when peak demands are occurring. Storage is even more valuable if

---

[4] These facilities are usually built on rivers with steady natural flows or regulated flows discharged from upstream reservoirs. These units have little or no storage capacity, and power is generated using the river flow and water head. Run-of-the-river hydro power plants are less appropriate for rivers with large seasonal fluctuations.

intermittent sources of electricity, such as solar or wind, are hooked into the system (Morales Pedraza, 2008).

Classification of Hydro Power Plants

According to the capacity of the hydro power plants they can be classified as follows[5]:

a) Large conventional hydro power plants: These facilities have a generation capacity of more than 300 MW;

b) Medium conventional hydro power plants: These facilities have a generation capacity from 100 MW to 300 MW (having a dam and a reservoir) and between 10 MW and 100 MW for others (run-of-river facilities). Medium-scale hydro power plants can sometimes be an economically viable for rural electrification, particularly in those rural areas that have adequate hydro power technical potential;

c) Small conventional hydro power plants[6]: These facilities have a generation capacity from 1 MW to 10 MW. Small-scale hydro power plants can sometimes be also economically viable for rural electrification, particularly in those rural areas that have adequate hydro power technical potential;

d) Mini-hydro power plants: These facilities have a generation capacity from 100 kW to 1 MW;

e) Micro-hydro power plants: These facilities have a generation capacity of less than 100 kW.

The Share of Hydro Power in the Energy Balance of the Region

Today, electricity generation from hydro power makes a substantial contribution to satisfy the increasing world's electricity demand. Most countries in the Latin American and the Caribbean region use already a good portion of their hydraulic potential to generate electricity. However, most operations lie in the multi-megawatt range, seeking economies of scale characteristic of hydroelectric technologies. This practice has left a large portion of the small hydroelectric potential yet to be exploited in several countries. Given the high rainfall indices, and the rough topography of many countries, small hydro power plants offer a good alternative to supply electricity, especially in remote sites (Huacuz, 2003).

Hydro power is the world's second most important source for the production of electricity, and one of the three main sources of energy used in the world for this specific purpose. The other two are fossil fuels and nuclear energy.

---

[5] It is important to stick out that there is no worldwide consensus on definitions regarding size categories of hydro power plants (Egre and Milewski, 2002).

[6] In general, small hydro power plants can use existing infrastructure such as dams or irrigation channels for electricity generation; are located close to villages to avoid expensive high-voltage distribution equipment; can use pumps as turbines and motors as generators for a turbine/generator set; and have a high level of local content both in terms of materials and work force during the construction period and local materials for the civil works (Kumar et al., 2011).

It is important to stress that of all renewable energy sources used for the generation of electricity, hydro power enjoys the most even distribution across the regions of the world. East and Southeast Asia has become the leader producer region of electricity using hydro power plants, with 23.4% of the world's total. North and South America are neck-and-neck with 20.7% of global output.

The contribution of hydro power to modern society has grown significantly supporting economic and social development worldwide. There are hydro power plants in operation in 150 countries in all regions, twenty nine of them in the Latin American and the Caribbean region. It is important to know that twenty four countries from different regions depend on hydro power plants for 90% or more for their electricity supply. South America shares 28% of the hydroelectricity generated worldwide in 2009; more than 50% of the electricity generated comes from hydroelectricity. Nevertheless, South America uses only between 20% and 21% of the exploitable hydro resources available in the region, making it, with Africa and Asia, one of the regions with the largest potential for hydro expansion in the coming years (Rudnick, 2008). The goal for the region for 2020 is to reach an increase up to 25% in the production of electricity using hydro power plants.

During the period 1999-2009, hydro power plants generated 603.2 TWh of electricity, occupying the second place behind fossil fuels. Hydro power plants provide, at least, 50% of the total electricity supply in more than sixty countries. Besides the fact that hydro power currently makes up a substantial share of the total's amount of electricity generated in the world, the arguments for continuing and increasing utilization of hydro power are based on its advantages in comparison with other sources of energy.

From 1985 to 1990, the share of hydroelectricity generation in Central America increased from 79% to 89%; this represents an increase of 10% in only five years (2% per year as average). But between 1990 and 1995, hydro's share dropped from 89% to 63%, a decrease of 26% with a corresponding increase in power generated from oil products, and the introduction of a small amount of coal-fired capacity. The drastic changes observed in Central America's energy matrix from 1985 to 1995, were mainly driven by changes in the energy matrix of Guatemala. Production from hydroelectric sources in Guatemala increased more than three times between 1985 and 1990 but dropped 5% by 1995.

In the specific case of South America, the production of electricity by hydro power in 2009 outperformed the others raising it by 21.2 TWh. The sub-region increased the production of electricity using hydro power by 2.8% per year during the period 1999-2009, adding 160.7 TWh to the total electricity produced in the sub-region in that period. With a total capacity of 723 GWe (21% of the world's electrical capacity), hydro power generates, in 2009, a total of 3 810.3 TWh (16% of the world's electricity generation).

In 2010, hydro power continues to be the first source of energy for electricity generation in Uruguay, Paraguay, Peru, Costa Rica, Brazil, Venezuela and Mexico. The estimated region's hydro power potential is 659.5 GW but only a small fraction of these potential capacities is being used, leaving significant possibilities for building new hydro power plants in several Latin American and the Caribbean countries in the future.

South America has a very large hydro electrical potential, with several countries relying in a significant manner in its contribution. The planned capacity, considering projects that have been proposed for eventual development, focuses in Brazil with 60%, followed by Colombia with 16%. Figure 10 shows the significant growth of hydroelectricity generated in the region during the period 1965-2007.

It is important to stress that current tendencies in the region clearly show that several countries will continue to rely on hydro power plants for electricity generation at least in the near future in order to satisfy their foreseen increase in the demand of electricity. However, the role of hydro power in the generation of electricity is not the same in all countries of the region. Figure 9 shows the role of hydro power in a group of countries in Central and South America.

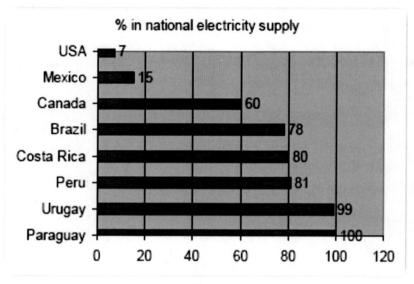

Source: Hydro Québec.

Figure 9. Percentage in national electricity supply in some countries of the region.

From Figure 9, the following can be stated: According to Hydro Quebec, Paraguay is the Latin America country with the largest participation of hydro power in the generation of electricity with a share of 100%, followed by Uruguay with a share of 99%, Peru with a share of 81%, Costa Rica with a share of 80%, and Brazil with a share of 78%.

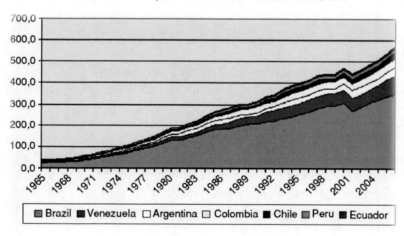

Source: BP Statistical Review of World Energy 2007.

Figure 10. Hydroelectric power generation in Terawatt-hours in South America.

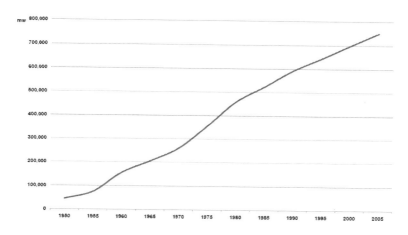

Source: Energy Information Administration.

Figure 11. The growth of hydro power generating capacity during the period 1950-2005 (MW).

From Figure 11, the following can be stated: In the last fifty five years, the use of hydro power plants for the generation electricity grew significantly, moving from around 50 000 MW in 1950 to over 700 000 MW in 2005; this represents an increase of 1 400%.

Hydro Power Potential

Hydro power is a key component in the energy mix required to meet fluctuating power demand, while reducing dependence on fossil fuels for the generation of electricity. The hydro power potential by country is shown in Figure 12.

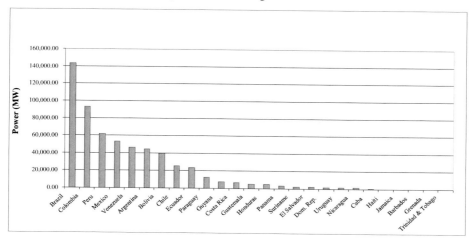

Source: OLADE, 2005.

Figure 12. Hydropower potential.LAC.

From Figure 12, the following can be stated: Brazil is the country with the largest hydro power potential in the region, followed by Colombia, Peru, Mexico, Venezuela, Argentina, Bolivia, Chile, Ecuador and Paraguay. In other countries the hydro power potential is very small.

Advantages and Disadvantages in the Use of Hydro Power Plants for Electricity Generation

The following are some of advantages and disadvantages in the use of hydro power plants for electricity generation:

1. Advantages

a) Fuel is not burned so there is minimal pollution. By far the cleanest way to produce electricity. Hydro power plants play a major role in reducing greenhouse gas emissions during the generation of electricity;
b) Water to run the hydro power plant is provided free by nature;
c) Relatively low operations and maintenance costs;
d) The technology is reliable and proven over time;
e) It is renewable - rainfall renews the water in the reservoir, so the fuel is almost always there with the exception of severe dry season;
f) Supports the development of other renewable energy sources;
g) Fosters energy security and price stability. Offers stable electricity rates, as it is independent from fuel price fluctuations;
h) Contributes to fresh water storage. Reservoirs also offer the opportunity for enhanced fresh water management enabling: a) Flood control; b) Irrigation; and c) Water based transport;
i) Improves electric grid stability and reliability. Reservoirs serve as energy storage to provide more flexibility and stability to the electric grid in peak-hours or emergency situations;
j) Helps fight climate change;
k) Makes a significant contribution to sustainable development. Allows countries to benefit from their domestic resources;
l) Means clean and affordable power;
m) Is a driving force for regional development.

2. Disadvantages

a) High initial investment costs;
b) Hydrology dependency on precipitation;
c) Inundation of land and wildlife habitat affecting the environment;
d) Loss or modification of fish habitat;
e) Changes in reservoir and stream water quality;
f) Displacement of large local populations.

Investment Cost Associated with Different Hydro Power Plant Sizes

The investment costs of large hydro power plants range from US$1,750 kWe to US$6,250 kWe. It is very site-sensitive, with a typical figure of about US$4,000 kWe. The investment costs of medium and small hydro power plants may range from US$2,000 kWe to US$7,500 kWe and from US$2,500 kWe to US$10,000 kWe, with indicative average figures of US$4,500 kWe and US$5,000 kWe, respectively,

Operation and maintenance costs are estimated between US$5 MWh to US$20 MWh for medium to large hydro power plants, and approximately twice as much for the small ones.

The resulting overall generation cost is between US$40 MWh and US$110 MWh (typical US$75 MWh) for large hydro power plants; between US$45 MWh and US$120 MWh (typically US$83 MWh) for medium hydro power plants; and from US$55 MWh to US$185 MWh (typically US$90 MWh) for small hydro power plants. The detailed analysis of the above costs is an important task that needs to be carried out by the competent authorities and the private energy industry of a country, during the consideration of the construction of new hydro power plants for the generation of electricity in the future.

From Figure 13, the following can be stated: Hydro power plants has a large capital investment representing a little bit more than 90% of the total, while the capital investment in gas and coal represent a little more than 20% and 40%, respectively. The operation and maintenance costs of hydro power plants is around 5% of the total investment, while in the cases of gas and coal are around 8% and 15%, respectively.

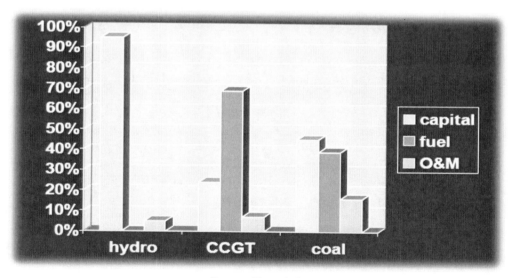

Source: Tractebel.

Figure 13. Typical kWh cost structure.

If one takes into account only some of the largest countries of the region, such as Brazil, Argentina, Peru, and Colombia in the next ten years, it is expected that they will have a significant increase in hydroelectric generation capacity, going from the current 100 GW to 139.9 GW at the end of the period; this represents an increase of 39.9% (3.99 % per year as average). Of these new generation capacity, Brazil will take the lead with nearly 27 GW.

Finally, it is important to stress the following: According to the Economic Commission for Latin America and the Caribbean, countries in the region would require an investment of US$572 billion in the electricity sector between 2007 and 2030, with the purpose of meeting the foreseen energy demand during this period. Who is going to provide these resources? According to the United Nations Framework for Climate Change, "more than 85% of the energy investment in this region will come from the private sector in the future", which seen to be an unrealistic approach, particularly, if the use of renewable energy sources for the generation of electricity is going to be promoted by several governments of the region in the coming years.

International and development banks have already committed funds to finance energy projects in several countries of the region, and the Inter-American Development Bank (IDB) is financing, since 2000, more than US$2.1 billion in the implementation of several renewable energy projects in the region. In addition, the United Nations' Clean Development Mechanism, which became operation in 2006, has been a key factor behind investment in the energy sector in the region. Of the 2 127 projects that were registered up to April 2010, a total of 461 of them were for the Latin American region, and more than 60% are related to the energy sector, especially the use of renewable energy sources for the generation of electricity. A combination of small hydro power plants, solar energy systems, wind farms, and biomass contributes to the majority of this investment. However, the resources already available to support the use of renewable energy sources for the generation of electricity for the whole region are only a small fraction of the total needed.

Hydro Power Plant Projects

Some of the current hydro power plant projects under implementation or that have been planned to be implemented in South and Central American sub-regions in the future are the following:

a) Brazil, with projects totalizing 26 638 MW of new hydroelectric generation capacity to be constructed until 2020, takes the lead in this regard. Among others, the country's environmental authorities recently approved the construction of the Belo Monte hydro power plant, which will have an installed capacity exceeding 11 000 MW, located on the Xingu River, a tributary of the Amazon River. Belo Monte hydro power plant would thus become the third largest hydro power plant in the world. Other large-scale power plants are the one in Rio Madeira, Santo Antonio, with a capacity of 3 150 MW, and the other in Jirau, with a capacity of 3 300 MW;

b) Peru, with announcements of over 20 000 MW of new capacities in hydro power, is another country of the region that is also taking the lead in the use of this type of enrgy for the generation of electricity. Former President Alan Garcia announced the construction of a complex of twenty hydroelectric power plants to be built in the next forty years (2050) in the country's jungle. The project aims to use the waters of the Marañón River to generate 12 400 MW of electricity;

c) Colombia, with projects of nearly 5 200 MW of new hydroelectric generation capacity to be constructed by the year 2020, has not been left behind. Already under construction is the El Quimbo hydro power plant on the Huila River, which will have

400 MW of power. In parallel, other major projects that have been announced are the Sogamoso hydro power plant, which will add 820 MW to the system, and the Pescadero-Ituango hydro power plant, with a capacity of 2 400 MW;

d) Argentina, with projects of more than 2 600 MW of new hydroelectric capacity to be constructed by 2020, has completed in 2010 the construction of the Yacyretá hydro power plant, which it shares with Paraguay. Now, the capacity of the hydro power plant is 2 250 MW, an increase of 67% respect the capacity of the plant in 2004. Moreover, the construction of the La Barrancosa-Cóndor Cliff hydroelectric plant is progressing. This complex will be located in Argentina's Patagonia, and will provide an electricity output of more than 1 700 MW;

e) Ecuador is considering the construction of eight hydroelectric power plants, among them the Coca Codo Sinclair (1 500 MW capacity), the Sopladora (312 MW capacity), and the Toachi-Pilatón (253 MW capacity), all of them under construction. In addition, there are five other hydro power plants of different sizes that are going to be built in the coming years. These are: Minas San Francisco (276 MW capacity), Delsitanisagua (115 MW capacity), Quijos (50 MW capacity), Mazar-Dudas (21 MW capacity), and Villonaco (15 MW capacity);

f) Costa Rica, with projects of 955 MW of new hydroelectric capacity to be constructed in the coming years, is taking the lead in Central America. This country will develop two hydroelectric projects one is Reventazón, with 305 MW capacity, and the other El Diquis, with 650 MW capacity.

Environment Impact

Hydro power is a clean source of energy as it burns no fuel and does not produce greenhouse gas emissions, other pollutants or any other of the wastes associated with the use of fossil fuels and the use of nuclear energy for the generation of electricity. However, the use of hydro power for the generation of electricity does cause indirect greenhouse gas emissions, mainly during the construction and flooding of the reservoirs. This is due to the decomposition of a fraction of the flooded biomass (forests and peat lands, among others), and of an increase in the aquatic wildlife and vegetation in the reservoir. However, it is important to stress that, according to certain expert calculations, hydro power's greenhouse gas emissions factor (between 4 grams to 18 grams CO_2 equivalent per kWh produced) is 36 to 167 times lower than the emissions produced by electricity generation using other types of fossil fuels. Compared to other renewable energy sources on a lifecycle basis, the use of hydro power for the generation of electricity releases fewer greenhouse gas emissions than the electricity generation from biomass and solar power, and about the same emissions from wind, nuclear, and geothermal power plants.

At the same time, the use of hydro power plants for the generation of electricity is not free from negative impact in the environment. These are, according to Petts (1984), Stanford et al (1996), Wirth (1997), Schmidt et al (1998), and d'Anglejan (1994), the following:

a) Habitat diversity is substantially reduced;

b) Native diversity decreases, while exotic species proliferate. The altered hydrologic, sediment, and temperature regimes do not provide adequate environmental conditions for most native species. Conversely, the homogenization of habitats allows exotics to compete better;

c) Water quality is altered downstream of the dam. Alterations to the temperature regime and increases in the fine organic material are often anticipated during project design but the severity of the problem was frequently underestimated.

One important element that needs to be considered during the construction of hydro power plants due to the negative impact in the environment, is the sedimentation associated to the construction of the dam. Sedimentation issues are not confined solely to the reservoir and downstream reaches.

The backwater reach can extend many kilometers upstream of the reservoir. The depositional environment immediately following implementation is confined to the delta region at the head of the reservoir. As this delta builds up, additional sediment is deposited in the upstream reach of the river due to the backwater effect. The aggradations in the reach in turn raise the local water surface elevations, creating additional backwater and deposition even further upstream.

This feedback mechanism allows the depositional environment to propagate much further upstream than the initial hydraulic backwater curve might suggest. Upstream effects include effects to the benthic communities due to deposition as well as the obvious barriers to fish migration corridors.

Conversely, the effects of the backwater due to dams is the potential drowning of natural migratory barriers within a basin, promoting the spread of some fish species beyond their pre-project domains (Goodwin, 2006).

Public Acceptance

The public acceptance has become a high-priority issue for hydro power development in many countries over the last two decades. Local citizens are now requesting to be fully consulted as part of the project development process for the construction of new hydro power plants. This has also implications for the financing of new hydro power plants. For instance, World Bank lending for hydro power bottomed out in 1999, due to growing opposition from environmental and other non-governmental organizations to the construction of new large hydro power plants.

Fortunatelly, now this situation has changed, and there is now a growing awareness that countries must follow an integrated approach in managing their water resources, planning hydro power development in co-operation with other water-using sectors, and taking environmental, safety, and social factors properly into account. World Bank lending is now expanding in this sector, reflecting a Water Resources Sector Strategy approved in 2003, which recognizes that significant levels of investment in water infrastructure are required throughout the developing world in order to satisfy the foreseen increase in the electricity demand in the coming years but without increasing the negative impact in the environment.

Looking Forward

The era of large hydro power projects began in the 1930s in North America, and has since extended worldwide. Today's large hydro power projects, either under construction or planned, are located in China, India, Turkey, Canada, and Latin America and the Caribbean. Significant potential remains around the world for both developing a large number of small hydro power projects, and for upgrading existing plants and dams.

Important technical potential for new hydro power capacity remains in Asia, Africa, and South America. A realistic figure totals from 2.5 to 3 times the current production. In the IEA Energy Technology Perspectives scenarios, hydro power capacity is projected to more than double (up to 1 700 GWe) between now and 2050, and the hydroelectricity production is projected to reach between 5 000 MW and 6 000 TWh per year by 2050; this represents an increase between 31% and 57.4% respect to 2009 (3 810.3 TWh).

Without any doubt, hydro power represents a strong option for a clean electricity generation for several countries in the Latin American and the Caribbean region. In 2003, hydro power was the first source of energy for electricity generation in the whole region. It has been in use for many years, and is now a conventional form of power generation used in many countries. Although there are hydroelectric projects under construction in about eighty countries in different regions, most of the remaining hydro potential in the world may be found in South and Central Asia, Central and South America, and Africa (see Figure 14).

It is important to stress the following: On the short-term, due to the high initial investment, the long construction periods and the long distant power transmission from the remote hydro power plants to populated areas, hydro power cannot compete in the production of electricity with e.g., highly-efficient gas-fired-power plants. Nevertheless, on the long-term, oil and gas reserves in the region will start to deplete, oil and gas price will continue to increase in the coming years and, for this reason, the use of hydro power plants is envisaged to obtain again a larger share in the energy mix of the region (Deutsche MontanTechnologie GmbH, OLADE and Ciemat, 2005).

Figure 14. Greatest undeveloped hydro power potential.

According to the outcome of a study made by GBI Research, in 2010 five key economies in South America have a hydro power installed capacity of 63.5% of the total. However, currently government policies and renewable energy legislations adopted by several countries, support the development and use of renewable energy sources for the generation of electricity, with Argentina, Brazil, Chile, and Colombia all enacting legislations to promote its development. The electricity production through hydro power has increased significantly over the past decade but it is expected to show moderate growth until 2020. With increasing legislative and financial support for renewable energy sources, the share of renewable energy in the generation of electricity is expected to increase in Brazil, Argentina and Chile, among other countries of the region.

However, future hydro power production could be affected by climate change. The potential impact is not yet well understood and, for this reason, must be investigated in more detail. Key issues and challenges for new hydro power projects include the general scarcity of water and land resources in most parts of the world, the social and the environmental impact of large hydro power plants, and the long distance from new hydro resources and consumers, particularly in the case of large Latin American countries. These challenges are likely to limit the use of the hydro power potential in order to satisfy the expected increase in the electricity demand in the region in the coming years.

There should be no doubt that the use of existing hydro power plants is one of the cheapest ways to generate electricity. Why? Because, most hydro power plants were built long time ago and the initial investment for dams and hydro geological infrastructure has been already fully amortized.

The market of large hydro power plants is dominated by a few manufacturers of large equipment, and a number of suppliers of auxiliary components and systems. Over the past decades, no major breakthroughs have occurred in the basic machinery used in the operation of hydro power plants. However, computer technology led to significant improvements in many areas such as monitoring, diagnostics, protection, and control. Manufacturers and suppliers need to invest significant resources in research and development to meet technology advance and market competition. In addition, large hydro power plants may have considerable impact on environmental and social economic aspects at regional level. Therefore, the link between industry, research and development, and policy institutions is central to the development of this important energy sector for several countries of the region in the coming years. Different from large hydro power plants, small hydro power installations involve a huge variety of designs, layouts, equipment, and materials. Therefore, state-of-the-art technologies, knowledge, and design experience are the key to fully exploit hydro local resources at competitive costs and with no significant environmental impact in the future.

According to several experts' opinion up rating is the best option available in all countries to maximize the energy produced from existing big and medium hydro power plants, and often may offer a cheap opportunity to increase hydroelectricity production. Gains between 5% and 10% are realistic and cost-effective targets for most hydro power plants now in operation. The potential gain could also be higher at locations where non-generating dams are available. Investment in repowering hydro power projects, however, involves not only technical risks but also risks associated to re-licensing of existing installations, often designed several decades ago, with limited records of technical documentation. As a consequence, a significant potential is left untapped. Fortunately, today's technologies allow for accurate analysis of geology and hydrology, accurate assessments of potential gains, operation and maintenance, and possible replacement of main machinery after several decades of operation.

Small hydro power plants may be operated for some fifty years without substantial replacement costs.

Finally, it is important to know that hydro power investment costs for new installations vary considerably between industrialized and developing countries. In developing countries and emerging economies, the construction of hydro power plants usually involve substantial civil work (dams, deviation of rivers, etc.), the cost of which largely depends on labor costs, which is substantially lower than in industrialized countries. The cost of pumped storage systems also depend strongly on site configuration but also on the operation service. The investment cost may be up to twice as high as an equivalent un-pumped hydro power system. However, depending on cycling rates, the generating cost may be similar to those of un-pumped systems as a pumped storage system receives substantial income from pumping during the night and generating during peak demand periods, based on a corresponding electricity price differential.

According to Yepez-García (2010), to maintain the current high share of hydro power in the energy balance of the countries in the Latin American and the Caribbean region, it is necessary to develop hydro power resources in Peru, Colombia, and Ecuador, countries with more than half of the hydro power potential outside of Brazil, and which today have developed only 10% of this potential. Greater integration among regional power markets could help to justify and attract financing for the development of larger hydro power projects in these countries in the future.

Constraints and Barriers

Notwithstanding the strong development rationale, the enormous technical potential, and the improved understanding of good practices scaling up, hydro power faces important constraints and barriers. According to the World Bank (2009) report, these constraints and barriers are, among others, the following:

a) Identification and management of environmental and social risks is challenged by limited institutional capacity and experience in implementing new standards. This means refining regulatory and policy frameworks at the country level, building capacity among developers as well as electricity companies and government, and enhancing transparency for stakeholders. It also means on-going research into important environmental issues such as emissions from reservoirs in shallow tropical sites, and continuous improvement in avoiding and mitigating impacts;

b) Infrastructure design based on poor hydrological data can severely compromise performance and decrease the very water management benefits the infrastructure is designed to generate. Climate change accentuates these risks for two reasons: The first one is that extrapolations of historical data are less reliable as the past becomes an increasingly poor predictor of the future; the second is that hydrology is ever-changing, placing a premium on designs that maximize flexibility and operations that embrace adaptive management;

c) While the potential for hydro power is known, there is a lack of planning and project prioritization. In particular, engineering studies completed years ago need to be updated with new knowledge (particularly of hydrology) as well as more sophisticated consideration of environmental and social values. As a public good, governments need to undertake strategic assessments and prefeasibility studies in order to develop a pipeline of projects, and identify high-value storage sites;

d) Against the demand for hydro power infrastructure is a shortage of financing, exacerbated by the current global financial crisis. This gap is most severe in the poorest countries, where the funds needed well exceed the resources of governments and donors/development banks. Yet increasing resources from the private sector requires a broad range of responses: i) Better policies and institutions; ii) Improving payments from energy consumers; iii) Clarity in regulations for developing and operating hydro power plants; and iv) Innovative financial structures that support public-private partnership projects with multiple (public and private) benefits.

THE USE OF WIND POWER PLANTS FOR THE GENERATION OF ELECTRICITY

In 2009, wind power became the number two within the renewable energy sources used for the generation of electricity (268.2 TWh), overtaking biomass for the first time but still far behind hydro power. It account only for 13% of world's electricity production, and 7% of the total generation of electricity using renewable energy sources. In 2009, growth in the wind power sector raised 22.1% respect to 2008. However, this percentage is slightly below the annual growth rate of 28.9% for the whole period 1999-2009.

Without any doubt, wind sector is the best placed renewable energy sector to back up the hydro power sector, and curb the trend to increase reliance on fossil fuels for generating electricity. At the end of 2009, world's installed wind power capacity stood at 150 GW, which is double the level reached in 2006.

The ten top countries with 85.5% of the total wind output production are: USA, Germany, Spain, China, India, UK, France, Portugal, Denmark and Italy. Regrettably, no Latin America and the Caribbean countries are included in this group. Table 3 contains the production of electricity by country of the region using wind power. From Table 3, the following can be stated: The country with the highest production of electricity using wind power is Brazil, with a production of 341 billion kWh, followed by Venezuela, Paraguay, Mexico, Colombia, Argentina, Chile, and Peru. The production of electricity using wind power in other countries of the region is very small.

From Figure 15, the following can be stated: Latin America and the Caribbean is one of the regions with the lowest level in the use of wind energy for the generation of electricity worldwide, very far from Europe, North America, and Asia and the Pacific. However, the region set to become a global wind powerhouse in the coming decade with a foreseen increase of more than 40 GW of wind capacity by 2025, according to recent forecast report prepared by IHS Emerging Energy Research.

The report expects growth to be fuelled by an increasing regional push to diversify energy supply, supported by the maturing of the project development market, and wind's decline in costs through local manufacturing. In 2006, unexploited potential as a per cent of the total amounts to around 62%, in the case of the Latin America and the Caribbean region.

As Latin American and the Caribbean countries has been relatively unaffected by the current global economic recession, power demand has continued to rise at regional level. Meanwhile, traditional reliance on hydro power and fossil fuels has led to a constrained supply during recent periods of unusually low precipitation, amid volatile oil prices. As a consequence, policymakers have paid greater attention to guaranteeing energy security with endogenous resources, particularly renewable energy sources. While renewable energy policy in developed countries is driven by climate change concerns, in Latin American and the Caribbean countries this issue still remains secondary. Governments seek technologies that are proven, cost-competitive, and can spawn local industrial activity. Wind is a clear favorite, along with geothermal energy, biomass and mini-hydro power plants.

Table 3. Wind electricity generation in 2007 and 2008

Rank	Country	Billion kWh
1	Brazil (2008)	341.0[1]
2	Venezuela (2008)	86.7
3	Paraguay (2007)	53.19
4	Mexico (2008)	48.34
5	Colombia (2007)	42.01
6	Argentina (2007)	31.67
7	Chile (2007)	25.49
8	Peru (2007)	19.78
9	Ecuador (2007)	8.95
10	Uruguay (2007)	8.12
11	Costa Rica (2007)	8.11
12	Guatemala (2007)	4.9
13	Panama (2007)	3.7
14	El Salvador (2007)	3.06
15	Bolivia (2007)	2.46
16	Honduras (2007)	2.35
17	Dominican Republic (2007)	1.42
18	Suriname (2007)	0.9
19	Nicaragua (2007)	0.89262
20	Cuba (2007)	0.43719
21	Jamaica (2007)	0.308
22	Belize (2007)	0.1774
23	Haiti (2007)	0.152
24	Dominica (2007)	0.03
25	St. Vincent and the Grenadines (2007)	0.02249
26	Trinidad and Tobago (2007)	0.009
27	Guyana (2007)	0.001

Note 1: By the end of 2009, the capacity increased up to 786 MW. In 2010, the wind capacity grew to 931 MW.

Source: Global Wind Energy Council.

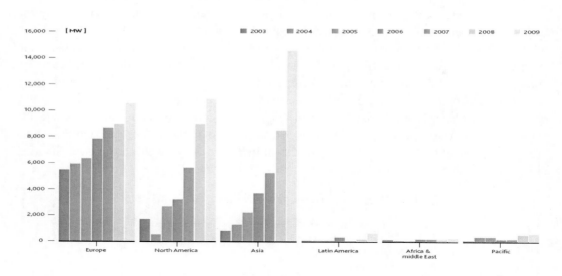

Source: Global Wind Energy Council.

Figure 15. Annual installed capacity by region 2003-2009.

Wind power has select growth opportunities to diversify supply and — led by Brazil, Venezuela, Paraguay, Mexico, Colombia, Argentina, Chile, and Peru — Latin America and the Caribbean is expected to reach 40 GW of total installed wind capacity by 2025, with a 12.6% compound annual growth rate of installations. The study entitled "Latin America Wind Power Markets and Strategies: 2010 – 2025" concludes that "Brazil will lead the region with 31.6 GW wind installed capacity by 2025 (79% of the total capacity to be expected to be installed in the region), followed by Mexico some way behind, with about 6.6 GW expected to be installed in the coming years (16.5% of the total). Chile will also add significant wind power, boosted by the country's Renewable Portfolio Standard."

In addition to Brazil, Mexico, and Chile, other countries such as Peru, Argentina, Uruguay, and Costa Rica host diverse market drivers, including supply security concerns and wind resources, although there is a lack of policy execution, which can limit the use of wind power for the generation of electricity in the future. Other countries have shown political will for the development of renewable energy sources but lack consistency. For example, Panama has seen multiple project cancellations and a pipeline disproportionate to its wind potential. Venezuela has also made repeated announcements on a political level but implementation plans remain vague.

Wind Power Market, Investment, and Technology Trends

Latin America and the Caribbean is an aggregation of markets with limited interconnection and diverse growth prospects due to differences in the power generation mix — including varying reliance on hydro — and in economic development, political orientation, and wind resources. Wind power is a relative newcomer to Latin American and the Caribbean countries, with yearly installations greater than 100 MW only in three of the past ten years.

The use of wind power for the generation of electricity has begun to stabilize thanks to maturing policies, resulting in a coherent context of growing pipeline, installations, and supply. The key factor in the growth in the use of renewable energy sources for the generation of electricity, particularly wind energy, apart from competing lower-cost technologies is country risk, which determines political will and policy support. Latin American and the Caribbean markets are relatively immature, given that wind resources are plentiful and barely tapped in the face of an urgent need for added generation electricity capacity.

Governments show support for the use of wind energy and other renewable energy sources for the generation of electricity but this has failed to turn into a transparent framework in most of the Latin American and the Caribbean countries. Local developers lack experience can hinder industry growth by underestimating costs, and create a nebulous pipeline of non-economical projects. Even so, with Latin America's large potential and limited installed capacity, developers are racing to secure market share in a single country, while those companies with more mature pipelines have initiated regional expansion. This trend is dominated by international players, while local firms are concentrating investment in their home markets.

On this issue, it is important to stress that European wind players are poised to dominate wind power development and ownership in Latin America and the Caribbean in the near-term, leveraging their experience and financial resources. With experienced European firms leading the way, smaller and inexperienced greenfield players are being bypassed in securing sites in markets where foreign competition is welcome. Locally, IMPSA Wind is currently the only Latin America developer with regional ambition. Nonetheless, domestic industrial players and independent power producers are expected to move to challenge these foreign entrants by the latter half of the decade, according to a study prepared by Emergency Energy Research.

Local entrepreneurs, meanwhile, are creating independent power producers that are securing sites, whereas local utilities lack the impetus and experience to build wind portfolios. But even starting from a small base, the installed capacity is quickly growing up from 0.5 GW at year-end 2008 to 1.3 GW at year-end 2009, an increase of 160%. Players' market shares have therefore yet to stabilize. For example, commissioning its only operational Latin American project, the 250 MW Eurus installations, made Spain's Acciona Energía, the regional market leader.

Latin America's inconsistent march toward a more developed wind power market is beginning to take shape around technology trends seen in other more mature regions. Tapping high-wind resource sites, with lower-cost more easily installed proven machines, has served to kick-start the market with projects in Costa Rica, Mexico, Brazil and Argentina. With increasing experience with the technology, imports of newer larger models will reach Latin America and the Caribbean with a steadier level of demand. Orders placed for 2010-2011 delivery in Latin America and the Caribbean totalling nearly 4.5 GW represent key developments in firming up the supply side of an industry that has, until recently, been more focused on solidifying demand.

Significant developments include Brazilian developers, which began turbine sourcing discussions in early 2009 for independent power producers, winning projects from a capacity tender in December the previous year. Over 1 GW was initially committed in 2009 and, after this year, a steady flow of firm turbine supply agreements has been discussed in order to finalize these commitments.

Source: International Journal of Distributed Energy Resources, ISSN 1614-7138, Volume 1 Number 3, 2005.

Figure 16. Brazil's largest wind park: Prainha (30 km from Fortaleza, in the northeast of Brazil).

Mexican orders are also gaining in scale, reflecting a short-term surge in wind demand — up to almost 1.8 GW of new orders — as self-supply power purchase agreements for players such as CEMEX, and for local municipalities that are seeking power supply, provide independent power producers opportunities under CFE-backed private off-take deals. Other markets offer one-off opportunities. Chile, Venezuela, and Argentina are the only other markets with 100 MW or more turbines on orders in the Latin American and the Caribbean region.

Given the growth trajectory of Latin America's wind turbine market, underpinned by diverse country-specific demand drivers, experts anticipates a total investment level scaling from under US$1 billion in 2009 to over US$2.2 billion by 2015, an increase of 120% for the whole period. Key assumptions behind this expected increase include falling prices in 2010-2011 as financing challenges soften market demand. Experts anticipate relatively flat demand in the region, around 1.3 GW, with prices per MW installed falling. Brazil is still likely to depend on foreign imports at a premium as well as Mexico. Leveling out in 2012-2013 as import competition increases, increased supplies from additional European, US and Asian players will likely stabilize prices. Furthermore, localization and economies of scale are expected to emerge through 2015 and impact the cost curve. Beyond 2013, several experts anticipate significant regional production capacity to be in place across the component supply chain, increasing this downward price pressure.

When the role of wind energy in the world's energy balance is analyzed, the following important element needs to be taken into account: Wind cannot be analyzed in isolation from the other components of the electricity system, and all systems differ. The size and the inherent flexibility of the power system are crucial aspects determining the system's capability of accommodating a high amount of wind power. Experience has shown that combining a diverse mix of creative demand and supply solutions allows large wind power penetration in an electricity grid without adverse effect. Three major trends have dominated the economics of grid connected wind turbines in recent years:

a) The turbines have grown larger and taller;
b) Turbine efficiency has increased. A mixture of taller turbines, improved components and better sitting has resulted in an overall efficiency increase between 2% and 3% annually over the past fifteen years;
c) Investment costs have decreased.

In the use of wind power for the generation of electricity, the turbine comprises about 80% of the total cost. The other main cost elements (20% of the total) are operational costs and maintenance costs, including repairs and insurance. Manufacturers aim is to shrink these costs significantly through development of new turbine designs requiring fewer regular service visits and, consequently, reduced downtime.

Wind technology has become very reliable, operating with availabilities of more than 98%, and having a design life of twenty years or more. Moreover, as the costs of wind turbines have steadily declined, technical reliability has increased making the use of this technology for the generation of electricity more competitive in many countries in the past years. The main factors that currently limit wind energy's market penetration include variability, public acceptance, and grid reliability. However, recent developments in electricity market reform, which promote better grid integration and improved management of natural cycles of renewables, diminish the technological barriers that have constrained market penetration.

In the area of wind energy, continued research and development is essential to provide the necessary reductions in cost, and uncertainty to realize the anticipated level of deployment. Other research and development priorities include increasing the value of forecasting power performance, reducing uncertainties related to engineering integrity, improvement and validation of standards, reducing the cost of storage techniques, enabling large-scale use, and minimizing environmental impacts.

Further expansion of wind power will promote significant reductions in greenhouse gases. With further deployment support, wind power may become generally competitive with conventional technologies by 2015-2020; off-shore wind will likely become competitive to a degree after that.

Wind Energy and the Impact in the Environment

Besides the positive effects of wind energy on the environment, especially in the replacing of fossil fuels for the generation of electricity and consequent reduction in CO_2 and other gas emissions, wind energy potentially have also negative environmental impacts. These can be divided into impact on ecology, and visual and other-sense impacts. The first category includes potential impacts on the populations, for example, collision, diversion, habitat disturbance, impact on migration routes, and effects on sea floor organisms and fish, as well as on sea mammals for off-shore applications. The second category includes acoustic sound emissions, visual impact, shadow effects and "flicker" and safety. The Latin American and the Caribbean region increased in the past years the use of wind energy for the generation of electricity. Southeast Mexico and most of the Central American and Caribbean countries are under the influence of "Trade Winds", while southern Mexico and Central America are also exposed to strong and almost constant thermally driven winds, produced by the temperature difference between the waters of the Atlantic and the Pacific oceans (Huacuz et al., 1992). Windy places can also be found in the southern hemisphere.

It is important to stress that low winds cannot be effectively used to produce electricity, while excessively strong winds may be a major threat to wind generators. This situation should be in the mind of all governments during the selection of sites for the construction of wind farms. Few countries in the Latin American and the Caribbean region, among them Argentina, Brazil, and Cuba, have developed wind maps to guide project developers. A low resolution wind map of the region was developed over a decade ago by OLADE.

Summing up, the following can be stated: Wind power has many benefits that make it an attractive source of power for both utility-scale and small distributed power generation applications. The beneficial characteristics of wind power include:

a) Clean and inexhaustible fuel: Wind power produces no emissions and is not depleted over time. A single one MWe wind turbine running for one year can displace over 1 500 tons of carbon dioxide, 6.5 tons of sulfur dioxide, 3.2 tons of nitrogen oxides, and 60 pounds of mercury, based on the USA average utility generation fuel mix;

b) Local economic development: Wind power can provide a steady flow of income to land owners who lease their land for wind development, while increasing property tax revenues for local communities;

c) Modular and scalable technology: Wind applications can take many forms, including large, medium and small wind farms, distributed generation, and single end-use systems. Utilities can use wind resources strategically to help reduce load forecasting risks and stranded costs;

d) Energy price stability: By further diversifying the energy mix, wind energy reduces dependence on conventional fuels for the generation of electricity that are subject to price and supply volatility;

e) Reduced reliance on imported fuels: Wind energy expenditures are not used to obtain fuels from abroad, keeping funds closer to home and lessening dependence on foreign governments that supply these fuels.

THE USE OF SOLAR POWER SYSTEMS FOR THE GENERATION OF ELECTRICITY

According to the IEO (2009) report, solar power is one of the fastest-growing sources of renewable energy worldwide. Many nations, concerned about the environmental impacts of electricity generation from fossil fuels or from large-scale hydro power plants, have been turning to solar power as an environmentally benign alternative. Two solar power technologies are widely employed today for the generation of electricity: a) Solar photovoltaic; and b) Solar thermal.

Solar Photovoltaic

Solar photovoltaic technology converts sunlight directly into electricity by using photons from the sun's light to excite electrons into higher states of energy. The resultant voltage differential across cells allows for a flow of electric current. Because individual solar cells are very small, and, for this reason, produce a few watts of power at most, they are connected together in solar panels that can be arranged in arrays to increase electricity output. The arrangement of arrays is one major advantage of solar photovoltaic technologies, because they can be made in virtually any size to fit a specific application.

One popular application of solar photovoltaic is in solar panel installations on residential roofs, which can be scaled to accommodate house size and electricity needs. Although the technology now is used most often in small residential applications, it can be scaled up to create larger solar power plants, such as the 14 MW Nellis solar power plant in Nevada, with some 70 000 solar panels installed, and the 11 MW solar power plant in Serpa, Portugal, with 52 000 solar panels installed.

At present, the cost of electricity produced from solar photovoltaic generally is too high to compete with wholesale electricity. In sunny locations, however, the cost can be as low as 23% per kWh, which may be competitive with the delivered price of electricity to retail customers, in areas where electricity prices are high.

It is important to stress that, on the basis of installed cost per megawatt, solar photovoltaic installations are relatively costly, because the panel components are expensive, and the conversion of solar energy to electricity in the cells still is inefficient. From conversion efficiencies between 5% and 6% for the first solar cells built in the 1950s, there has been an improvement to efficiencies between 12% and 18% for modern commercial wafer-silicon cells, which is higher but still very low. Efficiency gains, coupled with other technological advances, have reduced the cost of solar photovoltaic capacity from approximately US$300 per watt in 1956 to less than US$5 per watt in 2009. IEO (2009) projects that by 2030 overnight capacity costs for new generating plants using solar photovoltaic technology will be 37% lower than the 2009 costs. In addition, the efficiency of solar photovoltaic applications is expected to improve as the technology continues to be developed. Although prices for electricity from solar photovoltaic may not become widely competitive with wholesale prices for electricity from conventional generating technologies within the next twenty five years, they may be competitive with high retail electricity prices in sunny regions in a shorter period.

Already, solar photovoltaic technology is gaining market share in countries where declining prices and government-backed financial incentives to use renewable energy sources for the generation of electricity have been adopted.

Solar Thermal

Solar thermal technology produces electricity by concentrating the sun's heat to boil a liquid and using the steam to rotate a generator turbine, in much the same way that electricity is produced from steam plants powered by oil, coal or natural gas. There are two main types of solar thermal power plants: a) Towers; and b) Parabolic troughs. A solar power tower consists of a large array of sun-tracking mirrors, which are used to reflect the sun's rays onto a central tower. When the rays hit the tower's receiving panel, their heat is transferred to a fluid medium that is boiled to produce steam. Solar power towers have been demonstrated successfully but they still are in the early stages of technology development. The world's largest solar power tower, located in Spain, is the 15 MW Solar Tres Power Tower.

The most commonly used solar thermal technology is the parabolic trough, in which a parabolic reflector focuses the sun's rays on a heat pipe that runs the length of the trough, and transports heated fluid to a central power station. Most solar parabolic trough installations consist of a field of reflectors concentrated on a central location, where the working fluid is heated to produce steam. The world's largest solar parabolic trough installation is the Kramer Junction Solar Electric Generating System located in in California, USA, which consists of five 30 MW parabolic trough arrays. This is currently the cheapest and most generally used technology for solar power generation.

Using solar parabolic collector technology, solar power can be produced in capacities of between 10 MW and 200 MW. The modular character of a solar array makes any initial capacity possible. From a commercial point of view, the larger, the better.

Through the establishment of mass production for mirrors and absorbers and the further development of heat storages, solar parabolic collector power plants will in future be economically comparable with conventional power plants in medium-load operation.

Solar thermal power plants are designed to be large scale grid-connected power plants but at present, they generally cannot be used as base load generators, because they do not produce heat at night or during the day when clouds block the sun. Some advances have been made in storing solar energy by using it to heat liquid sodium, which can be used later to boil water and produce the steam needed to power a generator turbine. The process is time-limited, however, and can extend a plant's operations by only a few hours at best. In some cases, storage times of 4 to 16 hours have been achieved, sufficient to allow electricity from solar thermal generators to be sold when it is more valuable, during the peak demand hours of 7-9 am and 5-7 pm.

Source: Concentrating solar power from research to implementation, European Commission.

Figure 17. Solar collector elements of a parabolic system.

Source: Concentrating solar power from research to implementation, European Commission

Figure 18. Solar power solar system.

Looking Forward

Solar technologies have benefited from much research and development over the past two decades, bringing down the delivered price of solar electricity. Today, electricity from residential solar photovoltaic is marketed to compete with high-priced retail electricity. In the future, it is possible that utility-scale solar photovoltaic power plants will compete with wholesale electricity generation, provided that further technological advances are achieved. Solar thermal power plants are intended to compete with wholesale electricity generation, especially from peaking power plants, and they may become more competitive over time, if heat storage technologies improve, costs decrease, and/or policies to mitigate carbon dioxide emissions are adopted by interested governments in the promotion of the use of this type of technology for electricity generation.

In the specific case of Latin American and the Caribbean region, solar energy is more evenly distributed, as good portions of the region lie within the so-called "Sun Belt Region" of highest solar radiation. Thus, except for site specific adverse microclimates, solar energy is a predictable and reliable energy resource, susceptible of being transformed to heat and electricity by means of several technologies in different stages of development and commercial availability. Solar irradiance maps are available for Mexico, Colombia[7], Brazil, Argentina, and a few other countries (Huacuz et al., 1992). For this reason, wind power is a realistic option for the generation of electricity in a clean manner for many Latin American and the Caribbean countries.

---

[7] In the case of Colombia, the installed solar panels are limited to a few pilot decentralized electrification projects. However, private investors are beginning to express an interest in the use of solar power for the generation of electricity, and are planned more projects but still for decentralized applications.

THE USE OF GEOTHERMAL ENERGY FOR THE GENERATION OF ELECTRICITY

Steam and water heated by earth's crust have long been used for cooking and bathing but it was not until the beginning of the 20th century, that geothermal energy was utilized for industrial and commercial purposes. In 1904, electricity was first produced using geothermal steam at the vapor-dominated field in Larderello, Italy.

Source: Image courtesy of Yellowstone National Park, National Park Service.

Figure 19. Geothermal site.

Since that time, other hydrothermal developments—at The Geysers, in California, USA; Wairakei, in New Zealand; Cerro Prieto, in Mexico; Reykjavik, in Iceland; and in Indonesia and the Philippines —have led to an installed world's electrical generating capacity of nearly 10 000 MWe, and a direct-use non-electric capacity of more than 100 000 MWt, at the beginning of the 21st century.

Geothermal heat originates from Earth's fiery consolidation of dust and gas over 4 billion years ago. At the center of the Earth (8 800 km deep) temperatures may reach over 4 245° C. Geothermal energy resources can be found in areas of high volcanic activity in many parts of the world.

Geothermal energy sources can be classified as follows: a) Hydrothermal; b) Geo-pressured; c) Hot-dry rock; and d) Magma. Presently, all commercial operations are based on hydrothermal systems where wells are about 2 000 meters deep, with reservoir temperatures ranging from 180° C to 270° C.

Types of Hydrothermal Steam Power Plants

There are three types of hydrothermal steam power plants, depending on the way the energy is generated. The first one is hydrothermal dry steam power plant. This type of plants produces energy directly from the steam generated underground. In this case, there are no need additional boilers and boiler fuels because the steam (and no water) directly fills up the wells, passing through a rock catcher, and directly operates the turbines. The use of such type of geothermal sources is not popular because the natural dry steam reservoirs are very rare.

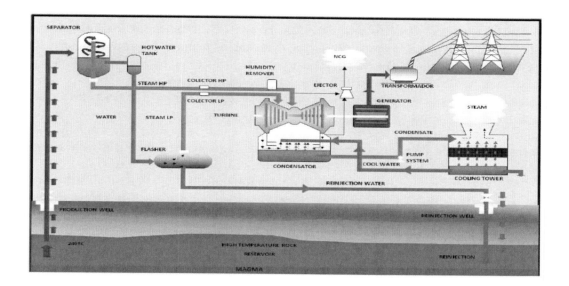

Source: Lopez (2011).

Figure 20. Simplified process flow diagram for a geothermal power plant.

The second type is hydrothermal flash steam power plant, which is use when there is a liquid hydrothermal resource with high temperature (over 177° C). The operating principle is the following: when the hot water is released from the pressure, it is collected in a flash tank where the liquid is flashed to steam. The latter is separated from the liquid, and it is used to run the turbines. The waste water is re-injected into the reservoir.

The third type is hydrothermal binary steam power plant. This type of plants is employed when the hydrothermal resource is with lower temperature (38° C). The operating principle is the following: the hot water is passed to a heat exchanger, where it is compound with secondary liquid with lower boiling point. This mixture vapor and its steam run the turbine. The waste mixture is recycled trough the heat exchanger. The geothermal fluid is condensed and it is returned to the reservoir. Since the most geothermal resources available in the Earth are with lower temperature, the hydrothermal binary steam power plants are more common than the others two.

Small Geothermal Power Plants for Rural Electrification

Rural electricity services can be improved by installing individual systems and mini-grids. Individual systems are generally too small to be cost-effective applications of geothermal technology. However, a region where individual systems would be appropriate could be even better served with small geothermal power plants (plants with less than 5 MW of capacity), if extensive economic development changed the market conditions. For small geothermal projects to be used under these circumstances a region would need to be far from any existing grid and undergo long-term intensive economic development that would greatly increase the region's load density and the demand for and ability to pay for the electricity consumed (Vimmersted, 1998).

Small geothermal power plants, either binary or flash steam, can be manufactured and can be operated in remote areas but each type of technology enjoys different advantages, and faces different challenges. For example, binary steam plants can typically operate with lower temperature resources and this could help a small project hold down drilling costs; however, greater system complexity can complicate operation and maintenance. The flash steam plant's simpler and less expensive design is especially welcome in a small system. However, flash steam plants are typically used with higher temperature resources that could be more expensive to obtain than lower-temperature ones. Using a flash steam plant with a lower-temperature resource, might not be cost effective because of reduced efficiency.

Finally, the complexity of managing scale deposition is likely to impose greater costs in flash steam plants than in binary steam plants. The choice between these two designs for small geothermal power plants will be site specific, and will depend on resource temperature, chemical composition of the geothermal fluid, and maintenance preferences. However, the site-specific characteristics of geothermal resources, the little number of small remote geothermal power plants, and the limited amount of published data comparing operation and maintenance costs between a flash team and binary steam plants, complicate the comparison between the two designs (Vimmersted, 1998).

It is important to single out that the costs of small geothermal projects depend significantly on power plant costs, drilling costs, resource quality, and costs of financing. Costs of small geothermal generation are in the same range as competitor technologies for rural electricity markets. Figure 21 shows one estimate, in which the cost of small-scale geothermal generation substantially overlaps that of diesel. The actual and modeled costs suggest that small rural geothermal electricity projects have the potential to achieve competitive technology costs, as low as US$0.05 per kWh.

Table 4. Geothermal power capital cost by project development phase

	200 kW binary steam plant	20 MW binary plant	50 MW flash plant
Exploration	300	320	240
Confirmation	400	470	370
Main wells	800	710	540
Field and other costs	120	120	60
Power plant	4 250	2 120	1 080
Contingency	880	190	120
Total costs	6 750	3 930	2 410

Source: World Bank (2005).

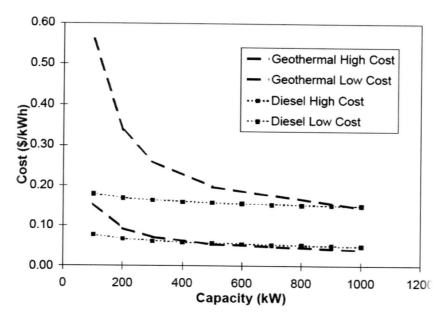

Source: National Renewable Energy Laboratory.

Figure 21. Cost of diesel generation and geothermal generation vs. capacity.

The costs of geothermal energy have dropped substantially from the systems built in the 1970s. For example, generation costs at current geothermal power plants in the United States are between US$0.015 and US$0.025 per kWh. New geothermal power plants can deliver power between US$0.05 and US$0.08 per kWh, depending on the quality of the resource. However, geothermal power is accessible only in limited areas of the world, the largest being the United States, Central America, Indonesia, East Africa and the Philippines.

Challenges to expanding geothermal energy include very long project development times, and the risk and high-cost of exploratory drilling, among other factors. Examining size distributions of geothermal units throughout the world shows that small geothermal power units are numerous, that the number of units increases at smaller sizes, and that many units are smaller than 5 MW. Although this might indicate that small remote geothermal projects are more common and easily completed, further studies shows that this is not the case, because most of the operating geothermal units (5 MW or smaller) are installed at a site where the total generation is much larger. The sites where less than 5 MW of capacity has been developed are generally not remote; many are at sites very near larger developments or at sites where there were plans for additional development to a much larger size (Huttrer, 1995). The existing small projects show that small geothermal power plants are technically sound and these projects could be used to gather installation, operation and maintenance data relevant to remote geothermal sites. However, the success of small systems at large project sites is insufficient to demonstrate their viability in remote locations.

In summary, the following can be stated: The current applications of small geothermal power plants are primarily within larger geothermal developments, which provide valuable technical data. However, remote applications face different obstacles and more economic and logistical data is needed on them in order to reach the adequate conclusion. Both binary and flash steam geothermal technologies could be used in small geothermal projects. The resource characteristics and feasibility of meeting their respective requirements for operation and maintenance help to determine, which technology to use at a given site.

The Use of Geothermal Power Plants for the Generation of Electricity

Geothermal energy meets a significant portion of the electrical power demand in several developing countries, including some in the Latin American and the Caribbean region. Individual geothermal power plants can be as small as 100 kW or as large as 100 MW, depending on the energy resource available in the site and the power demand in the area.

Without any doubt, this technology is suitable for rural electrification and may be especially important and significant in developing countries where no local fossil fuel resources exist, such as oil, coal or natural gas, and in which areas of high volcanic activity can be found. However, when characterizing resources for geothermal projects, the developer must inexpensively identify resources of sufficient quality, to permit a group of economically viable projects to be developed.

Table 5. The biggest geothermal power plants in the region

Country	Plant	Unit	Year	Capacity (MW)	Type
México	Cerro Prieto II	1	1986	110	Double Flash
México	Cerro Prieto II	2	1987	110	Double Flash
México	Cerro Prieto III	1	1986	110	Double Flash
México	Cerro Prieto III	2	1986	110	Double Flash

Source: Bertani (2010).

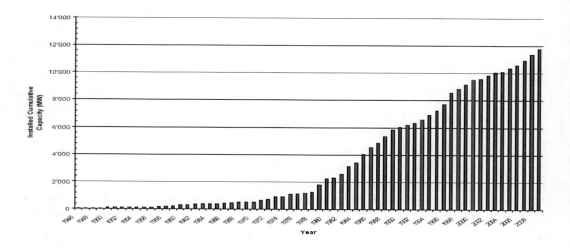

Source: Bertani (2010).

Figure 22. Cumulated geothermal power capacity during the period 1946 and 2011.

From Figure 22, the following can be stated: In the past twenty one years, the installed cumulative geothermal capacity increased from almost 6 000 MW in 1990 to almost 12 000 MW in 2011; this represents an increase of 100%.

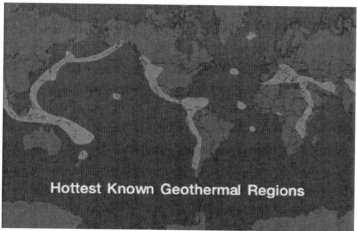

Source: Courtesy University of Texas.

Figure 23. Hottest known geothermal region.

From Figure 23, it can be easily confirm that the whole Pacific coast of the Central America, South America and the Caribbean Sea, are areas in which geothermal sources can be found. In the Central American sub-region, five countries are using geothermal energy sources for the generation of electricity. These countries and their installed capacities in 2010 are Mexico (958 MW), El Salvador (204 MW), Costa Rica (166 MW), Nicaragua (88 MW) and Guatemala (52 MW) (see Figure 24).

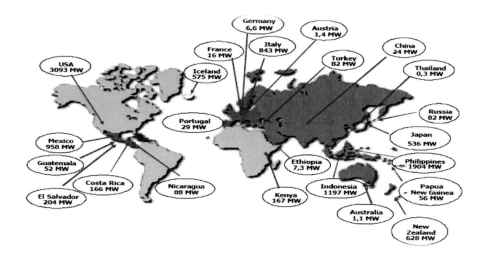

Source: Bertani (2010).

Figure 24. Installed geothermal capacity for electricity production in 2010 in different countries (10.7 GW).

In addition to the five countries mentioned above, geothermal sources are used for electricity generation in Guadeloupe and Panama. In Costa Rica, El Salvador, Guatemala, and Nicaragua ther are several geothermal projects in development (see Table 7).

A major drawback for the development of geothermal energy resources is capital. Companies in developing countries are usually not large or diversified enough to assume the high investment risks, as well as the high up-front costs associated with geothermal energy exploration. The magnitude of technical and financial assistance required to develop the region's geothermal energy potential goes far beyond the capabilities of many governments, particularly, in the Central American and the Caribbean sub-regions.

In South America, energy demand and consumption is expected to increase in the coming years. However, plans for the use of geothermal energy sources for the generation of electricity are limited to two countries only: Argentina and Chile (see Table 7).

From Table 6, the following can be stated: it is foreseen an increase in the geothermal installed capacity from 6.8 GW in 1995 to 140 GW in 2050, and an increase in the electricity production from 38 035 GWh per year in 1995 to 1 103 760 GWh per year, in 2050. The capacity factor of the geothermal power plants is foreseen that reach 90% in 2050; this represents a 26% increase in the period considered.

On the other hand, it is important to stress that the electricity production from geothermal energy sources is strongly related to the plant capacity factor. Since 1995, it has been continuously increasing from the initial value of 64% to the present one of 73%; this represents a 9% increase. Better technical solutions for the power plants improve their performances; the most advanced approaches for the resource development (reinjection, inhibitors against scaling/corrosion, better knowledge of the field performances, and parameters using advanced geophysical surveys) should increase the capacity factor linearly to the limit of 90%, presently already reached by many geothermal fields in exploitation (Fridleifsson et al., 2008).

Table 6. World installed capacity, electricity production and capacity factor of geothermal power plants

Year	Installed capacity (GW)	Electricity production (GWh per year)	Capacity factor (%)
1995	6.8	38 035	64
2000	8.0	49 261	71
2005	8.9	56 786	73
2010	11.0	74 669	77
2020	24,0	171 114	81
2030	46.0	343 685	85
2040	90.0	703 174	89
2050	140.0	1 103 760	90

Source: Fridleifsson et al. (2008).

Table 7 includes information on the current installed geothermal power capacity in a select group of counties in the Latin American and the Caribbean region, and the forecast for 2015. In South America, only two countries are planning to use geothermal energy sources for the generation of electricity in 2015. These countries are Argentina (30 MW) and Chile

(150 MW). In the Caribbean sub-region, only one country has concrete plans for the use of geothermal energy sources for the generation of electricity; this country is Nevis (35 MW). The major investment in geothermal energy sources are located in Mexico (7 047 MW), El Salvador (1 422 MW), and Costa Rica (1 131 MW). According to Table 7, in 2015 the geothermal power capacity in this group of countries will be increased in 7%, and the production of electricity in 15%.

Table 7. Installed capacity and produced energy using geothermal energy sources for 2010 and forecasting for 2015

Country	Installed in 2010 (MW)	Energy in 2010 (GWh)	Forecast for 2015 (MW)
Argentina	0	0	30
Chile	0	0	150
Costa Rica	166	1 131	200
El Salvador	204	1 422	290
Guatemala	52	289	120
Honduras	0	0	35
Mexico	958	7 047	1 140
Nevis	0	0	35
Nicaragua	88	310	240
Total	1 468	10 199	2 240

Source: Bertani (2010).

Environmental Impact for the Use of Geothermal Energy for the Production of Electricity

The use of geothermal energy for the production of electricity has the environmental benefit of being a relatively clean fuel. However, potentially negative environmental impacts for the use of geothermal energy for the production of electricity are:

a) The impact of the drilling on the nearby environment. This requires the installation of a drilling rig and equipment, as well as construction roads. Depending on the distance that needs to be drilled, the area needed for the drilling rig could vary from 300 m^2 to 1 500 m^2. Drilling could also lead to surface water pollution (e.g., through blow-outs) and emission of polluting gases into the atmosphere;

b) The pipelines to transport the geothermal fluids will have an impact on the surrounding area;

c) The reduction in the pressure in the aquifers. This could lead to subsidence of the ground in the geothermal facility sites. Re-injection of the condensed and/or cooled water back into the reservoirs could neutralize the subsidence. Re-injection also reduces the risk that the steam is exhausted into the atmosphere or that used water is discharged into surface water (see Figure 20).

Looking Forward

According to Fridleifsson et al. (2008), geothermal energy is a renewable energy source that has been utilized economically in many parts of the world for decades. A great potential for an extensive increase in worldwide geothermal utilization has been proven. This is a reliable energy source that serves both direct use applications and electricity generation. Geothermal energy is independent of weather conditions, and has an inherent storage capability that makes it especially suitable for supplying base load power in an economical way, and can thus serve as a partner with energy sources that are only available intermittently. In addition, geothermal energy can contribute significantly to the mitigation of climate change, and more so, by working as partners rather than competing with each other.

Presently, the geothermal utilization sector growing most rapidly in the Latin American and the Caribbean region is heat pump applications. This development is expected to continue in the future, making heat pumps the major direct utilization sector. The main reason for this is that geothermal heat pumps can be installed economically all over the region.

One of the strongest arguments for putting more emphasis on the development of geothermal energy resources for electricity generation in the Latin American and the Caribbean region is the limited environmental impact compared to most other energy sources used for this specific purpose. The CO_2 emission related to direct applications of geothermal energy sources for the generation of electricity is negligible and very small compared to the CO_2 emission related to the use of fossil fuel for the same purpose.

The geothermal exploitation techniques are being rapidly developed, and the understanding of the reservoirs has improved considerably over the past years. Combined heat and power plants are gaining increased popularity in many Latin American and the Caribbean countries, improving the overall efficiency of the geothermal energy sources utilization. Also, low-temperature power generation with binary steam plants has opened up the possibilities of producing electricity in some countries, which do not have high-temperature fields. Enhanced Geothermal Systems (EGS) technologies, where heat is extracted from deeper parts of the reservoir than conventional systems, are under development. If EGS can be proven economical at commercial scales, then the development potential of geothermal energy will be limitless in many countries and regions of the world in the future.

Central America is one of the world's richest regions in geothermal energy resources. Geothermal power plants provide about 12% of the total electricity generation in the following four countries: Costa Rica, El Salvador, Guatemala and Nicaragua. The electricity generated in the geothermal fields is, in all cases, replacing electricity generated by imported oil. With an interconnected grid, it would be relatively easy to provide all the electricity for the four countries using renewable energy sources. The geothermal potential for electricity generation in Central America has been estimated in some 4 000 MWe but less than 500 MWe have been harnessed so far (12.5% of the total). With the larger untapped geothermal energy resources, and the significant experience in geothermal as well as hydro development in the region, Central America may become an international example of how to reduce the overall emissions of greenhouse gases in a large region (Fridleifsson and Georgsson, 2011).

However, the future role of geothermal energy sources in the generation of electricity in the Latin American and the Caribbean region will be driven, from the technological point of view, by the following six primary technologies:

a) Hydrothermal systems: Hydrothermal (or hot water) resources arise when hot water and/or steam is formed in fractured or porous rock at shallow-to-moderate depths (between100 m to 4.5 km), as a result of either the intrusion in the earth's crust of molten magma from the planet's interior or the deep circulation of water through a fault or fracture. High-temperature hydrothermal sources (with temperatures from 180° C to over 350° C) are usually heated by hot molten rock. Low-temperature resources (with temperatures from 100° C to 180° C) can be produced by either process. More than 9 000 MW of the world's power is generated from conventional geothermal reservoirs;

b) Enhanced geothermal systems: This technology is still experimental, and several challenges, such as creating a pervasively fractured large rock volume, securing commercial well productivity, and minimizing cooling and water loss, will need to be overcome before it could become commercially viable. But because it offers the promise of worldwide distribution, it offers the most potential;

c) Conductive sedimentary systems: Many sedimentary formations, including some that contain oil or gas, may be hot enough to serve as commercial geothermal reservoirs. Though no fracturing will be needed for this commercially unproven technology, it may require deeply drilled wells. According to several expert's opinion, this system could be commercially feasible if reservoir flow, capacity, and temperature are high enough;

d) Oil and gas field waters: Hot water produced with deep drilling for oil or gas or from depleted oil/gas wells is being used more and more. But, though it poses few technical challenges, the power cost using this process may not always be attractive;

e) Geo-pressured systems: Geo-pressured geothermal resources consist of hot brine, saturated with methane, found in large deep aquifers under high pressure. The water and methane are trapped in sedimentary formations at a depth between 3 km to 6 km, and the temperature of the water is in the range of 90° C to 200° C. Three forms of energy can be obtained from geo-pressured resources: thermal energy, hydraulic energy from the high pressure, and chemical energy from burning the dissolved methane gas. The major region of geo-pressured reservoirs discovered to date is in the northern Gulf of Mexico. The method consists of drilling a bore into a geo-pressured-geothermal reservoir, allowing the fluid within the reservoir to escape through the bore, and using the fluid to turn an electricity-generating turbine. The concept has not been commercially proven yet, though a demonstration has shown technical feasibility. Even so, it poses a variety of technical challenges to making power at a cost that is commercially viable, not to mention that its distribution is very restricted;

f) Magma Energy: Magma, the largest geothermal energy source, is molten rock found at depths of 3 km to10 km and deeper. It has a temperature that ranges from 700° C to 1 200° C. The concept of using this heat source theorises that thermal energy contained in magmatic systems could represent a huge potential resource of energy. This technology is far from becoming commercially viable, however, not only is it extremely localized, but it also poses a host of technical challenges, including developing drilling and completion techniques, as well as developing a technology for extracting heat from magma.

THE USE OF BIOMASS FOR THE GENERATION OF ELECTRICITY

It is important to know that in 2009 biomass was overtaken by wind power and slipped to the world number three renewable electricity source with 1.2% of the world's electricity produced in that year.

As a natural consequence of the solar radiation available, photosynthetic activity in most of the region of study is rather high, and hence the high production of biomass. On top of that, many countries in the region have an economy based on agriculture, so that agricultural waste, forest residues, and other residues from animal raising constitute important forms of biomass.

Without any doubt, biomass combustion for heat and power is a fully mature technology. According to the IEA (2007) report, biomass offers both an economic fuel option, and a ready disposal mechanism of organic wastes at local and industry level.

Regrettably, the industry has remained relatively stagnant in the use of biomass for the generation of electricity over the past decade, even though demand for biomass, mostly wood, continues to grow in many developing countries, particularly those classified as least developing countries, and without important conventional energy sources available for the generation of electricity.

One of the problems facing the use of biomass for the generation of electricity is that material directly combusted in cook stoves produces pollutants, leading to severe health and environmental consequences, and a negative impact in the environment. A second problem is that burning biomass emits CO_2, even though biomass combustion is generally considered to be "carbon-neutral", due to the fact that carbon is absorbed by plant material during its growth, thus creating a carbon cycle.

First-generation biomass technologies can be economically competitive but may still require deployment support to overcome public acceptance, and small-scale issues. However, it is important to be aware that the use of biomass for the generation of electricity in a large scale could accelerate deforestation and desertification, preventing large volume of natural fertilizers entering the soil, and the disappearance of forests threatens the habitat of valuable species causing, for example, in the Amazon rain forest, the extinction of at least one specie every week. The use of biomass for the generation of electricity in a large scale in the Latin American and the Caribbean region could also represent a hazard for the health of families, and this situation should be evaluated very carefully, before a decision is adopted to increase the production of biomass or its use for the generation of electricity in the region.

Biomass electricity output across the world increased 4.3% over 2008, whereas total electricity production decreased by 1.1%. The main contributing regions in 2009 were Western Europe with 12.7 TWh, and South America with 4.2 TWh[8].

Without any doubt, world's biomass electricity production should continue its upward trend over the next few years, primarily through the development of cogeneration plants that optimize biomass energy yield by producing electricity and heat simultaneously[9].

---

[8]According to World Bank data, in the specific case of Cuba, combustible renewables and waste produced 13.1% of the total energy produced in the country.

[9] Cuba's State-owned Zerus S.A. recently signed a MoU with Havana Energy Ltd., a U.K.-based renewable energy company, to develop a 30 MW pilot project for generating electricity from sugarcane stalk residue, or bagasse, at a sugar mill in Ciro Redondo. It is the first step of a larger project that has the potential to satisfy almost half

Technological progress in the area of biomass gasification could offer new venues for the development of biomass electricity in the future.

THE USE OF HYDROGEN FOR THE GENERATION OF ELECTRICITY

One of the most significant global trends arriving in the near future is a shift away from fossil fuels towards hydrogen. According to some expert's opinion, the future world's economy will be powered by hydrogen, not by oil.

According to the Annual Report on World Progress in Hydrogen (2011), it has been predicted that the world's hydrogen and fuel cell market will grow to US$16 billion by 2017, while others estimate that it will grow to US$26 billion by 2020. Global spending on hydrogen and fuel cell innovation exceeded US$5.6 billion in 2008, and is growing in manufacturing, research and development demonstrations, and other market sectors.

Global revenues in hydrogen and fuel cells are expected to range between US$3.2 billion and US$9.2 billion in 2015 and between US$7.7 billion and US$38.4 billion in 2020, respectively. By 2050, the 2009 Renewable Energy Data Book (2010) suggests that the industry could grow to as high as US$180 billion.

According to the Annual Report on World Progress in Hydrogen (2011), in Latin America a growing population and an increase in energy demand have made hydrogen a focus in many countries. Argentina, Brazil, and Mexico, for example, are among the hydrogen and fuel cell leaders in the region. The national governments of Argentina and Brazil are both aggressively supporting research and development in hydrogen and fuel cell technologies, through the approval of appropriate legislation, tax benefits, and direct financial support.

Producing, storing, and transporting hydrogen is a multi-path, multi-step process and, for this reason, the production of hydrogen near its point of use would be the most viable solution. There will be applications for hydrogen in remote electricity grids where population density is low, and where the operating margins for power suppliers are limited, since it is difficult and costly to extend transmission and distribution capacity to remote areas. Hydrogen systems offer a potential solution in the form of off-grid generation storage, which may include wind-hydrogen or solar photovoltaic-hydrogen with battery back-up.

Although hydrogen is perhaps most viable and promising as a clean energy alternative to conventional energy, experts generally agreed that hydrogen energy technology development should be based upon existing primary energy sources, including fossil fuels.

Coal-to-hydrogen production received due consideration since large coal deposits are collocated with some of the world's largest economies, and hydrogen from natural gas was cited as a proven low cost technology. However, renewable energy resources for the production of hydrogen should be preferred in the interest of achieving long-term sustainability. Despite of the above, it is important to stress that, in general, the existing suite

---

of the island's 3 000 MW power needs and to possibly deliver a return on investment in just five years. In 2009, the production of electricity using bagasse was 389 GW, representing 2.2% of the total electricity produced by the country in that year. Sugarcane bagasse has contributed to Cuba's energy supply for decades, but as the "Special Period" progressed, power generation from this source dropped significantly, particularly when the government restructured the sugar industry in the early 2000s.

of hydrogen energy technologies is not yet ready for mass production and development. Further research and development is needed to advance the most promising options, making them more reliable and cost-effective.

The Hydrogen Economy

The hydrogen economy is important for the advancement of humanity for several reasons:

a) Reduce pollution;
b) Reduce global warming;
c) Reduce the fight for the control of resources;
d) Unlimited supply.

Beyond the problems with the oil economy, there are additional reasons why a hydrogen economy offers unprecedented benefits to the quality of life of people everywhere:

a) Hydrogen is everywhere: Hydrogen is in water, and can be found in abundance at the bottom of the ocean in frozen gas hydrates. They are found off the coasts of Canada, Japan, Alaska, Russia, China, Iceland, and the countries of northern Europe. Technology now exists to harvest these frozen gas hydrates, store them at liquid nitrogen temperature, and convert them into usable hydrogen gas by allowing them to melt at normal atmospheric pressure. However, the extraction of frozen gas hydrates from the bottom of the ocean is not an easily task. Hydrogen also can be found in natural gas, petroleum, and the byproducts of microbial activity. One of the important features of hydrogen is that it is not limited to a few geographic regions of the planet, making it a resource that automatically reduces geopolitical tension over the control of limited oil resources;
b) Hydrogen is clean: Through fuel cell technology, hydrogen can be converted to electricity with no harmful waste products. Hydrogen does not pollute cities, rivers, streams or oceans, and does not cause global warming. Shifting to a hydrogen economy could save millions of lives each year in terms of human health effects alone, not to mention its effects on the health of the planet, and its various forms of life;
c) Hydrogen is renewable: Unlike fossil fuels, hydrogen is renewable. Converting hydrogen gas to electricity in fuel cells does not destroy the hydrogen; it just alters its state. For this reason, hydrogen molecules can be used repeatedly to store and release electrical potential;
d) Hydrogen solves serious global problems: By shifting to a hydrogen economy, the humanity will simultaneously solve a long list of problems tied to the oil economy (pollution, limited resources, global warming, etc.) (Morales Pedraza, 2008).

Limiting Factors in the Use of Hydrogen for the Generation of Electricity in a Large Scale

One of the current limiting factors in the use of hydrogen as energy source for electricity generation is, according to several experts, the weight and cost of the hydrogen's batteries, particularly due to the use of platinum, which is a very expense raw material. Materials used in the fuel cell system are not very expensive but required significant research investments, in order to improve fuel cell durability, and hydrogen storage densities. Industrial processes and volumes are not yet there to optimize production costs, and it will certainly take years, if not decades, to get there. However, in the past years, the weight and cost of the special badges of hydrogen's batteries diminished in 90%, making possible the use of hydrogen as an important energy source in the near future.

Another limiting factor in the use of hydrogen as energy source is the need to use other energy sources to produce it. Hydrogen as an energy vector can be produced from a variety of sources, including renewables, nuclear, and fossil fuel sources. The production of hydrogen today is mainly performed by steam reforming, partial oxidation of gaseous or liquid fuels or the gasification of coal. Electrolysis is used when a small amount of pure hydrogen is required at a specific site. The purification of hydrogen rich gases is an important step in improving the quality of hydrogen produced, depending on eventual use. Certain fuel types require very high purity hydrogen.

Distribution of hydrogen is done through pipelines or using trucks carrying hydrogen in high-pressure gas cylinders or cryogenic tanks. The latter involves an energy-intensive liquefaction step, though the energy required just to compress gaseous hydrogen is itself significant.

In the short-to-medium-term, the lack of readily available non-fossil sources means that the bulk of hydrogen produced will come from fossil fuels, firstly without carbon capture and sequestration (CCS), and later with CCS in the medium-term. The long-term goal is to produce hydrogen from indigenous carbon-free and carbon-clean energy sources. (Directorate-General for Research Sustainable Energy Systems, 2006) or using renewable energy sources or nuclear energy.

The shift to a hydrogen economy will, of course, require a major support from government in the form of mandated usages of this new type of energy, particularly for the generation of electricity or by limiting the use of carbon or any other energy sources more contaminant from the point of view of the environment.

THE USE OF RENEWABLE ENERGY SOURCES FOR THE GENERATION OF ELECTRICITY IN DIFFERENT SUB-REGIONS

Central American and the Caribbean

Most Central American and Caribbean countries are under the influence of the so-called "Trade Winds," while the whole Central American is exposed to strong and almost constant thermally driven winds. This special situation makes wind power an excellent alternative for the generation of electricity in countries located in these two areas. For this reason, there is a potential capacity in the use of wing power that can be exploited by several countries in the coming years.

With regards the use of other renewable energy sources for the generation of electricity in the Central American and the Caribbean sub-regions, it is important to stick out the following: Some Central American economies have engaged in an economic diversification strategy favoring tourism, labor intensive manufacturing, and the service sector. As a result, the economies are more exposed to the cost of energy, in particular the cost of imported oil products to satisfy an increase energy demand. In order to address these energy challenges, efforts at diversifying the region's energy matrix have been heavily discussed, with an emphasis on increasing the incorporation of different renewable energy sources such as biomass, wind, and geothermal energies for the generation of electricity.

In addition, a long-discussed integration effort, the SIEPAC project aimed at creating an integrated power market across the region, has picked up speed and is under construction. Important obstacles for security of energy supply, diversification and integration are numerous, including regulatory and geopolitical issues but governments are ready to find acceptable solutions to eliminate these obstacles and to increase the use of renewable energy sources for the generation of electricity in the most economic manner in the coming years.

Finally, it is important to stress the following: Central American countries, except Costa Rica and Panama, retain a large dependence on biomass, and have a severely underutilized potential in hydro and other renewable energy sources. The use of imported diesel and fuel oil for the generation of electricity has been increased in the sub-region in the past years, growing its unhealthy dependence on these types of energy sources for the generation of electricity. This situation should be changed in the future with the adoption of new energy policies promoting the use of renewable energy sources for the generation of electricity and the reduction of CO_2 emissions.

In the specific case of Cuba, the major island in the Caribbean, it is important to take into account the following: According to government sources, the main renewable energy sources come from forest biomass and sugar cane, solar, wind and hydro energy. It is the intention of the government to increase its renewable energy production by 12% over the next eight years in order to consolidate security and energy sovereignty". Today only 3.8% of the energy generated in the country is obtained from the use of different renewable energy sources; over the next eight years the intention of the government is to reach 16.5%[10], an increase of 12.7%. The sugar agro-industry will be "the mainstay" of this development and there is potential to increase production from biomass by 10% for 2013.

Cuba is also expected to build a wind farm of 50 MW in the eastern region of the island, while nationwide study for the installation of eight new wind farms with total power of 280 MW by 2020 are carried out by national competent authorities.

For its part, the country is working on the construction of a solar photovoltaic Park 1 MWp which is expected to begin to be exploded in December 2012, and it is projected the construction of others in 2013 with total capacity of 10 MWp. According to government sources, the potential of solar energy recognized in the country exceeds the 2 000 MW but currently the country has only small solar photovoltaic installations that are not connected to the national electric system and provide services only in isolated areas of the country.

---

[10] Cuba aims to generate more than 100 MW from hydro power plants of different sizes.

Other options will be the development of renewable energy sources such as biogas, forest biomass and the windmills in agriculture.

The emerging use of water and wind sources allowed in 2011 the replacement of 31 150 tons of fuel and stop broadcasting more than 100 000 tons of CO_2, representing a decrease of 20% of Cuban emissions over the 1990.

Andean Community

The First Meeting of the Council of Andean Community Ministers of Energy, Electricity, Hydrocarbons and Mines underscored the importance of linking up renewable energy sources with the implementation of the Andean Community's Integral Plan for Social Development. The launching of studies was proposed to give special priority to the use of renewable energy sources for the generation of electricity in antipoverty programmes. These programmes also promote access to basic services and their intensive use for meeting energy requirements in border and isolated rural areas and, in general, of the population lacking energy sources.

The First Meeting of Energy and Environment Experts on the Use of Renewable Energy Sources for the Generation of Electricity, held in Lima, Peru, in May 2004, identified the following criteria for deepening the analysis on the use of renewable energy sources for the generation of electricity in the sub-region:

a) The sub-region's renewable energy potential can play a key role in the region's energy system by guaranteeing sustainable development and its ability to create new forms of cooperation among Latin American and the Caribbean countries and between these and developed countries, within the context of international environmental conservation commitments;

b) New strategies and policies must be adopted with the purpose of allowing the rational use of endogenous energy sources and to enable new and renewable energy sources to contribute to the security of the energy supply, while considering the particular needs of the individual member countries;

c) Renewable energy sources constitute an asset for negotiation and their development can open up new opportunities for investment in local and sub-regional development;

d) Despite the advances made in electricity coverage in the Andean sub-region in 2008, nearly 12.8 million people continue to live in isolated communities without electrical services. Renewable energy sources can help enormously to provide those communities with sustainable electric power and other forms of energy;

e) Inasmuch as access to energy sources helps improve the living conditions of people in the sub-region, it is essential to link up this theme with the formulation and implementation of the Integral Plan for Social Development (IPSD-Decision 553), in keeping with the United Nations Millennium Development Goals;

f) It is important to evaluate the role renewable energy sources can play in the provision of power by and the productive development of the integration hubs in which the Andean Community is involved, within the framework of the South American Regional Infrastructure Integration Initiative (IIRSA).

The Andean Community should play an active role within the Johannesburg Renewable Energy Coalition. The meeting concluded by identifying the need to lay the groundwork for a future Andean Renewable Energy Strategy, with the purpose of increasing the use of renewable energy sources for the generation of electricity, reducing at much as possible the use of fossil fuels for this specific purpose.

Southern Cone

In Argentina the most important legal instruments for the promotion of renewable energy sources for the generation of electricity are Law 25,019 of 1998 and Law 26,190 of 2007. The 1998 Law, known as the "National Wind and Solar Energy Rules", declared wind and solar generation of national interest and introduced a mechanism that established an additional payment per generated kWh. The 2007 Law complemented the previous Law adopted in 1998, declaring of national interest the generation of electricity from any renewable energy source intended to deliver a public service. The 2007 Law also set an 8% target for renewable energy consumption in the period of ten years and mandated the creation of a trust fund whose resources will be allocated to pay a premium for electricity produced from renewable energy sources.

The aim of the above laws is to increase the use of renewable energy sources for the generation of electricity, and includes specific feed-in tariffs for energy production from renewable energy sources: US$0.33 per kWh for solar photovoltaic and US$0.51 per kWh for wind, geothermal energy, biomass, biogas, and small hydro power plants. It involved a fifteen year payment period.

Furthermore, the objective of the National Plan for Renewable Energy is to install 1 000 MW of renewable energy capacities, including 500 MW of wind energy in the coming years.

In the case of Chile, besides hydro power, no other renewable energy source has a significant contribution to the Chilean energy mix. Hydro power accounted in 2009 for 43.7% of the total electricity produced by the country in that year. The other renewables used for the generation of electricity are biomass with 5.8% and wind energy with 0.2% of the total electricity produced in the country in 2009. Although there is still much to be done, the fruits of this effort can already be seen. By early 2009, non-conventional renewable energy projects, representing more than 1 600 MW, had already been approved or were waiting to be approved by the government. In addition, practically all the electricity generators in Chile are presently developing or evaluating projects with these characteristics; new companies have been created exclusively to implement this type of initiative, and there is a significant number hoping to soon follow suit (Palma Behnke et al., 2009).

It is important to stress that renewable energy is currently mostly used in Chile for rural electrification or other small-scale power generation. However, Chile has huge solar, wind and geothermal power potential that can increase the role of renewable energy sources in the energy balance of the country in the near future.

As in other countries, and given global energy prices, renewable energy options have become today more attractive in Chile. The government aims to almost double the installed capacity from renewable energy sources in the coming years, and point to adequate legal and regulatory support (the Short Laws I and II) to enable these developments. Short Law II included language aimed at eliminating any discrimination against the implementation of renewable energy projects. Yet, some of the authorities feel that additional incentives are necessary in order to increase the use of renewable energy sources for the generation of electricity in the near future.

An important element of the effort to increase renewable energy development is the role of CORFO, the Chilean investment promotion agency. CORFO is currently funding fifty three feasibility studies for the same amount of renewable energy projects in different locations of the country.

Despite all efforts made until now by Chile to increase the use of renewables for the generation of electricity, the participation of renewable energy technologies in the energy mix, except hydro power, is still very low (Palma Behnke et al., 2009).

Chile's answer to its energy challenges is to press forward with efforts to incorporate more renewable energy sources into its power equation. Following the approval of the General Law of Electricity Services in 1982, Chile laid the basis for the creation of a competitive electricity system. The associated regulatory framework has been improved over the years, maintaining its original goal as a system operated at a minimum global cost.

The changes introduced to the General Law of Electricity Services, which became official in March 2004 through Law 19.940, modified several aspects of the electricity market affecting all generators by introducing elements especially applicable to non-conventional renewable energy sources for the generation of electricity. Likewise, Law 20.257 that came into force on April 1, 2008, made it mandatory for electricity companies selling directly to final customers to incorporate a certain percentage of renewable energy into the electricity they trade. This Law consolidates the efforts of the Chilean State to remove barriers to the incorporation of renewable energy into the national power mix, thereby contributing to the objectives of supply security and environmental sustainability that govern Chile's energy policy (Palma Behnke et al., 2009).

Legislation passed in 2008 requires renewable energy to account for at least 10% of the energy supplied by Chile's electric utilities by 2024. Power providers must integrate renewable energy sources —such as wind, solar, and small hydro power— into the power supply system, progressively increasing the amount to meet the 10% goal or face fines.

Chile has begun to look beyond its immediate neighbors for energy financing, courting international investors who have continued to fund renewable energy power projects despite the global economic downturn. Foreign investment has been facilitated by Chile's stable regulatory framework and by the United Nations Clean Development Mechanism, which allows developing countries to earn certified emission reduction credits for projects that reduce emissions, including renewable energy ventures. These credits can then be traded and sold, and industrialized countries can use them to help meet emissions reduction targets established by the Kyoto Protocol.

According to Energici sources, the use of renewable energy sources in Paraguay for the generation of electricity represented 99.93% of total installed capacity in the country in 2008, an increase of 0.01% over a five year period. This renewable energy capacity generated 54.91 billion kWh of electricity (99.99% of the total), primarily from hydro power plants (100% of the total electricity generated).

There is no geothermal, solar, wind, biomass and waste energy capacity installed in Paraguay yet but there are 8 130 MW hydroelectricity installed capacity in 2008, the same capacity over the previous year. Its share of total installed capacity increased from 99.92% in 2004 to 99.93% in 2008; its share of renewable installed capacity remained unchanged at

100% in 2008. Hydroelectricity generated 54.91 billion kWh of electricity in 2008, equating to 99.99% of the total electricity generated in that year. This is equivalent to 6.75 billion kWh of electricity per million kW of capacity, which was the highest ratio amongst renewable energy sources within the country. Paraguay has 5.95% of the total regional capacity for hydroelectricity and ranks at number 20 in the world for hydroelectricity installed capacity.

According to Energici sources, renewable energy installed capacities in Uruguay represented 69.21% of the total installed capacity in the country in 2008, a decrease of 1.7% over a five year period. A total of 10 MW of new capacities was added since 2007. These new capacities generated 5.25 billion kWh of electricity, primarily from hydroelectricity (85.01% of the total kWh generated), biomass and waste (14.99% of the total kWh generated).

There are no geothermal and solar energy capacities installed in Uruguay. Hydroelectricity had an installed capacity of 1 538 MW in 2008. Its share of total installed capacity decreased from 70.91% in 2004 to 68.74% in 2008, and its share of renewable installed capacity decreased from 100% in 2004 to 99.33% in 2008. Hydroelectricity generated 4.46 billion kWh of electricity in 2008, representing 52.63% of the total electricity generated in that year. This is equivalent to 2.9 billion kWh of electricity per million kilowatt-hour of capacity, which was the highest ratio amongst renewable energy sources within the country. Uruguay has 1.13% of the total regional capacity for hydroelectricity and ranks at number 60 in the world for hydroelectricity installed capacity.

Wind energy had an installed capacity of 10 MW in 2008. Its share of total installed capacity increased from 0% in 2004 to 0.47% in 2008, and its share of renewable installed capacity increased from 0% in 2004 to 0.67% in 2008. Uruguay has 1.81% of the total regional capacity for wind energy and ranks at number 56 in the world for wind energy installed capacity.

It is important to stress that Uruguay has no fossil fuel resources. As Uruguay's Secretary of Energy Ramón Méndez explained to the Clean Energy Congress in March 2011, Uruguay has "no oil, no natural gas, and no coal". Between 2003 and 2007, a total of 68% of Uruguay's energy needs were met by hydroelectric dams on the Uruguay River. The largest of these dams, called "The Salto Grande" is a facility shared with Argentina and has generated more than half of Uruguay's electricity in the past. Thus, when there has been a shortfall in energy generation in Uruguay due to a severe dry season, it has been necessary to import not only oil, but also electricity from neighboring Argentina and Brazil – a policy which could be economically unsustainable over the long-term. This imported electricity is a vital source of energy for Uruguay when hydroelectric generation falls short of demand during periods of protracted drought.

As demand for electricity increases and the industrial sector continues to grow, Uruguay's large-scale hydroelectric power plants do not appear to have the capacity to meet the energy needs of future Uruguayans. To address these challenges, the government is creating an energy plan designed both to secure the future of energy generation up until 2030, and to replace hydrocarbons with different renewable energy resources. At the center of this plan is Uruguay's most abundant natural resource: wind. Uruguay's strong wind currents make it a prime location for wind power generation, leading the Mujica administration to set a target of installing 500 MW of wind power capacity by 2015. Earlier this year, Méndez commented that while the government's official target is to generate 15% of its power from wind and biomass sources by 2015, it may actually be able to generate between 25% and 28%. The goal, Méndez said, was to "go as high as possible" in the production of electricity using renewable energy sources, with Montevideo awarding contracts to energy technology companies such as the Spanish firm Abengoa SA to build large-scale wind farms. Studies confirmed that the energy generated by wind farms is significantly cheaper than the electricity produced at fuel and diesel oil thermoelectric plants, which range between US$81.15 and US$86.26 per MW hour from wind generation as opposed to US$135 and US$140 per MW hour from oil generation. However, using wind to produce energy is not free of a number of challenges. Due to the unpredictability of wind strength, wind generation alone cannot be used to power Uruguay. On very windy days, farms may produce a surplus of energy that far exceeds demand, placing pressure on the country's electricity infrastructure but on very calm days, turbines may not generate sufficient electricity to satisfy the current energy demand. Furthermore, initial construction of the wind farms will require a massive investment of Uruguayan State capital, costing an estimated US$100 million per farm, placing a financial burden on a country whose GDP in 2010 was estimated to be a relatively small (US$40 billion).

Alongside its investment in wind power, Uruguay is also trying to increase the amount of energy generated using biomass. The nation's agricultural sector produces a large quantity of agro-industrial waste, which the government hopes to use to produce biofuel. In March 2010, Uruguay already had installed ten biomass power plants, and plans to have 200 MW of installed biomass generation capacity by 2015. In conjunction with its hydroelectric generation, investment in biomass will enable Uruguay to completely wean itself off foreign oil energy imports, a goal which the government hopes that can be achieved by 2013.

CONCLUSION

Hydroelectricity is by far the most important renewable energy source for the production of electricity in the Latin America and the Caribbean region, both historically and over the coming two decades. However, it is important to know that even with a dramatic hydroelectricity expansion in the coming years the share of hydroelectricity, in the total electricity generation, is likely to decline.

Most Central American and Caribbean countries are under the influence of the so-called "Trade Winds", while Central America is exposed to strong and almost constant thermally driven winds. Windy places can also be found in the Southern Hemisphere. This special situation makes wind power an excellent alternative for the production of electricity in countries located in these two sub-regions.

With regards the use of renewable energy sources for the generation of electricity in Central America and the Caribbean sub-regions, it is important to know that some Central American countries retains a large dependence on biomass, and has a severely underutilized potential in hydro and other renewable energy sources, while electricity generation has seen an increase in the unhealthy dependence on imported diesel and fuel oil in the past years.

In the case of the Andean Community of Nations, the first meeting of the Council of Andean Community Ministers of Energy, Electricity, Hydrocarbons and Mines, underscored the importance of linking up renewable energy sources with the implementation of the Andean Community's Integral Plan for Social Development (IPSD). The launching of studies was proposed to give special priority to the use of renewable energy sources in antipoverty programmes, and to foster access to basic services and their intensive use for meeting energy requirements in border, isolated and rural areas, and, in general, of the population lacking energy sources.

The first meeting of energy and environment experts on the use of renewable energy sources for the generation of electricity, held in Lima, in May 2004, for its part, identified the following criteria for deepening the analysis of renewable energy sources in the sub-region:

a) The sub-region's renewable energy potential can play a key role in the world's energy system by guaranteeing sustainable development and its ability to create new forms of cooperation among developing countries, and between these and developed countries. within the context of international environmental conservation commitments;

b) New strategies and policies must be adopted with the purpose of allowing for the rational use of endogenous energy sources, and to enable new and renewable energy sources to contribute to the security of the energy supply, while considering the particular needs of the individual member countries;

c) Renewable energy sources constitute an asset for negotiation, and their development can open up new opportunities for investment in local and regional development;

d) Despite the advances made in electricity coverage in the Andean sub-region, in 2008, nearly 12.8 million people continue to live in isolated communities without electrical services. Renewable energy sources can help enormously to provide those communities with sustainable of electric power and other forms of energy;

e) Inasmuch as access to energy sources helps improve the living conditions of people in the sub-region, it is essential to link up this theme with the formulation and implementation of the Integral Plan for Social Development (IPSD-Decision 553), in keeping with the United Nations Millennium Development goals;

f) It is important to evaluate the role that renewable energy sources can play in the provision of energy, and the productive development of the integration hubs in which the Andean Community is involved, within the framework of the South American Regional Infrastructure Integration Initiative (IIRSA);

In the case of the Southern Cone the situation can be summarized as follows: Paraguay and Uruguay use hydro power plants for the generation of almost 100% of their electricity needs. For this reason, in both countries the use of other renewable energy sources is very low or almost nonexistence. The situation is, somehow, different in the cases of Argentina and Chile. In Argentina, the National Promotion Direction (DNPROM) within the Energy Secretariat (SENER) is responsible for the design of programmes and actions conducive to the development of renewable energies (through the Renewable Energy Coordination) and energy efficiency (through the Energy Efficiency Coordination) initiatives. Complementarily, the Secretariat for the Environment and Natural Resources (SEMARNAT) is responsible for environmental policy and the preservation of renewable and non-renewable energy resources.

The most important legal instruments for the promotion of renewable energy sources for the generation of electricity in Argentina are Law 25,019, of 1998 and Law 26,190 of 2007. The 1998 Law, known as the "National Wind and Solar Energy Rules," declared wind and solar generation of national interest and introduced a mechanism that established an additional payment per generated kWh which, in 1998, meant a 40% premium over market price. It also granted certain tax exemptions for a period of fifteen years from the Law's promulgation. The 2007 Law complemented the previous one adopted in 1998, declaring of national interest the generation of electricity from any renewable energy source intended to deliver a public service. This Law also set an 8% target for renewable energy consumption in the period of ten years, and mandated the creation of a trust fund whose resources will be allocated to pay a premium for electricity produced from renewable energy sources. The 2007 Law aims to increase the use of renewable energy sources for the generation of electricity, includes specific feed-in tariffs for energy production from renewable energy sources: a) US$0.33 per kWh for solar photovoltaic; and b) US$0.51 per kWh for wind and other removable sources (geothermal, biomass, biogas and small hydro).

In the case of Chile, besides hydropower, no other renewable energy source has a significant contribution to the Chilean energy mix. Hydropower accounted, in 2009, for 43.7% of the total electricity produced by the country in that year. The other renewable energies used for the generation of electricity are biomass and wind. Although there is still much to be done, the fruits of this effort can already be seen. Wireless Energy Chile (WEC) has announced plans to develop three 5 MW wind power plants in the country, while Endesa plans to develop a 10 MW wind power plant. In addition, SN Power is installing the 46 MW Totoral wind farm power project, which began operating in 2009, along with GDF-Suez who completed the 38 MW Monte Redondo wind farm in the same year. Southern Chile has some of the most promising wind power potential in the world.

It is important to know that renewable energy is currently mostly used in Chile for rural electrification or other small-scale power generation. However, Chile has huge solar, wind and geothermal potential that can increase the role of renewable energy sources in the energy balance of the country in the future.

If Latin America and the Caribbean wish to maintain the current proportion of around 60% of renewable electricity in its generation mix, the use of non-hydro renewable energy would need to expand by about 150 TWh by 2030 (with non-hydro renewables going from 2% to 4% of total power generation), while still meeting the aggressive targets for hydropower.

REFERENCES

A Review of the Power Sector in Latin America and the Caribbean, Evolution in the Market and Investment Opportunities for CFTs (2005); Deutsche MontanTechnologie GmbH Essen, Germany; OLADE, Latin American Energy Organization, Quito, Ecuador, and CIEMAT, Madrid, Spain; March 2005.

Bertani, Ruggero (2010); *Geothermal Power Generation in the World 2005–2010 Update Report*: Proceedings World Geothermal Congress; Bali, Indonesia; April 25-30; 2010.

Birgir Fridleifsson, Ingvar; and Georgsson, Ludvik S. (2011); Geothermal Energy in the Worldand a Glimpse of Central America; Paper presented at *"Short Course on Geothermal Drilling, Resource Development and Power Plants"*, organized by UNU-GTP and LaGeo, in Santa Tecla, El Salvador; January 16-22, 2011.

Energy Statistics Manual (2005); Energy Statistics Division of the International Energy Agency (IEA) in co-operation with the Statistical Office of the European Communities (Eurostat); Paris, France; 2005.

Goodwin, Peter; Jorde, Klaus; Meir, Claudio; and Parra, Oscar (2006); Minimizing environmental impacts of hydropower development: transferring lessons from past projects to a proposed strategy for Chile; IWA Publishing; *Journal of Hydroinformatics*; 2006.

Holm, Alison; Blodgett, Leslie; Jennejohn, Dan; and Gawell, Karl (2010); Geothermal Energy: International Market Update; *Geothermal Energy Association*; 2010.

Huacuz, J.M., and Martínez, A.M. (1992); PV Rural Electrification: Early Mexican experience; *ATAS Bulletin*, Vol. 8; 1992.

Huacuz, J. (2003); Overview of Renewable Energy Sources in Latin America; Non-Conventional Energy Unit, Alternative Energy Division, Electrical Research Institute (IIE); International Electrical Research Exchange, Central American Forum; San José, Costa Rica; 2003.

Huttrer, G.W. (1995); *The Status of World Geothermal Power Production 1990-1994*; Proceedings of the World Geothermal Congress, 1995; Florence, Italy; May 18-31, Vol. 1;1995.

International Energy Outlook 2007; Energy Information Administration, DOE/EIA-0484 (2007); Washington, DC, USA; 2007.

International Energy Outlook 2009; Energy Information Administration, DOE/EIA-0484(2009); Washington, DC, USA; May 2009.

International Energy Outlook 2010; Energy Information Administration, DOE/EIA-0484(2009); Washington, DC, USA; September 2010.

Lopez, Godofredo A. (2011); Operation and Maintenance of Ahuachapan Power Plant, El Salvador; Paper presented at *"Short Course on Geothermal Drilling, Resource Development and Power Plants"*, organized by UNU-GTP and LaGeo, in Santa Tecla, El Salvador; January 16-22, 2011.

Morales Pedraza, J. (2008); The Current Situation and the Perspectives of the Energy Sector in the European Region, Chapter 1 of the book entitled *"Energy in Europe: Economics, Policy and Strategy"*; Nova Science Publishers; New York, USA; 2008.

Palma Behnke, Rodrigo; Jiménez Estévez, Guillermo; and Alarcón Arias, Ignacio (2009); *Non-Conventional Renewable Energy in the Chilean Electricity Market*; Comisión Nacional de Energía (CNE) and Deutsche Gesellschaft für Technische Zusammenarbeit (GTZ) GmbH; ISBN: 978-956-8066-05-5; Santiago de Chile, Chile; October 2009.

Petts, G. (1984); Impounded Rivers. *Perspectives for Ecological Management*; John Wiley and Sons, Chichester; 1984.

Rudnik, Hugh; Barroso, Luis A; Mocarquer, Sebastian; and Bezerra, Bernando (2008); A Delicate Balance in South America. The Challenges of Balancing the Need for Hydroelectricity with the impact on the Environment; *IEEE Power and Energy Magazine*; July- August 2008.

Schmidt, J. C.; Webb, R. H.; Valdez, R. A.; Marzolf, G. R.; and Stevens, L. E. (1998); Science and values in river restoration in the Grand Canyon; *Bioscience* 48 (9); 1998.

Stanford, J. A.; Ward, J. V.; Liss, W. J.; Frissell, C. A.; Williams, R. N.; Lichatowich, J. A.; and Coutant, C. C. (1996); A general protocol for restoration of regulated rivers; *Regul. Rivers Res. Mngmnt*; 12, 1996.

Vimmersted, L. (1998); *Opportunities for Small Geothermal Projects: Rural Power for Latin America, the Caribbean, and the Philippines*; National Renewable Energy Laboratory, U.S. Department of Energy, Colorado, USA; November 1998.

Yepez-García, Rigoberto; Ariel, Johnson; Todd, M,; and Andrés, Luis Alberto (2010); Meeting the Electricity Supply/Demand Balance in Latin America and the Caribbean; *The World Bank*; September 2010.

Wirth, B. D. (1997); Reviewing the success of intentional flooding of the Grand Canyon. *Hydro Rev.* Apr 1997.

In: Research and Applications for Energy ...
Editor: Riad Benelmir

ISBN: 978-1-62948-892-9
© 2014 Nova Science Publishers, Inc.

Chapter 9

CLIMATE POLICY, EMISSION TRADING AND THE EU ETS: A REVIEW

*Vincent Bertrand**

Centre de Recherche sur les Statégies Économiques (CRESE)
University of Franche-Comté, France

ABSTRACT

This paper reviews the main characteristics of climate policy, emission trading and the European Union Emission Trading Scheme (EU ETS). First, we present the origins of emission trading and climate policy. We also discuss the last negotiations on how to prolong the Kyoto Protocol and the international climate policies beyond 2012. Second, we review previous experiences of emission trading prior to the launch of the EU ETS. Finally, we give a wide overview of the EU ETS. The main factors that affect the functioning of the EU ETS are then discussed, as well as the changes that will be effective for Phase 3 (2013-2020).

Keywords: Climate Policy, Emission Trading, EU ETS

1. INTRODUCTION

In ratifying the Kyoto Protocol, the European Union committed itself to reducing its greenhouse gas (GHG) emissions by 8% relative to the 1990 level in the first Kyoto commitment period (2008-2012). In January 2005, to meet this target in a cost-effective way, the European Union established the European Union Emission Trading Scheme (EU ETS), a cap-and-trade system for carbon emissions in the energy and industrial sectors. It is the world's largest emissions trading system to date. According to the 2003/87/EC directive, the

---

* CRESE, 30 Avenue de l'Observatoire, BP 1559, 25009 Besançon Cedex, France. E-mail: vincent.bertrand@univ-fcomte.fr.

EU ETS covers about 11,000 installations,[1] which represent almost 50% of CO_2 emissions and 40% of total GHG emissions in the European Union.

Even though the EU ETS is still, by far, the more ambitious emission trading program for GHG emissions, many others GHG emissions trading schemes have been implemented in the last few years and several are on the horizon. There are now GHG emissions trading schemes in America, Europe and Oceania. These programs are closely related to the Kyoto Protocol Flexibility Mechanisms: the Joint Implementation mechanism, the Clean Development Mechanism, and the Emissions Trading mechanism. What is now commonly called "carbon trading" or "carbon finance" is becoming an important issue, not only for covered installations but also for financial companies that provide trading facilities (exchanges, clearing houses, etc) and financial services (analyses, brokerage, portfolio and risk management, etc). Banks and investment funds are also interested in carbon markets because they provide new opportunities for making money and for portfolio diversification. The aim of this paper is to provide a wide overview of climate policy and carbon trading. In particular, we analyze in details all the particularities of carbon trading in Europe and the last developments within the EU ETS.

The remainder of this paper is organized as follows. In section 2 we present the history of climate policy and the main characteristics of the Kyoto Protocol mechanisms. We also discuss the last negotiations on how to prolong the Kyoto Protocol and the international climate policies beyond 2012. Section 3 introduces the concept of emission trading. First of all, we present the economics of pollution control and the origins of emission trading. Next, we review the emission trading experiences prior to the launch of the EU ETS. Section 4 gives a detailed presentation of the EU ETS. We present the main characteristics of the scheme and the changes that will be effective for Phase 3 (2013-2020). Section 4 concludes.

2. THE KYOTO PROTOCOL AND INTERNATIONAL CLIMATE POLICY

2.1. The Origins of Climate Policy

At the end of the 1980s, the observation of an average temperature increase near the Earth's surface[2] of about +7°C since the pre-industrial period has raised the question of the impact of human activities. This has been further suggested by the intriguing concomitance of recorded sharp increases in temperatures and GHG concentrations since 1850 (see Figures 1 and 2).

Following conclusions of the Intergovernmental Panel on Climate Change (IPCC), there was a wide consensus among scientists and policymakers in the early 1990s to recognize that the influence of anthropogenic GHG emissions (i.e. human-made GHG emissions) on the

---

[1] Covered installations are those defined in Annex 1 of the 2003/87/EC directive. Combustion installations of the energy sector with installed capacities superior to the threshold of 20 thermal MW are notably concerned. Other installations are those of sectors such as cement, refineries, pulp and paper, iron and steel.

[2] The scientific reliability of calculation of a globally averaged surface temperature is disputed by some scientists. However, most of the scientists agree that regional climate variations can modify climatic conditions in other regions of the world. Accordingly, "climate change" is a more accurate terminology than "climate warming" in describing this phenomenon.

observed increase in globally averaged temperatures is very likely. However, human activities are not the only source of GHG emissions.

Natural phenomena such as solar activity or volcanic eruptions also contribute to temperature variations and GHG concentration. Moreover, no formal proof of human influence on temperatures and climate has been given yet. Accordingly, there are a few scientists who dispute the idea of a human-caused climate change.

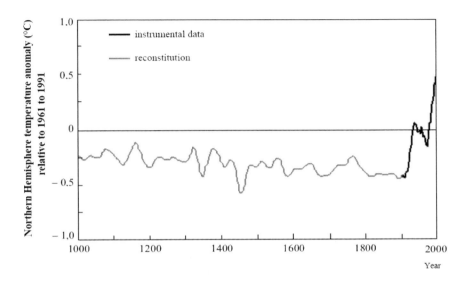

Figure 1. Northern hemisphere temperature variations from IPCC [2001] and Guesnerie [2003].

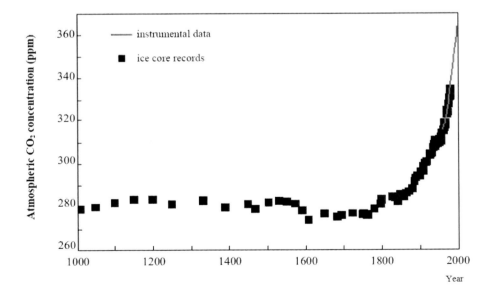

Figure 2. Atmospheric CO_2 concentrations from IPCC [2001] and Guesnerie [2003].

Nevertheless, while there do remain scientific uncertainties about the human influence, the correlation between high increases in temperature variations (and possible global warming) and anthropogenic GHG emissions give strong presumptions. From an economic point of view, those uncertainties do not justify delaying immediate actions to reduce human-made GHG emissions. The nature and scale of potential risks (as well as the fact that some effects could be irreversible and could accelerate processes) are so huge that inaction, if unfavorable events occur, may be more costly than action, even though occurrence is uncertain.[3]

After all, should we refuse to insure our house because we cannot be sure that it will burn? As pointed out in the Stern Review on the economics of climate change (Stern [2006a]), stabilization of atmospheric CO_2 concentrations at 550 ppm[4] would be five to twenty times less costly than the cost of inaction.[5]

Such considerations have brought policymakers to develop an international response to the problem of climate change. Following the precautionary principle,[6] many countries have committed to implementing climate policies, i.e. policies established to address the problem of climate change by reducing GHG emissions and financing a low-emission development. Most of those initiatives have been decided at an international level. They are reviewed in what follows.

2.2. Review on International Climate Policies

The Kyoto Protocol has extended the United Nations framework originated from the United Nations Framework Convention on Climate Change (UNFCCC) of 1992. The UNFCCC was the first step in international treaties dealing with reducing temperature increases and anthropogenic climate change (i.e. climate change with presumption of human influence). With the Kyoto Protocol, adopted in the United Nations summit of Kyoto in December 1997,[7] an international GHG emissions reduction commitment was set for the first time. Developed countries listed in Annex B of the Protocol have committed to reduce collectively their CO_2 emissions by 5.2% compared with the 1990 level, between 2008 and 2012 (i.e. taking as reference the year 1990 for each year).

Among these countries, individual contributions to the global effort span from -8% (the European Union-15) to +10% (Iceland), depending on historical contributions to concentration of CO_2 in the atmosphere (see Table 1).

---

[3] Due to irreversibility and acceleration in the increase of the greenhouse effect with higher GHG concentrations, inaction may create more and more damage and increase the cost of delayed actions. See Guesnerie [2003] and Stern [2006b].

[4] Ppm (parts per million) is the measure of the number of GHG molecules in the total number of molecules of dry air. For example, 550 ppm means 550 molecules of a GHG per million molecules of dry air. See IPCC [2007].

[5] Note that the Stern Review's methodology is subject to numerous discussions that we do not report here.

[6] While the precautionary principle is sometimes criticized as an absurd call for "zero risks" required by anxious people, the extraordinary nature of potential consequences of climate change makes it probably much more relevant in this case.

[7] While adopted in 1997, the Kyoto Protocol did not come into force before February 2005 due to late ratification of Russia. Australia is the latest Annex B country (i.e. countries with binding emission reduction targets in the Kyoto Protocol) to have ratified the Protocol on December 2007. So far, the United States is the only signatory (Annex B) country which has not ratified the Protocol.

Countries' targets are converted into Assigned Amount Units (AAU)[8] which are received by governments of Annex B countries ("Annex B Parties"). In order to facilitate the achievement of emission reduction objectives and to minimize the overall cost, an international emissions trading system offers the possibility to trade AAUs among Annex B Parties. The Emissions Trading mechanism allows countries that have AAUs in excess – due to higher emission reductions than their targets – to sell these spare units to countries that are over their targets.

Table 1. Annex B countries emission reduction targets (in the period 2008-2012) compared to the 1990 levels, based on Brohé [2008]

Country	Target (in %)
Iceland	10
Australia	8
Norway	1
New Zealand, Russian Federation, Ukraine	0
Croatia	-5
Canada, Hungary, Japan, Poland	-6
United States	-7
Bulgaria, Czech Republic, Estonia, Latvia, Liechtenstein, Lithuania, Monaco, Romania, Slovakia, Slovenia, Switzerland	-8
European Union - 15	-8

Other emissions units can be traded (and used for compliance) under the Kyoto Protocol's emissions trading system. These units are the Emission Reduction Units (ERUs) and the Certificates of Emission Reduction (CERs). The ERUs are units issued from the JI mechanism. The JI mechanism allows an Annex 1 country (i.e. a country listed in Annex 1 of the UNFCCC)[9] to earn ERUs from an emission reduction project in another Annex 1 country.

The CERs are units generated through the CDMs. The CDMs encourage emission reduction projects by Annex 1 countries in non-Annex 1 countries. The aim is to assist developing countries (i.e. non-Annex 1 countries) in achieving a sustainable low-carbon development.

---

[8] Each unit gives the right to emit one tonne of CO_2.

[9] The UNFCCC distinguishes between Annex 1 and non-Annex 1 countries. Annex 1 countries are developed countries with high past emissions, whereas non-Annex 1 countries are developing countries. Annex 1 countries had committed themselves to reducing their GHG emissions under the UNFCCC. They agreed to maintain their emissions to the 1990 levels by 2000, even though these targets were not legally binding (as opposed to targets of Annex B countries under the Kyoto Protocol, which are legally binding). Annex 1 and Annex B countries are often assimilated in practice, since most of Annex 1 countries are also Annex B countries (and vice versa). Turkey is the only country included in Annex I but not in Annex B, while Croatia, Liechtenstein and Monaco are included in Annex B but not in Annex 1 (see Brohé [2008] and the UNFCCC website).

There are also units that can be used for compliance although they cannot be traded. These are the Removal Units (RMUs, articles 3.3 and 3.4 of the Kyoto Protocol) which are issued on the basis of emission reduction projects through the Land Use, Land Use Change and Forestry (LULUCF) activities.10 In each case, the CERs, ERUs and RMUs are delivered after a validation and certification process that warrants effective emission reductions. Those certification are guaranteed by the CDM Executive Board (CDM EB), for the CDMs, and by the JI Supervisory Committee (JISC), for the JI and JI-LULUCF.11 It has to be noted that there is a major difference between the JI mechanism and the CDMs regarding accounting of emission credits. While CERs are additional credits, issued in addition to AAUs, ERUs are converted AAUs (i.e. a volume of AAUs equivalents to the volume of emission reductions is converted into ERUs). This was decided in order to avoid "double accounting" of emission reductions. Indeed, if the host country of the project is an Annex B country, and if the ERUs were created in addition to the host country's AAUs, emission reductions would be counted twice: as ERUs for the investing country and as unused AAUs (due to emission reductions from the project) for the host country.

Negotiations for a post-Kyoto agreement began with the Conference of the Parties (COP) of Bali in December 2007. It introduced a new negotiation process with the aim to reach an agreement for the post-2012 period at the COP of Copenhagen in December 2009. In the meanwhile, the European Union has adopted the "Climate and Energy Package", in December 2008, which extends the EU's climate policy after 2012. The package includes three "20 targets" to reach by 2020: reducing GHG emissions by 20%, reaching 20% of renewable energy in the total energy consumption and increasing energy efficiency to save 20% of energy consumption. Besides, the EU ETS has been confirmed for a Phase 3.

Despite the great hope in the Copenhagen Summit, it did not achieve the global binding agreement that was expected to prolong the Kyoto Protocol. The Copenhagen Accord was notable in that it referred to a collective commitment to allocate new resources to finance climate policies in developing countries: 30 billion USD for the period 2010-2012. It also stated that actions should be taken to stabilize an average temperature increase at +2°C, as recommended by the IPCC. However, no explicit binding emission targets were specified in the Accord. By contrast, the signatory countries stated what actions they are willing to take if a binding agreement is achieved in the future (see Table 2).[12]

At the same time, no economic mechanism has been provided in the Accord, as it was the case in the Kyoto Protocol with the Flexible Mechanisms.

One year after the Copenhagen Summit, the next COP was held in Cancun in December 2010. While the Cancun Agreements reaffirmed the principles of the Copenhagen Accord, no precise decision was adopted on the legal form of countries' binding emission targets,

---

[10] Note that only afforestation and reforestation are eligible as project-based emission reductions in non-Annex 1 countries, whereas all kind of LULUCF activities are eligible in Annex 1 countries (afforestation, reforestation, revegetation, forest management, cropland management, grazing land management). Accordingly, projects in LULUCF are sometimes referred to as JI-LULUCF. See JMOE and GECF [2006].

[11] There is another type of project-based units outside the Kyoto Protocol regime. These are the Verified Emissions Reductions (VERs) which are issued from projects that do not follow all the JI and CDM requirements, and are not subject to certification of the CDM EB or JISC. They are traded in the voluntary markets.

[12] The Copenhagen Accord has specified a "variable geometry" commitment system, with different targets from one country to another. This is a different approach with respect to the Kyoto Protocol which provided a collective emission target for Annex B countries. For a detailed analysis of the Copenhagen Accord, see Casella et al. [2010].

financial resources and economic mechanisms for the post-Kyoto period. Nevertheless, Cancun has yielded some success. Notably, the enshrining of the main elements of the Copenhagen Accord into the UNFCCC framework (e.g. stabilization of average temperature increase at +2°C, calling on developed countries to reduce their GHG emissions, helping developing countries to implement a low-emissions development) and the reassurance of the intention to continue with market-based mechanisms (CDMs, Emissions Trading, etc) even in the absence of a post-Kyoto commitment. Moreover, a "Green Climate Fund" was mentioned with the goal for developed countries to mobilize jointly 100 billion USD per year by 2020 to assist developing countries in financing emission reductions and adaptation. However, there was no agreement on how money will be raised to feed that fund.

Table 2. "Variable geometry" commitments of some of the main signatory countries to the Copenhagen Accord, from Casella et al. [2010]

Country	2020 emission reduction target	Benchmark year
Annex 1 countries		
Australia	between 5% and 15% (if there is an international agreement that includes the developing countries), or even 25% (if there is a target not to exceed 450 ppm of GHG in the atmosphere)	2000
Canada	17%	2005
EU - 27	20% or 30% (if there are equivalent commitments from the other developed countries and an adequate contribution from developing countries)	1990
Japan	25% (if there is a fair and ambitious international agreement that includes the main economies)	1990
New Zealand	between 10% to 20%, if there is a full international agreement (aiming not to exceed a 2°C rise in temperature, comparable efforts from the other developed countries, adequate measures from developing countries, rules on LULUCF, access to an efficient international carbon market)	1990
Russia	15% to 25%, depending on the recognition of forests and the main emitter's commitment to reducing their emissions	1990
United States	around 17% (subject to Congress voting on the international legislation)	2005
Non-Annex 1 countries (developing countries)		
Brazil	between 36% and 39% compared with the "business-as-usual" assumption	2020
China	40% to 45% reducing in GDP CO_2 intensity	2005
India	20% to 25% reducing in GDP GHG intensity (excluding agricultural emissions)	2005

Many important decisions were agreed on during the COPs of Copenhagen and Cancun, even though Parties were often very vague regarding concrete enforcements. Among those decisions, the recognizing of the +2°C global target and the creation of a fund to finance the clean development of developing countries, are particularly important. However, there was no agreement on how to extend the Kyoto Protocol beyond 2012. Besides, although a majority of signatory countries have confirmed their support for the Copenhagen Accord, emission reduction targets remain unbinding and often undefined precisely.[13] Thus, the primary concern of the next rounds of negotiations will be to adopt a new global agreement that prolongs the Kyoto Protocol, with legally binding emission targets, new economic mechanisms and institutions. Recently, the COP of 2011 was held in Durban in December 2011. Once again no legally binding agreement was achieved. However, the outcomes include a decision by Parties to adopt a universal legal agreement no later than 2015 (Durban Platform for Enhanced Action). The Green Climate Fund has also been confirmed. The next COP will be held in Qatar in December 2012.

So far we have reviewed how the problem of climate change has been tackled at the international level in climate policies. We have also reported the negotiations which are currently under way to prolong international climate policies beyond 2012. Let us now discuss origins of the concept of emission trading and give a presentation of first experiences that were implemented before the EU ETS.

3. EMISSION TRADING: THEORY AND PRACTICE

3.1. The Economics of Pollution Control and Emission Trading

An externality exists when an agent takes decisions that are not accounted for in a market price even though they affect other agents' well-being. Accordingly, producers of externalities do not have any incentives to take into account the effects of their decisions on others. Pollution is generally considered as a negative externality. A negative externality causes divergence between social and private costs. The private cost of polluting activities is under-estimated with respect to the social cost, since it neglects the "external" cost of damages created by pollution. As a result, the chosen level of pollution is higher than the socially optimal level (i.e. the level which equalizes the social marginal cost to the social marginal benefit of pollution).

The problems of excessive pollution are sometimes also tackled in terms of "public good" or "common asset". A public good is a good that exhibits properties of non-excludability (i.e. no one can be excluded from using the good) and non-rivality (i.e. the consumption of the good by one individual does not reduce the availability of the good for others). The open access to public goods leads to a problem which is well known by economists: free-riding, that induces over-exploitation and potential destruction of "common assets" ("the tragedy of the commons", as defined by Hardin [1968]). Environmental goods

---

[13] Note that reaching unanimity among Parties is a very important task since unanimity is required to enforce legally binding agreements under the UNFCCC's rules (Casella et al. [2010]). In that respect, the Kyoto Protocol was an exception since the condition for the Protocol to be enforced was the ratification of at least 55 Parties of the Convention representing 55% of the global emissions of the Parties in 1990.

and services are particularly exposed to that kind of inefficiency. Ecosystem services such as waste absorption capacities are typical examples of public goods which are subject to over-exploitation and this results in excessive pollution.[14] The problem of climate change is unusual in that respect, since it concerns a global public good: climate stability.

However pollution is referred to – negative externality or deterioration of a public good – it leads to a market failure that results in inefficient outcomes. For economists, the solution consists in putting a price on pollution in order to "internalize" the cost of pollution in private decisions. Basically, there are two categories of economic instruments to internalize pollution: Pigouvian tax and emissions trading scheme ("cap-and-trade"). Both have been advocated by economists because they minimize the overall cost of environmental regulation compared to rigid "command-and-control" approaches. Command-and-control regulations generally apply uniform emissions limits on regulated firms, regardless of the fact that firms are not equally efficient in reducing emissions. By contrast, with economic instruments, individual firms are free to choose how much they will reduce their emissions by comparing their abatement costs with the price of pollution. As a consequence, firms with lower costs make higher share of the overall effort of emissions reduction, and vice versa. This leads to the "least-cost solution" in which each firm equalizes its marginal abatement cost to the price of pollution.

Pigouvian tax was introduced by Pigou [1920] as a way to restore market efficiency in presence of negative externalities. In his famous example, Pigou explains that social benefits of railway services in the England of the 19th century was over-estimated due to negligence of damages caused by sparks from engines. To correct the negative externality, Pigou proposed to place a tax on railway companies varying with the amount of smoke produced and equivalent to the monetary value of the externality (i.e. equivalent to the difference between the social cost and the private cost). Hence, by making companies financially liable for the damages created by sparks, the Pigouvian tax gives an incentive to reduce the output to the socially optimal level.

The concept of the emission trading scheme was introduced by Dales [1968],[15] based on the Coase theorem. Coase [1960] proposed a solution that consists in establishing property rights on emission of externalities. If transaction costs are negligible, Coase shows that parties – i.e. "disrupters" and "victims" – can achieve a socially optimal level of externality by bargaining, regardless of who initially received the property rights. The socially optimal level of externality is attained when the marginal benefit of the externality (i.e. profits arising from the activity which generates the externality) is equal to the marginal cost of the externality.[16] Moreover, a market price emerges for the externality. Based on the Coasian approach, market-based instruments (MBIs) have been popularized as an efficient way to reduce pollution. They work with a central authority which sets a cap on the total amount of pollutant that can be emitted. The cap is converted into allowances that give the right to emit a certain

---

[14] Pollution is sometimes referred to as a "public bad" to point it out as a negative externality deteriorating an environmental public good.

[15] First references to emission trading can be found in Crocker [1966].

[16] In his 1960 paper, Coase argued that the traditional Pigouvian approach may lead to results "which are not necessarily" the true social optimum, because it neglects the "reciprocal nature" of externalities: inducing disrupters to reduce harm on victims also inflicts harm on disrupters. He proposed his solution as a way to overcome this problem.

amount of pollutant. Allowances are allocated to polluters, and they can be traded on a secondary market.

A market price emerges[17] and buyers pay that price to increase their emissions, while sellers can earn money by selling unused allowances. Thus, polluters with low abatement costs have an incentive to reduce their emissions by more than needed, and those with high abatement costs can buy more allowances rather than engage in costly emission reductions. Accordingly, MBIs theoretically achieve emission reduction targets at the lowest cost to society. Such a "least-cost" solution implies equalization of marginal cost of abatement among polluters. Montgomery [1972] formalized this result and showed that it is verified in the equilibrium of the market for allowances.[18]

3.2. Emission Trading Experiences Prior to the Launch of the EU ETS

Before the EU ETS and the Kyoto Protocol, MBIs were used in many previous programs to reduce different kinds of pollution. The first experiences appeared in the United States in the 1970s and 1980s. The US Environmental Protection Agency (EPA) started in 1976 with the adoption of the "offset" mechanisms that became part of US legislation with the 1977 Clean Air Act Amendments (CAAAs) to the Clean Air Act of 1970. The 1977 CAAAs allowed emission trading among facilities subject to emission restrictions regarding six air pollutants (ozone, particulate matter, carbon monoxide, sulfur dioxide, nitrogen oxide and lead), under the National Ambient Air Quality Standards (NAAQS).[19] Other examples of early MBI implementations are the 1980 Wisconsin's program to reduce BOD (Biochemical Oxygen Demand) discharges in the Fox River, the 1982 EPA lead reduction program for gasoline refiners[20] or the Regional Clean Air Incentives Market (RECLAIM, 1994) for SO_X (sulfur oxide) and NO_X (nitrogen oxide) emissions in California. However, the first nation-wide emission trading program in the US appeared in 1995 with the US Acid Rain Program (ARP), established under Title IV of the Clean Air Act Amendments of 1990. The ARP sets annual reduction targets for SO_2 emissions of power plants. SO_2 emissions of affected facilities were capped annually at about half of their 1980 levels. Ex-post evaluations of the ARP have demonstrated high cost savings with respect to previous command-and-control approaches (see Ellerman [2003]).

Emission trading schemes related to pollutants responsible for acid rains have also been implemented in Europe. On the basis of the national NO_X and SO_2 reduction targets established under the 2001/81/EC directive (the "National Emission Ceilings" directive),

---

[17] Emission trading schemes are sometimes referred to as "quantity instruments" because they fix the overall emission level (quantity) and allow the price to vary according to supply and demand conditions (i.e. according to scarcity of allowances, which is set by volume of emissions). By contrast, a Pigouvian tax on emissions is a "price instrument" because it fixes the price and allows quantities (i.e. emissions) to vary.

[18] Montgomery [1972] provides formal proof that such an equilibrium exists under certain conditions (competitive market, no transaction-costs, etc).

[19] While the offset-mechanisms introduced a market for emissions reduction credits, it was only designed for new facilities. Thus, it was limited in size.

[20] While the lead reduction program was recognized as a success with annual cost savings estimated at 200 million USD by the EPA (see Newell and Kristian [2003]), the Fox River program ended in failure with only one trade in five years due to numerous administrative requirements discouraging the trading of allowances (see Hahn [1989] and [1991]).

Slovakia (2002) and the Netherlands (2005) have set legally-binding caps for NO_X (the Netherlands) and SO_2 (Slovakia) emissions of industrial thermal facilities.[21] The Slovakian SO_2 trading program came into operation in 2002. The aim was to reduce SO_2 emissions in 2010 to 36% of the 1999 emissions. It applied to sources with installed thermal capacities above 50 MW, and it represented about 90% of the Slovakian SO_2 emissions in 1998. There were very few trades. The Dutch NO_x emissions trading system applies to approximately 250 facilities with installed thermal capacities of more than 20 MW. It covers about 85% of industrial emissions and 25% of the overall Dutch emissions. Between 2005 and 2010, the Dutch government set a target of 55,000 tonnes of NO_x emissions per year for affected facilities, compared to 1995 base year emissions of 122,000 tonnes. Nevertheless, the allowance price was very low. Yet, the Dutch NO_x trading program has been prolonged until 2013. Discussions about the future of the program for after 2013 are currently under progress.[22]

However, the first national MBI in Europe was the Individual Transferable Quotas (ITQ) system in the fishery sector in Iceland (1984). Between 1945 and 1983, the value of capital stock in the Icelandic fishery sector increased by 1,200%. The fishery stocks were clearly over-fished, which motivated the introduction of the ITQ system. The program allocated quotas attached to boats. However, transfers of quotas were not allowed, unless boats were wrecked or sold abroad. These restrictions have led to incentives to destroy boats in order to sell quotas. To avoid such destruction, unrestricted transfers of quotas were allowed in 1991. The ITQ system reduced the number of fishing boats in Iceland, and brought the fishery sector better in line with fish stocks (see EEA [2006]). ITQ systems were also used in Canada (1983), Australia (1984) and New Zealand (1986). In Europe, ITQ systems have been implemented in the fishery sector of Denmark, Italy, the Netherlands, Portugal and the UK (see Branch [2004]).

Another example of the MBI system which is not related to GHG emissions can be found in the packaging waste regulation. In the wake of the EU Packaging and Packaging Waste Directive (94/62/EC), the UK government implemented in 1997 the Packaging Recovery Note (PRN) system which allows affected companies to trade quotas limiting packaging discharges. So far, the UK PRN is the only application of MBIs to limit packaging.

Due to the interest in promoting renewable energies in Europe, MBIs have been designed to foster penetration of renewables. The EU adopted a directive in 2001 (2001/77/EC) to increase the share of green electricity in the total electricity consumption. It established different national targets for Member States in order to meet an overall objective for the EU.[23] To achieve this aim, markets for "Tradable Green Certificates" (TGCs) – or "Tradable Renewable Energy Certificates" (TRECs) – have been established in several EU Member States, including the UK, the Netherlands, Italy, Denmark, Belgium, Sweden, and Austria

---

[21] See EEA [2005], EEA [2006], IEA [2006] and Ecofys [2010].

[22] For several years the EU has been assessing opportunities on developing an EU-wide NO_x and SO_2 trading scheme for IPPC installations, i.e. installations subject to the directives 96/61/EC and 2008/1/EC about Integrated Pollution Prevention and Control (see EC [2010]). However, in March 2011, the Commission officially announced that it will not be pursuing further work on NO_x/SO_2 trading due to potential conflicts with the Industrial Emissions Directive (the IDE directive 2010/75/EU) and uncertainties about the impact on local air quality (see Eurofer [2011]). Same questions about interferences with the IDE directive are the main topic regarding the future of the Dutch NO_X trading program.

[23] This was confirmed in 2008 with the Climate and Energy Package.

(see Bertoldi and Rezessy [2004]). TGC schemes impose quantified obligations on electricity buyers (e.g. retailers or consumers). The obligated buyers must surrender to an authority a number of certificates corresponding to a percentage of their total electricity sales or consumption. The authority issues (a fixed number) and distributes certificates to producers of green electricity (typically, one certificate refers to one MWh of green electricity). Certificates are sold by power producers to obligated buyers and they vanish after submission. TGC schemes can be regarded as market-based subsidies rather than pure MBIs as defined before.

MBIs are particularly appropriate for GHG emissions since greenhouse effect is a global process, and thus local differences in air concentrations do not matter. Created in 1996, the Canadian PERT (Pilot Emission Reduction Trading) program was the first emission trading scheme applying to GHG emissions. The PERT was a voluntary market for industrial emissions in the Ontario region. While the initial focus was NO_x and VOC (Volatile Organic Compound) emissions, the program was expanded in 1997 to include CO_2 and carbon monoxide emissions. It operated between 1996 and 2001, and it was directly linked to the Canadian government through supervision of the Canadian federal environmental agency. It appears that only a small number of trades were completed during the program.[24] The Greenhouse Gas Abatement Scheme (GGAS) is another example of emission trading scheme applying to GHG emissions. It was introduced by the New South Wales (NWS – Australia) state government in 2003 (see GGAS [2008]). It is a mandatory emission trading scheme. The program covers GHG emissions of electric generators and large consumers of power. The GGAS establishes an annual state-wide target for emissions which is converted into NSW Greenhouse Abatement Certificates (NGACs). Individual sources receive each year an initial allocation of NGACs, with the ability to buy and sell those certificates to meet their obligations. The GGAS remains operational to date.[25]

Prior to the creation of the EU ETS, the first European CO_2 trading schemes were introduced in Denmark and in the UK.[26] The Danish CO_2 emissions trading system came into operation in 2000, after the "Electricity Reform" and the "CO_2 Quota Act" were passed by the Danish parliament in March and June 1999, respectively. The system covered the eight largest electricity producers in Denmark, representing approximately 90% of the CO_2 emissions from the Danish electricity production, and about 30% of the total GHG emissions in Denmark. It operated between 2000 and 2004. Legally-binding allowances were allocated each year to affected producers, representing 66% of their average annual emissions between 1994 and 1998. However, the low non-compliance fees of DKK 40 (i.e. about EUR 5.40) per tonne made the constraint less restrictive. The program obtained contrasted results with very few trades and several companies that failed to comply in 2002 and 2004, while they were collectively long of allowances. Nevertheless, efficiency was not the first objective of the program. The aim was rather to prepare the country for the EU ETS. In that respect, it was a success. The UK ETS (United Kingdom Emission Trading Scheme) was a voluntary scheme launched in the UK in April 2002 for the five-year period 2002-2006, and which formally ended in March 2007. It intended to prepare the UK companies for the EU ETS, and London's

---

[24] For further details see LECG [2003].

[25] Even though it has been delayed several times since 2007, an Australian Federal Emission Trading Scheme is expected to be operationnal in 2013.

[26] See Pedersen [2000], EEA [2005], EEA [2006], DEFRA [2006] and Green [2008].

financial place for emissions trading. The UK ETS was the world's first economy-wide GHG emissions trading scheme, since it covered a wide range of sectors. The reduction targets (with respect to baseline emission levels between 1998 and 2000) were set through an auction in March 2002. Sources sold their reduction targets to the government, and received tradable allowances in exchange. The aim was to provide a financial incentive for companies to adopt emission reduction targets voluntarily. The thirty-three direct participants committed to reducing collectively their CO_2 emissions by 3.96 million tonnes by the end of the scheme. However, over the life of the program, a total of 7.2 million tonnes of CO_2 were reported.

Following the European leadership on carbon trading, several GHG emissions trading schemes have been implemented in the last few years and others are on the horizon. Examples are the Specified Gas Emitters Regulation (SGER, state of Alberta, Canada, 2007), the New Zealand Emissions Trading Scheme (NZ ETS, New Zealand, 2008) and the Regional Greenhouse Gas Initiative (RGGI, United States, 2008). There are now GHG emissions trading schemes in America, Europe and Oceania. However, the EU ETS is still, by far, the more ambitious program. The main characteristics of the EU ETS are presented in the following.

4. THE EU ETS

The EU ETS officially started in January 2005. It is nowadays the central piece of the European climate policy which was initiated in 1991, with the first Community strategy to limit CO_2 emissions and increase energy efficiency. It is made up of consecutive "Phases" which are trading periods of several years. Phase 1 covered the period 2005-2007. It was designed as a pilot phase to "learn by doing" and gain experience for subsequent Phases. Phase 2, which is currently in progress, corresponds to the first Kyoto commitment period, i.e. 2008-2012. Phase 3 will start in 2013 and end in 2020. It is supposed to be part of a post-Kyoto agreement.

The EU ETS was established to help the EU Member States to fulfill their commitments in the Kyoto Protocol. Under the Burden-Sharing-Agreement of 1998 (EU Council Document 97/02/98), the EU-15 collective target (see Table 1) has been translated into differentiated national targets for each Member State (see Table 3). Moreover, ten of the twelve Member States that were not part of the EU in 1997 have individual commitments under the Kyoto Protocol (see Table 1).

In order to meet national targets, each Member State has to set a national cap on CO2 emissions for each Phase of the EU ETS. Indeed, the Directive 2003/87/EC establishes that each Member State has to develop a National Allocation Plan (NAP) stating the total number of allowances it intends to allocate for the Phase (the cap), how it proposes to allocate them (free allocations or auctions), what the receiving installations and the new entrant reserves are. Each NAP has to be approved by the European Commission before validation. In the case of incompatibility with criteria listed in the Directive 2003/87/EC or if allocations are judged too generous with respect to obligations, the European Commission may reject NAPs and send them back to Member States for revisions.

The EU ETS is a decentralized system, in which Member States have a lot of freedom in designing their NAPs. But, on the other hand, the European Commission decides the general rules (e.g. which are the affected sectors and facilities). Thus, it is halfway between an EU centralized system and a fully decentralized system (Kruger et al. [2007]).

Table 3. Distribution of the EU-15 Kyoto target in the Burden-Sharing-Agreement, from Guesnerie [2003]

National targets of the EU-15 countries under the Burden-Sharing-Agreement (emission reductions in the period 2008-2012 compared to the 1990 levels)					
Country	Target (in %)	Country	Target (in %)	Country	Target (in %)
Austria	-13	Germany	-21	Netherlands	-6
Belgium	-8	Greece	25	Portugal	27
Denmark	-21	Ireland	13	Spain	15
Finland	0	Italy	-6.5	Sweden	4
France	0	Luxembourg	-28	UK	-12.5

4.1. Allocation

The EU ETS concerns facilities with energy consumption or installed thermal capacities which exceed some thresholds (see Annex 1 of the Directive 2003/87/EC) in sectors of power and heat, refineries, cement and lime, iron and steel, pulp and paper, glass, ceramic, metal ore processing and coke ovens.[27] Based on accepted NAPs, each participating installation receives a certain volume of EUAs (European Union Allowances) at the beginning of each year, on 28th February. Each EUA gives the right to emit one tonne of CO_2, and can be traded on several exchanges (i.e. organized market places) across Europe.

Options for allocation of EUAs in the EU ETS are grandfathering (i.e. free distribution of allowances on the basis of historical emissions) or auctioning.[28] Auctioning has been widely advocated by economists,[29] who support that it can reduce adverse effects associated with grandfathering such as unfair distributional effects (transfer of resources "from the poor to the rich")[30] or perverse dynamic incentives to emit more now in order to receive a larger allocation in the future. Moreover, auctioning is likely to be more efficient than free allocation because it ensures that more allowances are received by firms which need them more (i.e. firms with higher abatement costs) and it offers scope to reduce distortionary taxes in the economy by "recycling" the auction revenue. According to the Directive 2003/87/EC, Member States can auction up to 5% of the total number of EUAs allocated for Phase 1, and up to 10% for Phase 2. Nevertheless this only gives an upper limit and Member States can

---

[27] With the start of Phase 3 in 2013, new sectors will be covered by the EU ETS such as aviation, petrochemical or aluminium.

[28] Allocations based on benchmarking (i.e. allocations on the basis of specific benchmarks) are also allowed. They seem to yield better outcomes compared to grandfathering (see Betz et al. [2006]), that we do not discuss here. In practice, benchmarking is often used for new entrant allocations. Only France used benchmarking for existing installations in Phase 1, and very few countries in Phase 2 including Belgium, Malta and Cyprus.

[29] See Crampton and Kerr [2002], Hepburn et al. [2006] and Mougeot and Naegelen [2009].

[30] Most of the rent from grandfathered allowances ultimately accrue to shareholders of the profiting firms, who tend to be wealthier than the general population. See Hepburn et al. [2006].

determine freely the exact volume of allowances they want to auction. During Phase 1, only four countries decided to use auctioning: Denmark (5%), Hungary (2.4%), Lithuania (1.5%) and Ireland (0.5%). For Phase 2, eleven countries decided to include auctioning in their NAPs. Examples are Germany (8.8%), the UK (7%), the Netherlands (3.7%) or Hungary (2%).[31] There will be change in Phase 3. The Directive 2009/09/EC, which sets out changes to the EU ETS from 2013 onwards, states that 100% of the allocation will be auctioned in the electricity sector. In other industrial sectors, with limited exposure to international competition, the allocation via auction will increase from 20% in 2013 to 70% in 2020 (and 100% in 2027). Besides, firms of the newly-included aviation sector will have to buy 15% of their EUAs at auction. Thus, the auctioning of EUAs will sharply increase in Phase 3, with more than one billion EUAs auctioned annually, compared to less than 150 million in Phase 2.[32]

According to the Phase 1 NAPs, about 2181 million EUAs per year have been distributed between 2005 and 2007. In Phase 2, yearly allocations account for about 2082 million EUAs. This corresponds to a reduction of about 217 million EUAs per year compared to Phase 1 (excluding the Romanian and Bulgarian Phase 2 NAPs of calculation to make Phases 1 and 2 comparable since those countries did not have Phase 1 NAPs). Regarding the repartition of EUA allocations, there are strong disparities between Member States (see Figures 3 and 4). During Phase 1 Germany distributed 499 million EUAs annually, while the following countries were Italy, Poland and the United Kingdom, with about 235 million EUAs allocated a year. Six countries (France, Germany, Italy, Poland, Spain and the UK) total 70.5% of EUAs distributed in Phase 1, and 66.7% in Phase 2. The volume of EUA allocated in Germany is particularly high due to its massive carbon emissions from electricity, which is largely generated with coal and lignite in this country. Germany is by far the biggest carbon emitter in Europe. For instance, in 2005, carbon emissions in Germany were twice as high as in the UK, the second biggest carbon emitter (see Ellerman and Buchner [2008]).

Regarding differences between allocations and verified emissions, an allowance surplus of 155.7 million EUAs was recorded during Phase 1, equivalent to 2.5% of the three-year allocations (Trotignon and Delbosc [2008]).

This surplus decreased from 83 million tonnes in 2005 to 36 million tonnes in 2007. However, positions are heterogeneous between Member States. Some countries recorded a net deficit of allowances (e.g. the UK, Spain or Italy), despite the overall surplus (see Figure 5). For the first time the EU ETS revealed a deficit of 115 million tonnes EUAs in 2008 (Trotignon [2009]), the first year of Phase 2, while 2009 ended with a surplus of 170 million tonnes EUAs due to reductions of CO_2 emissions that came with the economic recession (Trotignon [2010]). Excluding auctioned allowances, the 2009 net surplus is 85 million tonnes EUAs. In 2010, the economic recovery reduced the surplus to 55 million tonnes EUAs (excluding auctioned allowances) even though the EU ETS is still globally long (Trotignon and Stephan [2011]).

---

[31] See Charpin [2009] for an overview on main characteristics of auction procedures adopted by Member States in Phases 1 and 2.

[32] See Charpin [2009], Delbosc [2009], Mougeot and Naegelen [2009] and Sator [2010].

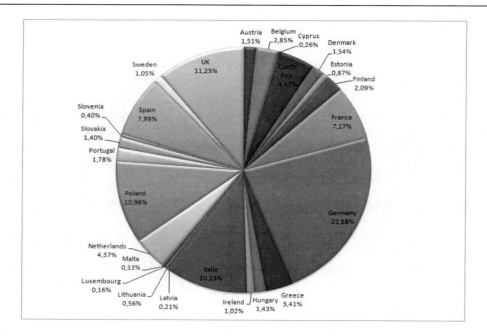

Figure 3. Phase 1 NAPs in percentages of total EUA allocations (based on CITL data, available at www.ec.europa.eu/environment/ets).

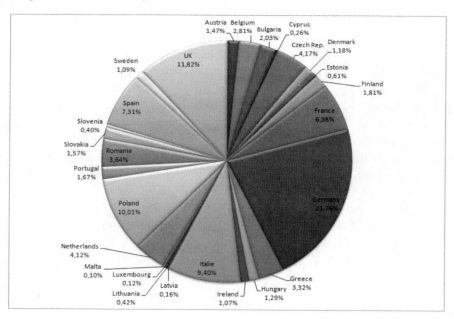

Figure 4. Phase 2 NAPs in percentages of total EUA allocations (based on CITL data, available at www.ec.europa.eu/environment).

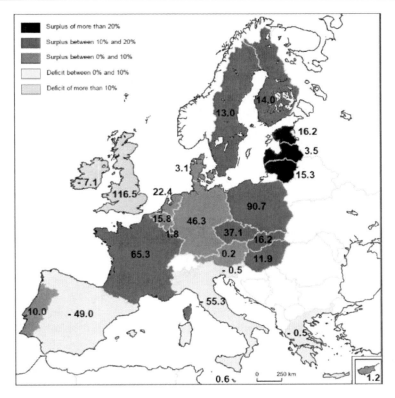

Figure 5. Net positions of Member States in Phase 1, from Trotignon and Delbosc [2008]. Shortages and surplus are expressed as percentages of the national allocations (colored areas) and in million tonnes CO2 (numeric values).

4.2. Monitoring, Reporting and Trading

Rules for monitoring and reporting of emissions are defined in the Decision 2007/589/EC amending the Decision 2004/156/EC of the European Commission (Brohé [2008]). It states that each Member State has to report its previous year's verified emissions (recorded between January 1 and December 31) to the European Commission before March 31 of the following year, and that affected firms must surrender the allowances corresponding to their previous year's verified emissions before April 30 (see Mansanet-Bataller and Pardo [2008]). For example, for the 2005 emissions, reports had to be submitted before March 31 and April 30, 2006 was the deadline to surrender allowances corresponding to verified emissions. Once all reports have been submitted and approved, the European Commission can officially publish, on May 15 of the following year, the previous year's verified emissions (see Chevallier [2010]). This monitoring and reporting process is summarized in Figure 6.

In Phase 2, if an installation fails to surrender enough allowances to cover its verified emissions, it must pay a penalty of 100 Euros per tonne of CO_2 in excess (in Phase 1 the penalty was 40 Euros per tonne of CO_2). In addition to paying penalties, firms are compelled during the following year to return all allowances that were not surrendered for compliance in the previous year.

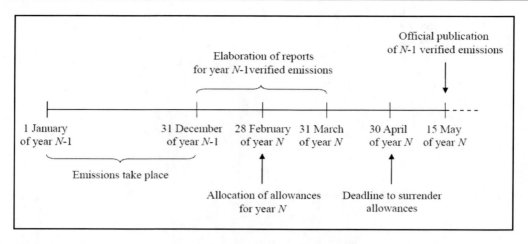

Figure 6. The EU ETS monitoring and reporting deadlines, based on Mansanet-Bataller and Pardo [2008] and Chevallier [2010].

According to the European Parliament and Council Decision 280/2004/EC, each Member State has to establish a registry where the balance of bought and sold allowances of each participant is recorded, as well as verified emissions. Therefore, registries are used to check the compliance of each participant. The national registries are linked to the Community Independent Transaction Log (CITL), the European registry that centralizes all information contained in the national registries. Since October 16, 2008, the CITL is connected to the UNFCCC International Transaction Log (ITL), the international registry system under the Kyoto Protocol.[33] Thus, participants are now allowed to meet part of their obligations with international credits (CERs and ERUs).

Participants can trade allowances through organized trading platforms (exchanges) or in over-the-counter (OTC) transactions. Several organized exchanges exist where it is possible to trade EUAs and related financial products such as futures contracts or options. Eight are based in Europe: BlueNext (Paris), Climex (Amsterdam), EEX (European Energy Exchange, Leipzig), EXAA (Energy Exchange Austria, Vienna), GME (Gestore Mercato Elettrico, Rome), ICE-ECX (Intercontinental Exchange - European Climate Exchange, London),[34] NordPool (Oslo) and SendeCO$_2$ (Spain). Another is located in the United States: GreenX (Green Exchange, New York Mercantile Exchange). As for stock exchanges, these platforms offer standardized contracts and provide clearing and settlement services.[35] In terms of size, BlueNext is the most important market place for spot contracts with 73% of total spot volume in Phase 1, while ECX is the most important platform for future contracts with 96% of total

---

[33] Information available at http://cdm.unfccc.int/Registry. Note that the European Commission announced on July 7, 2011 that it intends to set a single European Union registry (EUTL – European Union Transaction Log) to replace all Member States registries which are centralized in the CITL (information available at http://ec.europa.eu/environment).

[34] ECX is a former subsidiary of the Chicago Climate Exchange (CCX). In 2006, ECX, CCX and CCFE (Chicago Climate Futures Exchange) were grouped in the "Climate Exchange Plc" holding. In 2010, ICE acquired Climate Exchange Plc, after a five-year partnership between ICE and ECX.

[35] For a detailed presentation of products and services in the different exchanges, see Kristiansen et al. [2006] and Mansanet-Bataller and Pardo [2008].

transactions in Phase 1 (Mansanet-Bataller and Pardo [2008]).[36] ECX and GreenX are the only platforms offering the possibility to trade options on EUAs. EUA/CER and EUA/ERU swaps are traded bilaterally, over-the-counter.

4.3. Banking, Borrowing and Linkage

In principle, firms have to build a compliance strategy for each year since, at the end of each year, they have to surrender a number of allowances equal to their verified emissions. However, the EU ETS rules allow them to bank and borrow allowances. Therefore, in practice, abatements can be smoothed over time, and allowances can be traded between years. Despite the Directive 2003/87/EC which gives the Member States the possibility to allow banking between Phases, all countries decided to prohibit the transfer of allowances between Phase 1 and Phase 2.[37] Thus, during Phase 1, it was impossible to bank EUAs in order to use them in Phase 2. Borrowing EUAs from Phase 2 to cover Phase 1 emissions was also forbidden. Banking and borrowing were only allowed within the same Phase.[38] Since the beginning of Phase 2, it is now allowed to bank allowances between Phases (i.e. in Phase 2 for Phase 3) in all the Member States.[39] By contrast, borrowing allowances between Phases is still forbidden.

Since the CITL is connected to the ITL, installations can use international credits to comply with their obligations.[40] Firms are allowed to import CERs and ERUs in the EU ETS, up to a certain percentage of their initial allocations. The rules for using international credits in the EU ETS are stated in the linking Directive 2004/101/EC, amending the Directive 2003/87/EC. The linking Directive states that Member States may allow imports of international credits by specifying it in their NAPs. If permission is given, Member States have to set a limit on how many CERs and ERUs can be surrendered by installations. Limits are expressed in terms of percentage of the allocation of allowances to each installation. This translates into an overall limit for each country. Those limits vary from 0% of allocations in Estonia, to 20% in Germany, Lithuania and Spain. This means that installations in Germany can import 450 million credits over Phase 2, representing more than a fourth of the total volume of international credits in the EU ETS. CERs and ERUs can be obtained by investing in CDM and JI projects, or by purchasing them on the secondary market. As for EUAs, it is possible to trade international credits through organized exchanges or in over-the-counter transactions. NordPool, ECX, BlueNext and GreenX are example of exchanges which offer

---

[36] See also see Benz and Klar [2008] and Daskalakis et al. [2009].

[37] See Alberola and Chevallier [2009] for a discussion on reasons that justified these decisions.

[38] A "one-year" borrowing is allowed within the same Phase. That is firms are allowed to borrow allowances from the following year for compliance in the current year. For example, in 2005, permits could be borrowed from 2006, but not from 2007.

[39] The Directive 2003/87/EC establishes that allowances allocated for a given Phase have to be canceled by Member States at the end of this Phase. For example, EUAs that were part of Phase 1 NAPs had to be canceled after April 30, 2008. However, the Directive allows Member States to replace those canceled allowances with valid allowances of the next Phase (Phase 2 in our example), which leads to an "inter-phase" banking. In other words, the Directive states that inter-phase banking is possible in principle, and it gives the Member States the responsibility to decide if it is allowed in practice. With the European Union "Climate and Energy Package" of December 2008, the European Commission decided that inter-phase banking will be clearly allowed, at the EU level, from the beginning of Phase 2. This was confirmed later in the Directive 2009/09/EC.

[40] Before connection, issued international credits remained in the UNFCCC registries.

the possibility to trade CERs and ERUs. In 2008 and 2009, the overall quantity of international credits used for compliance in the EU ETS was about 85 million tonnes CO_2. In 2010, this quantity rose by almost 65%, to reach about 140 million tonnes CO_2 (see Trotignon and Stephan [2011]).

To date, about half the CERs and ERUs issued have been surrendered in the EU ETS. The use of credits is particularly high in Slovakia, Romania and Hungary, where about 50% of the total quantity allowed for the three years has already been surrendered. In other countries like Spain, Portugal, Finland and Germany, the use of credits has also not been negligible with about 30% of the allowed limit already surrendered. Here it is interesting to note that there has been a legal loophole in the EU ETS, regarding the use of international credits (Sator [2011]).

The loophole allowed credits already used for compliance in the EU ETS to re-enter the market and be traded again. This problem became evident in March 2010, when some of those CERs that were sill circulating on the EU ETS were identified. The Hungarian government had resold them even though they had already been used for compliance by Hungarian installations. To avoid such "dishonest dealings", an amendment to the EU registry legislation was decided in April 2010. The amendment states that surrendered credits must be placed in a specific retirement account from which the resale is forbidden.[41]

4.4. Sectoral Analysis

Among sectors covered by the EU ETS, the power sector is of special relevance. Both CO_2 emissions and allowance allocations in this sector account for more than half of the total volumes of the EU ETS (see Figures 7 and 8).[42] Hence, the power sector represents more than half of the potential demand and supply for EUAs, and thus, understanding its position is crucial. Moreover, power plant allocations represent more than 50% of the total power and heat allocations. As pointed out in Trotignon and Delbosc [2008], the share of power plants in the power and heat allocations is even higher in some Member States. During Phase 1, it ranged from 50% in France to more than 80% in Italy and in the UK.

Countries where emissions and allocations of the power sector are particularly high are those which generate large volumes of electricity with fossil fuels such as coal, natural-gas or lignite. These countries include Germany, Italy, Poland, Spain and the UK.

---

[41] Other kinds of fraud were observed on the EU ETS in 2010 and 2011, such as VAT frauds and allowance thefts (Sator [2011]). In VAT frauds, fraudsters set up an account in one country and buy allowances from a seller to another country without paying VAT in the purchase price (because EU VAT rules exempt cross-border sales of allowances from VAT). Next, the fraudsters resell allowances in domestic transactions with VAT added into the price. However, instead of refunding the collected VAT to the Sate, the fraudsters pocket it and disappear. Allowance thefts also occur when fraudsters acquire access details to accounts of some EU ETS operators. Thus, fraudsters can steal allowances by transferring them from the victim's account to another account. In order to access the victim's accounts, fraudsters can use fishing techniques (e.g. fake links or e-mails requesting access details to accounts) or trojan virus (e.g. the "Nimkey" trojan).

[42] See Point Carbon [2006], Ellerman and Buchner [2008] and Trotignon and Delbosc [2008].

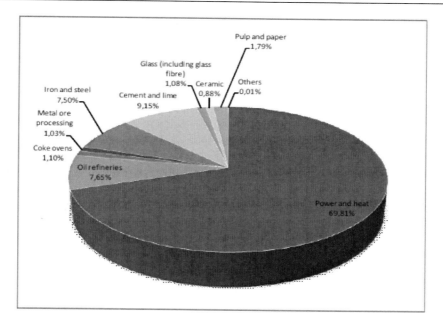

Figure 7. The 2006 EUA allocations by sector (data available at http://dataservice.eea.europa.eu/PivotApp).

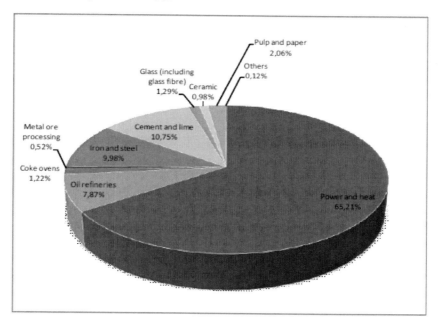

Figure 8. The 2009 EUA allocations by sector (data available at http://dataservice.eea.europa.eu/PivotApp).

Regarding the difference between allowance allocations and verified emissions, the position of the power and heat sector is also remarkable. In Phase 1, it was the only sector with a net deficit of allowances. The deficit accounted for about 1% of allocations in this sector, and it was mainly explained by the short position of power producers. The net deficit of power producers accounted for about 7% of the power plant's allocations, while other sub-sectors were long of allowances (see Trotignon and Delbosc [2008]). The net short position of the power and heat sector was confirmed and strengthened in Phase 2. In 2008, 2009 and 2010, the net deficit of allowances in the sector was respectively 240 (20% of allocations), 112 (9.3% of allocations) and 125 (10.2% of allocations) million tonnes CO_2. As a comparison, in 2006 and 2007 the power and heat sector net deficit was 24 (1.7% of allocations) and 33 (2.3% of allocations) million tonnes CO_2, respectively.[43]

4.5. Price Drivers

Numerous factors influence the price of CO_2 allowances. Like on other markets, the EUA price is driven by the balance between supply and demand, long-term investment decisions, market structure and institutional factors such as general rules or information disclosure.

On the supply side, the main price driver is the volume of EUAs allocated to installations, since it sets the overall stringency of the EU ETS. The lower the cap is with respect to business-as-usual emissions, the stricter the trading scheme will be. Uncertainties regarding the exact number of EUAs issued for a Phase may also be important. Because of special reserves for new entrants, the total amount of EUAs that would be available during a Phase is uncertain. It may be important if the market is stressed. Other factors influencing the supply side are the use of international credits and banking or borrowing between Phases. During Phase 1, both were irrelevant since inter-phases banking (and borrowing) was prohibited and the CITL was not connected to the ITL. However, as we have seen, inter-phase banking and the use of international credits are now possible in the EU ETS.

Political decisions and information disclosure also impact the EUA price. Regarding information disclosure, 2006 gave a good example. The publication by four countries (the Czech Republic, France, Spain and the Netherlands) of 2005 verified emissions (25 April 2006) and the European Commission communication announcing that the EU ETS was globally long for 2005 (15 May 2006), caused the EUA price crash of Spring 2006 (see Figure 9).

Another example is the price drop that occurred in October 2006, when the European Commission announced that Phase 2 validated NAPs of 17 Member States were stricter than submitted draft versions (see Figure 9).[44] This changed the perception of market participants, which realized that Phase 1 and Phase 2 were two different markets. Consequences have been a divorce between prices for Phase 1 and Phase 2. Due to banking restrictions, the EUAs issued for Phase 1 were useless at the end of Phase 1.

As information disclosures revealed that the market was oversupplied in Phase 1, the spot price of Phase 1 (and prices of futures contracts expiring in Phase 1) stabilized at around zero from Spring 2007 until the end of Phase 1. By contrast, prices of futures contracts expiring in Phase 2 ranged from 15 to 25 Euros (see Figure 9).

---

[43] Data available at http://dataservice.eea.europa.eu/PivotApp.

[44] The econometric paper by Alberola et al. [2008] reports statistical evidence of influence of those information disclosures on the EUA price.

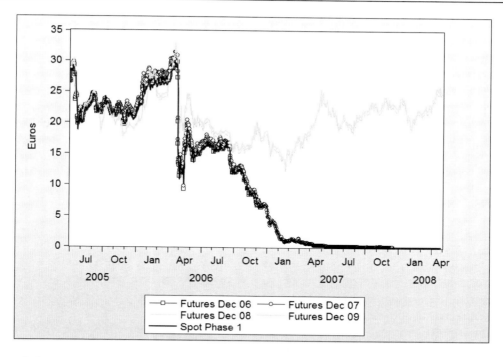

Figure 9. Spot and futures EUA prices in Phase 1. The spot price is the price of the BlueNext spot contract, and the futures prices are those of the ECX futures contracts with expiry in December 2006, 2007, 2008 and 2009 (data are available on the BlueNext and ECX websites).

Market structure is also important in price formation. With a small number of large buyers and sellers, the EUA price is expected to react strongly to individual decisions. As pointed out by Trotignon and Delbosc [2008], during Phase 1 more than half of the EUAs were held by thirty companies, among which there was a majority of power producers. Some authors argued that the level of prices before the crash of Spring 2006 could be explained by incentive for power producers to exert market power on the carbon market in order to keep high prices for EUAs (Betz et al. [2006]). In doing so, power producers would have tried to increase their windfall profits by passing through a higher carbon cost to the electricity price.[45]

The demand for EUAs is determined by the CO_2 emissions of covered installations. Power generation represents more than half of the total of CO_2 emissions in the EU ETS. Hence, factors that affect emissions in the power sector are the main drivers for EUA demand. They include energy prices, weather conditions (temperatures, rainfall, wind speed, etc) and economic activity. Because they determine electricity demand and the composition of power generation (i.e. the carbon-intensity of technologies that are used to produce), those factors drive the CO_2 emissions in the power sector, and thus the demand for EUAs of power producers.

---

[45] Hintermann [2010] has reported evidence of a "CO_2 bubble" in the EU ETS before the price crash of Spring 2006. He found that the EUA price was disconnected from its fundamentals (energy prices, temperatures, rainfall, etc) during this period, and driven by "self-fulfilling expectations" captured by lagged values of the EUA price.

Temperatures influence energy demand because they determine energy needs for heating (in winter) and cooling (in summer). As a consequence, temperatures influence carbon emissions and EUA prices. In particular, variations in carbon emissions depend heavily on extreme temperatures (i.e. extremely hot and cold temperatures) and on unexpected temperature changes (i.e. deviations from historical averages).[46]

The relationship between CO_2 emissions and economic activity is supposed to be positive, since, for example, an economic recession is expected to decrease energy consumption. However, there may be another simultaneous opposite effect. Indeed, it is sometimes argued that recessions can create some increases in carbon emissions, simultaneously with decreases that come with cuts in production (Declercq et al. [2011]). Because energy prices tend to decrease during recessions, there is an incentive to consume more energy and so to emit more CO_2. In 2009, which was a year of recession in Europe, verified emissions in the EU ETS sectors declined by 11% (compared to 2008), while they rose by 2.5% in 2010 with the recovery.[47] This suggests that the quantity effect (decrease in CO_2 emissions due to reduced production) dominates the price effect (increase in CO_2 emissions due to lower energy prices),[48] so that there would be a net positive relationship between CO_2 emissions and economic activity. This is confirmed by the decline in EUA prices observed in 2008 and 2009 (see Figure 10).

The depressive impact of the economic crisis has been accentuated by the credit crunch that came with the financial crisis. Thanks to emission reductions, regulated firms were able to sell large amounts of unused allowances in order to raise cash during the credit crunch.[49] This has translated into a stronger price decrease, especially on the spot market.

Rainfall, wind speed and cloudiness conditions also influence carbon emissions because they determine the share of power generation that can be obtained from hydroelectricity, wind and solar plants. The more hydro, wind and solar plants available to produce, the less electricity has to be generated by burning fossil fuels, and thus the lower the CO_2 emissions are. For example, a dry year in Nordic countries is likely to increase carbon emissions, because of high use of hydroelectricity in those countries. In such a situation, power producers have to replace hydroelectric capacities (from Norway and Sweden) by fossil-fuel-based capacities (coal plants from Denmark). Therefore, carbon emissions rise.

According to literature, fuel prices are the most significant price drivers for EUAs, due to the ability of European power producers to reduce their carbon emissions by switching fuels from coal to gas in electricity generation.[50] The basic idea of fuel switching is that relative fuel prices determine the demand for carbon allowances by setting the composition of power generation. In the EU ETS, this is known as the most important short-run abatement

---

[46] Several papers have shown that extreme temperatures and unexpected temperature changes are the most important weather variables for the EU ETS (see Mansanet-Bataller et al. [2007] and Alberola et al. [2008]). They matter more than temperatures themselves, which indicates that the relationship between temperatures and the carbon price seems to be non-linear.

[47] See Trotignon [2010] and Trotignon and Stephan [2011].

[48] Verified emissions have revealed a decrease of emissions in the power sector over the years 2008 (-30 million tonnes CO_2 compared to 2007) and 2009 (-130 million tonnes CO_2 compared to 2008). Data are available at http://dataservice.eea.europa.eu/PivotApp. Note however that the power sector have been globally short of allowances during this period. See Trotignon [2010], Declercq et al. [2011].

[49] See De Pertuis [2009], Sikorski [2009] and Charpin [2009].

[50] See Bertrand [2011] for a review of econometric and theoretical papers dealing with fuel switching.

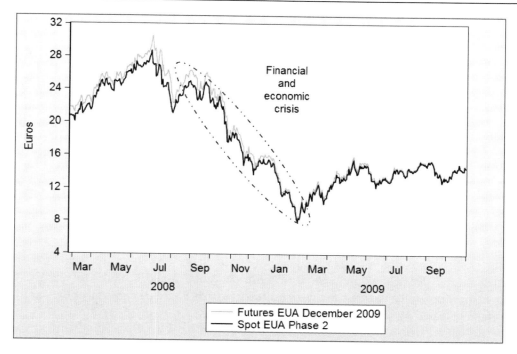

Figure 10. Decline in EUA prices during the 2009 recession.

option, since power producers are major actors in the scheme.[51] Thus, fuel prices strongly influence EUA prices. Without carbon price, coal plants are usually brought on line first, because of their cheaper fuel cost. Gas plants are used next, during shorter periods, when demand for power is higher. However, with a price for carbon emissions, gas plants may be preferable to coal plants, due to their lower carbon intensity. That is, if the cost of increased carbon emissions with coal plants is higher than the additional fuel cost associated with the decision to produce with gas rather than with coal, it is cheaper to use gas plants first instead of coal plants. If such a switching occurs, carbon emissions are reduced, because coal plants are brought on line during shorter periods. Therefore, all other things being equal, a relatively high gas price encourages the use of more coal, which drives up demand for allowances and the carbon price (and vice versa).

Among energy prices, the electricity price is another important driver of EUA prices in the short-run. This is explained by the short-run rent capture theory (Keppler [2010]). According to this approach, the electricity price influences the carbon price in the very short-run because no carbon abatements can be performed. This implies that power producers have to reduce their production to sell allowances. In this situation, the margin between the price of electricity (set by monopolistic suppliers) and its marginal cost will be captured in the carbon

---

[51] Fuel switching we refer to here involves coal plants and Combined Cycle Gas Turbines (CCGTs). Of course fuel switching can also take place with other plants for other levels of load. For example, switching can occur between oil plants and open cycle gas turbines, or also between coal and lignite. However, as quantities of carbon concerning switching between coal plants and CCGTs are much higher, this type of switching is the main focus of power producers and researchers (and the main EUA price driver).

price. In other words, power producers with market power have the ability to "monetize" on the carbon market their scarcity rents in the electricity market.[52]

In the long-run, the demand for allowances strongly depends on investment decisions. Investing today in measures such as carbon capture and storage, energy efficiency or in building new low-carbon power plants, will reduce carbon emissions in the future and thus the demand for allowances. However, high investment costs, uncertainties,[53] the time horizon before investments produce effects and irreversibility are many discouraging factors that often lead to delay investments.[54]

The long-run trends in energy markets are also important. In particular, trends in the gas market should be strongly influential, given the interest for gas in carbon abatement decisions. Thus, the EU ETS should be impacted by information about pipeline projects, non-conventional gas extraction or progresses in gas liquefaction. Regarding nuclear, the current debate in Europe about the renewal of installed capacities is of major importance for the EU ETS. Yet, Germany has already announced that it renounces to extend the life of its nuclear plants and the position of several other Member States has been uncertain since the Fukushima disaster. The consequences of those decisions would be huge for the EU ETS. This would drastically increase the demand for EUAs in Phase 3, and cancel the surplus of allowances created by recession in Phase 2.[55]

CONCLUSION

The aim of this paper is to provide a wide overview of climate policy, emission trading, and the EU ETS, from the beginning to nowadays. We analyze the main questions involved in these topics, giving an extensive review of them.

First, the history of climate policy and the main characteristics of the Kyoto Protocol mechanisms are presented. We also discuss the state of commitment of different countries, as well as the last negotiations on how to prolong the Kyoto Protocol and the international climate policies beyond 2012.

Second, based on this background, we introduce the concept of emission trading. First of all, we present the economics of pollution control and the origins of emission trading. Next, we review the early experiences of emission trading, prior to the launch of the EU ETS.

Finally, we give a detailed presentation of the EU ETS. We present the main characteristics of the scheme regarding allocations, monitoring, reporting, banking/borrowing, trading, and linkages with the United Nation carbon markets. Additionally, we review the

---

[52] Note that market power in the electricity market does not imply a permanent market dominance of some particular firms. This is rather a short-run rotating position during peak-load hours, depending on scarcity of capacities (see Keppler [2010]).

[53] As pointed out by Chao and Wilson [1993], purchases of allowances have an intrinsic advantage compared to investments in abatement measures, because they avoid uncertainties about volumes of abatements and their costs. As a consequence, allowances have an additional value (an "option value") with respect to investments in abatement measures, which justifies that the allowance price should exceed the marginal cost of abatements.

[54] In Phase 1, the EU ETS has triggered very few large-scale investment decisions with long amortization times (e.g. building new power plants). Covered firms have been mainly engaged in allowance trading or short-run abatement decisions to meet their obligations (see Hoffmann [2007]).

[55] For more details, see Berghmans [2011].

different drivers of the price of EUAs. We also discuss the changes that will be effective for Phase 3 of the EU ETS.

REFERENCES

Alberola, E., Chevallier, J., Chèze, B. (2008) Price drivers and structural breaks in European carbon prices 2005–2007, *Energy Policy*, 36. p. 787 - 797.

Alberola, E., Chevallier, J. (2009) European carbon prices and banking restrictions: evidences from Phase 1 (2005-2007), *The Energy Journal*, 30. p. 51 - 80.

Benz, E., Klar, J. (2008) *Price Discovery and Liquidity in the European CO_2 Futures Market*: An Intraday Analysis. Working paper, Bonn Graduate School of Economics.

Berghmans, N,. (2011) Nuclear freeze in Germany: the EU ETS overheats, *Tendances Carbone*, 58, Mission Climat – CDC Climat Research.

Bertoldi, P., Rezessy, S. (2004) *Tradable Certificates for Energy Efficiency: the Dawn of a New Trend in Energy Policy?* ACEEE (American Council for Energy-Efficient Economy).

Bertrand, V. (2011) *Interactions between carbon and energy prices: theories and evidence in Phase 2 of the EU ETS*. Working Paper, University of Franche-Comté.

Betz, R., Rogge, K., Schleich, J. (2006) EU Emission Trading: An Early Analysis of National Allocation Plans for 2008-2012, *Climate Policy*, 6. p. 361 – 394.

Branch, T.A. (2004) *The influence of individual transferable quotas on discarding and fishing behavior in multispecies fisheries*. Doctoral Thesis, University of Washington.

Brohé, A. (2008) Les marchés de quotas de CO_2. Larcier.

Casella, H., Delbosc, A., de Perthuis, C. (2010) *Cancun: Year One of the Post-Copenhagen Era*. Working Paper, Climate Economics Chair, Paris-Dauphine University and CDC Climat, Paris.

Chao, H., Wilson, R. (1993) Option Value of Emission Allowances, *Journal of Regulatory Economics,* 5. p. 233 - 249.

Charpin, J.M. (2009). *Report of the working group on the modalities for the sale and auctioning of CO_2 Allowances*. Elements relating to Phase III. MEEDDATT and Ministry of Finance, Paris.

Chevallier, J. (2010) *The European carbon market (2005-2007): banking, pricing and risk-hedging strategies*. Working Paper, University of Paris-Dauphine.

Coase, R.H. (1960) The Problem of Social Cost, *Journal of Law and Economics*, 3. p. 1 - 44.

Cramton, P., Kerr, S. (2002) Tradeable carbon permit auctions: how and why to auction not grandfather, *Energy Policy*, 30. p. 333 - 345.

Crocker, T. (1966) The structuring of atmospheric pollution control systems. In: Wolozin H, *The economics of air pollution*. New York, W.W. Norton.

Dales, J. (1968) *Pollution property and prices*. University of Toronto Press.

Daskalakis, G., Psychoyios, D., Markellos, R.N. (2009) Modeling CO_2 Emission Allowance Prices and Derivatives: Evidence from the European Trading Scheme, *Journal of Banking and Finance*, 33. p. 1230 - 1241.

Declercq, B., Delarue, E., D'haeseleer, W. (2011) Impact of the economic recession on the European power sector's CO_2 emissions, *Energy Policy*, 39. p. 1677 - 1686.

DEFRA. (2006) *Departmental Report 2006*. Department for Environment, Food and Rural Affairs, London, Crown copyright.

Delbosc, A. (2009) Phase III de l'EU ETS: Adjugé, *Tendances Carbone*, 32, Mission Climat – CDC Climat Research.

De Perthuis, C. (2009) Quotas de CO_2 contre liquidités, *Tendances Carbone*, 33, Mission Climat – CDC Climat Research.

Ecofys. (2010) Emissions trading for NO_X and SO_2 in the EU: consequences for the European cement sector. *Report for the European Cement Association*.

EC (European Commission). (2003) Directive 2003/87/EC of the European Parliament and of the Council of 13 October 2003, Establishing a Scheme for Greenhouse Gas Emission Allowance Trading within the Community and Amending Council Directive 96/61/EC. *Official Journal of the European Union*, L 275/32, 25 October 2003.

EC. (2010) *Assessment of the Possible Development of an EU-wide NO_X and SO_2 Trading Scheme for IPPC Installations*. Report for the European Commission, Entec UK Limited.

EEA (European Environment Agency). (2005) Market-based instruments for environmental policy in Europe. *EEA Technical Report* No 8/2005.

EEA. (2006) Using the market for cost-effective environmental policy: Market-based instruments in Europe. *EEA Technical Report* No 1/2006.

Ellerman, A.D. (2003) *Ex Post Evaluation of Tradable Permits: the US SO_2 cap-and-trade program*. Working Paper, Center for Energy and Environmental Policy Research, MIT.

Ellerman, A.D., Buchner B. (2008) Over-Allocation or Abatement? A preliminary analysis of the EU ETS based on the 2005 emissions data, *Environmental and Resource Economics*, 41. p. 267 - 287.

Eurofer. (2011) *Eurofer Annual Report 2010*. Eurofer, European Confederation of Iron and Steel Industries.

GGAS (Greenhouse Gas Abatement Scheme). (2008) *Introduction to the greenhouse gas reduction scheme* (GGAS). GGAS documentation.

Guesnerie, R. (2003) Les enjeux économiques de l'effet de serre. In: *Kyoto et l'économie de l'effet de serre*, Report of the French Council of Economic Analysis (CAE – Conseil d'Analyse Économique, French Prime Minister), La Documentation Française, Paris.

Godard, O. (2000) L'expérience américaine des permis négociables pour lutter contre la pollution atmosphérique, *Économie Internationale*, 82. p. 13 - 44.

Green, J.F. (2008) *The Regime Complex for Emissions Trading: Private authority, past and present*. Working Paper, Princeton University.

Grubb, M., Newbery, D. (2008) Pricing carbon for electricity generation: national and international dimensions. In: Grubb, M., Jamasb, T., Pollitt, M.G. *Delivering a Low Carbon Electricity System: Technologies, Economics and Policy*. Cambridge, Cambridge University Press.

Hahn, R.W. (1989) Economic prescriptions for environmental problems: how the patient followed the doctor's orders, *Journal of Economic Perspectives*, 3. p. 95 - 114.

Hahn, R.W. (1991) Reshaping environmental policy: the test case of hazardous waste, *American Enterprise*, 2. p. 72 - 80.

Hardin, G. (1968) The tragedy of the commons, *Science*, 162. p. 1243 - 1248.

Hepburn, C., Grubb, M., Neuhoff, K., Matthes, F., Tse, M. (2006) Auctioning of EU ETS phase II allowances: how and why? *Climate Policy*, 6. p. 137 - 160.

Hintermann, B. (2010) Allowance price drivers in the first phase of the EU ETS, *Journal of Environmental Economics and Management,* 59. p. 43 - 56.

Hoffmann, V.H. (2007) EU ETS and investment decisions: the case of the German electricity industry, *European Management Journal*, 25. p. 464 - 474.

IEA (International Energy Agency). (2006) *Slovak Republic Energy Policy Review 2005.* OECD/IAE.

IPCC (*Intergovernmental Panel on Climate Change*). (1996) *Climate change 1995: The Science of Climate Change.* Cambridge University Press.

IPCC. (2001) *Climate change 2001: The Scientific Basis.* Cambridge University Press.

IPCC. (2007) *Climate change 2007: Summary for policymakers.* IPCC, Geneva.

JMOE (Japanese Ministry of the Environment) and GECF (Global Environment Centre Foundation). (2006*) CDM/JI Manual for Project Developers and Policy Makers.* JMOE and GECF.

Keppler, J.H. (2010) The interaction between the EU ETS and European electricity markets. In Ellerman, A.D., Convery, F., de Perthuis, C. *Pricing carbon: The European Union Emissions Trading.* Cambridge University Press.

Kristiansen, T., Wolbers, R., Eikmans, T., Reffel, F. (2006) *Carbon Risk Management.* Paper presented at the 9th International Conference on Probabilistic Methods Applied to Power Systems, Stockholm, June 2006.

Kruger, J., Oates, W.E., Pizer, W.A. (2007) *Decentralization in the EU emissions trading scheme and lessons for global policy.* Working Paper, Resources for the Future, Washington.

LECG (Law and Economics Consulting Group). (2003) *Emissions Trading Market Study.* Report to the Ontario Ministry of Environment, LECG.

Mansanet-Bataller, M., Pardo, A., Valor, E. (2007) CO_2 prices, energy and weather, *The Energy Journal*, 28. p. 67 - 86.

Mansanet-Bataller, M., Pardo, A. (2008) What You Should Know About Carbon Markets, *Energies,* 1. p. 120 - 153.

Montgomery, W.D. (1972) Markets in licenses and efficient pollution control programs, *Journal of Economic Theory*, 5. p. 395 - 418.

Mougeot, M., Naegelen, F. (2009) EU-ETS Phase III: How to auction permits? *Revue d'Économie Politique*, 119. p. 165 - 184.

Nathan, R. (2010) *International Greenhouse Gas Offsets Under the Clean Air Act.* Working Paper, Resources for the Future, Washington.

Newell, R.G., Kristian, R. (2003) *The Market-based Lead Phasedown.* Working Paper, Resources for the Future, Washington.

Pedersen, S.L. (2000) *The Danish CO_2 emissions trading system*, Review of European Community and International Environmental Law, 9. p. 223 - 231.

Pigou, A.C. (1920) *The Economics of Welfare.* Macmillan, London.

Point Carbon. (2006) *Towards a truly global market.* Point Carbon.

Sator, O. (2010) Mise aux enchères de quotas en Phase III: un exercice d'équilibriste, *Tendances Carbone,* 47, Mission Climat – CDC Climat Research.

Sator, O. (2011) *Closing the door to fraud in the EU ETS*, Climate Brief, 4, Mission Climat – CDC Climat Research.

Sikorski, T. (2009) The EU ETS as a cash cow, *Tendances Carbone*, 35, Mission Climat – CDC Climat Research.

Stern, N., Peters, V., Bakhshi, A., Bowen, C., Cameron, S., Catovsky, D., Crane, S., Cruickshank, S., Dietz, N., Edmonson, S.L., Garbett, L., Hamid, G., Hoffman, D., Ingram, B., Jones, N., Patmore, H., Radcliffe, R., Sathiyarajah, M., Stock, C., Taylor, T., Vernon, H., Wanjie, Zenghelis, D. (2006) *Stern Review: The Economics of Climate Change*. HM Treasury, London.

Stern, N. (2006) What is the Economics of Climate Change? World Economics, 7. p. 1 - 10.

Trotignon, R. (2009) Déficit de quota en 2008: une première sur le marché européen, *Tendances Carbone*, 36, Mission Climat – CDC Climat Research.

Trotignon, R. (2010) Comment la crise économique a laissé son empreinte sur l'EU ETS, *Tendances Carbone*, 48, Mission Climat – CDC Climat Research.

Trotignon, R., Delbosc, A. (2008) Allowance trading patters during the EU ETS trial period: what does the CITL reveal? *Climate Report*, 13, Mission Climat – CDC Climat Research.

Trotignon, R., Stephan, N. (2011) 2010 compliance: weak recovery and high credit use, *Tendances Carbone*, 59, Mission Climat – CDC Climat Research.

UNFCCC (United Nations Framework Convention on Climate Change). (1998) *Kyoto Protocol of the United Nations Framework Convention on Climate Change*. United Nations.

UNFCCC. (2011a) *Report of the Conference of the Parties on its fifteenth session,* held in Copenhagen from 7 to 19 December 2009. United Nations.

UNFCCC. (2011b) *Report of the Conference of the Parties on its sixteenth session*, held in Cancun from 29 November to 10 December 2010. United Nations.

In: Research and Applications for Energy …
Editor: Riad Benelmir

ISBN: 978-1-62948-892-9
© 2014 Nova Science Publishers, Inc.

Chapter 10

RECOVERY OF RADIOISOTOPES FROM NUCLEAR WASTE FOR RADIO-SCINTILLATOR-LUMINESCENCE ENERGY APPLICATIONS

*Alfred Bennun**

Graduate School, Rutgers University, US
Nuclear American Society – Radioisotopes and Education Division
CONICET, AR, US

ABSTRACT

Extraction of the light weight radioisotopes (LWR) ^{89}Sr/^{90}Sr, from the expended nuclear bars in the Fukushima reactor, should have decreased the extent of contamination. Known technologies could be used to relate into innovative ways LWR, to obtain nuclear energy at scales smaller than those of nuclear reactors.

This would lead to devices without moving parts, because LWR interact by contact with scintillators. Their applications could pay for the extraction treatment of ^{89}Sr/^{90}Sr, by the added value of obtaining an additional source of energy, through conversion of β-radiation into light-energy.

INTRODUCTION

Fission plants use the reaction: $^{235}U^{92}+n\rightarrow ^{90}Sr^3+^{89}Sr^{38}+^{143}Xe^{54}+3n+\gamma$, to generate electricity. ^{143}Xe ($t_{1/2}$=30s) $\rightarrow ^{143}$Cs+β$\rightarrow ^{142}$Cs+n. ^{89}Sr is a produced as a fission products in slightly less quantities than ^{90}Sr, but their ratio is 166/1. ^{89}Sr has a specific activity of 28,200 Ci/g greater than 1g of radium, were as ^{90}Sr has a specific activity of 141 Ci/g.

Unfortunately, in Fukushima, the nuclear plant left untreated the expended reactor bars [1] [2]. Hence, the heat generated by radioactivity, inside the expended bars was mainly that

---

*E-mail: alfr9@hotmail.com.

of ^{89}Sr. The flooding from the reactor and by the sea dissolved these radioisotopes from the storage bars and carried them into the surrounding areas.

At 5 days after the accident, the measurement in Becquerel units (1 disintegration/s) the pollution in a neighboring town was found: 13-260Bq ^{89}Sr and ^{90}Sr 3.3-32Bq per kg of soil, amount strongly contaminating the cultivation areas. Radioactive Sr is extremely dangerous, because when ingested replaces Ca^{2+} in their physiological functions. ^{90}Sr^{38} decay ($t_{1/2} = 28.8$ years) $\rightarrow$ ^{90}Y^{39} ($t_{1/2}$= 64hs)+β (0.68MeV)+$\bar{v}$ $\rightarrow$^{90}Zr^{40}+β (2.28MeV) +$\bar{v}$. While: ^{89}Sr^{38} ($t_{1/2}$=50.55 days) $\rightarrow$ ^{90}Y^{39} +β(1.5MeV)+ $\bar{v}$. The ^{90}Y is generated at much lower quantities than required for full scintillation power, but in the adequate proportions in the presence of ^{89}Sr scintillates with a 2% light emission yield.

A potent large emission number of low penetrating power particles characterize ^{89}Sr, which allows that the highly radioactive ^{89}Sr involves a rather limited danger. Hence, storage for small amounts does not require lead, but requires containers made of glass or aluminum, and depending of quantity cooling conditions.

The difference in $t_{1/2}$ allows ^{89}Sr to deliver its energy at a rate 200 times higher than ^{90}Sr and by decaying 99% in one year allows a left-over of uncontaminated ^{90}Sr. This one becomes available for applications requiring long periods of time. β-radiation from ^{89}Sr damages animal tissues because ionize water, but penetrates through the skin about: 5 to 8 mm [3]. Thus, allowing manipulation of small amounts of ^{89}Sr with gloves, glasses and thick laboratory clothing. In solution ^{89}Sr has been administered as a palliative of pain of metastatic prostate cancer in doses of 150MBq [4]. Its bone-seeking properties favored its use at higher doses, in the treatment of bone cancer metastasis [5] [6] [7] [8] [9].

Evaluation of in-situ radiation treatments for replacing the therapeutic-radium on the treatment for prostate shrinking, skin cancer, etc., has involved many radioisotopes. For example, 1mg of ^{210}Po emits as many 5MeV-α-particles, than 5g of radium, but its use is very dangerous because is a volatile metal of extreme toxicity.

^{89}Sr shows higher radioactivity because decays at a rate 3 times faster than to ^{210}Po but decays with emission of β-particles of considerable weaker energy. Therefore, it is much less dangerous and allows many more practical uses. These properties provide an economic incentive for its recovering from the expended nuclear bars.

APPLICATIONS EVALUATION

In an insoluble form like ^{89}Sr silicate, a solid, could be used in the form of near microscopic implants, that inserted in quantities related to the tumors size could have a slow but persistent effects on reducing the extend of metastasis.

β-particle energy dissipates through the 5eV stopping power per molecule of water. Since, 460KJ/mol is the average energy of ionization, the mean energy of 1MeV per each β particle emitted by ^{89}Sr, allows a theoretical maximal ionization: 1.8×10^5 molecules of water. Hence, 1nmol of pure ^{89}Sr (89 ng equivalent to 95MBq) emits over 50 days 4×10^{14} MeV β-particles, which multiply by 1.8×10^5=7×10^{19} ionized water molecules or 1.2×10^{-1} mg of H_2O or ml. This number corresponds to the size of a small tumor, but the radiation characteristics of the radioisotope allow the use of a large number of ^{89}Sr-nano-implants for in-situ metastasis treatments.

Hence, one additional reason for the extraction of radioactive Sr from expended bars are the economics of cancer metastasis treatment, in which the ^{89}Sr has a clear advantage over radium due to its high efficiency versus costs ratio, much less dangerous and by its short-lived decay could not involve high disposal expenses.

However, the medical market is rather small for the overall quantities generated at nuclear facilities. However, if used as an alternative form of energy its consumption may match production and market offerings.

The scintillator-crystals act as a shield by absorbing the kinetic energy of β-particles to reach an excited quantum state and return to its initial state through photon emission. For large quantities, it could be used unbreakable glass as an additional covering shield because it is transparent to light.

[89]Sr light emitting panels allow an electric energy independent source of cheap energy to operate greenhouses located in Polar Regions. These radioisotope photo-cells emit light 24h without interruption, an engineering solution could be that of a rotating system which by displacement over 120 degrees, can illuminate every 8hs a different area, triplicating harvest yields. Alternatively, the ^{89}Sr light emitting could be re-directed some part of the day to activate photovoltaic cells.

FEASIBILITY

Efficiency of photovoltaic cell (PV) has been highly improved and basically a LWR-lamp or radioisotope light generator (RLG) coupled to a PV system could be used to generate electricity: radioisotope-light-electric-generator (RLEG), and recharge batteries. The electricity generated in-situ allows a battery operated electric motor which could not require fuel and the engineering of optical fibers permits transmission of light power.

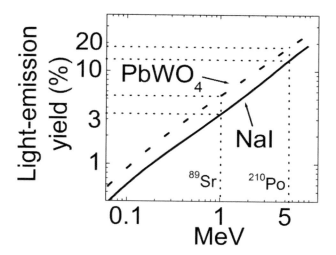

Figure 1. Performance-scintillator (η) vs. -Particle energy (MeV). Radioactive light generators (RLG) are based in the scintillator stopping power capable of exciting an orbital with photon emission. NaI (3.675 g/cm^3), average energy of excitation (a.e.e.) 458.0 eV, 2% Tl + β [1MeV] → hν (u.v.), η=3.4%; PbWO$_4$ (Mw=455g/mol at 8.28 g/cm^3), a.e.e.: 616.7 eV, 2% Tl+ β [1MeV] → hν (u.v.), η=5.4%; [210]Po, 5.4MeV α (^{4}He^{2+}), η=18.3% [10].

The silicates are materials based on the repeating unit SiO_4^{4-} tetrahedral. SiO_4^{4-} unit contains negative charges which are generally compensated by the presence of alkali metal ions like ^{89}Sr recovered and purified from mixed uranium fission products by dissolving with HCl. The [89]$SrCl_2$ titrated to the required pH to form [89]$Sr(HO)_2$ could then by processed by mixing with the dissolution of potassium/sodium silicate K/NaSiO$_3$ to obtain tetrahedral crystals of [89]$SrSiO_4$.

The silicate dissolution in water in the proportion of the molecular relationship between n=0.5 and n=4: nSiO$_2$+Na$_2$O (K$_2$O) are viscose liquids, with an alkaline increase of pH from 10 to 14, as a function of decreasing the value of n.

Wolfram W[74] also known as tungsten, with a melting point of 3,410°C, has a high traction resistance, very low vapor pressure and from all the metals is the one with lower dilatation coeficient. Since $_{74}$W participates in the molecular structure of as several scintillators like PbWO$_4$, the metal provide the advantage to form higly temperature and mechanical resistant crystals.

Tungstate in alkaline solutions depolymerizes to WO_4^{2-}. Increasing molar ratio of [WO_4^{2-}] to [[89]Sr^{2+}] modifies the morphology of the synthesized crystals of [89]$SrWO_4$ [11] [12] [13] from rods to other structures like dumbbells, or notched spheres. It could predicted that Tl[+]-doped RLG-chip design of [89]$SrWO_4$, could have as a scintillator a 3.8-4.4%, light emission yield. Perfect crystal integration of the radiactive and scintillator atoms in the absence of water would decrease loses to heat. These heat-resistant allows to manufacture small crystals, which in moderate amounts, could be cooled by attachment to a simple ventilator system.

Crystals of [89]$SrWO_4$ could be used instead of electricity, as the energy source to elicit the phosphor response of PbWO$_4$, which if incident in electrovoltaic cells may lead to an additional photo-current response of PbWO$_4$. The latter, has a green luminescent response at low temperature, and has been used to manufacture electrically switched light bulbes [12] [13]. Hence, PbWO$_4$ could be used as a covering to increasing light emission yield of [89]$SrWO_4$. This compound as a 87mg-Chip equiparates with a continuous electrical output of 15Watt with consumption over 50days. Higher manufacturing costs would be compensated by nill electrical costs.

The figure 2 indicates the convenience of using a scintillator mixture to obtain a better response for at the lower energy emitted particles. Ion dotting of a crystal like that of BaF$_2$:PbWO$_4$ could increase maximal transmittance [14]. The scintillator POPOP which can be used solid or liquid as secondary photon emission (λ), also extends λ-emission to 410nm in the violet of the visible spectrum. Crystals with added Al$_2$O$_3$ optimize light transmission and give a red shift of the emission spectrum. The omission of water in the engineering of the RLG crystals may decrease efficiency losses.

NASA developed thermo-electric nuclear batteries of [238]Pu (t$_{1/2}$=87.7años) with mass less than that required for a chain reaction but extremely dangerous and requiring heavy Pb shielding. The thermo-electric conversion yield is η=7%. However, its potential danger would prevent its widespread use. Russia to power buoy-lamps in the Arctic has used ^{90}Sr with η=4%. Radioactive thermo-electric generators (RTG) for satellites are being designed using [210]Po, which generates very high temperatures, it reaches T=750K with only 0.5g of [210]Po. The latter, interacting with PbWO$_4$ which at higher temperature increases light emission could allow the development of integrative RLEG-RTG design for more efficient devices.

Table. Comparative advantages of radioisotopes as energy sources in RTG vs. RLEG

Projects	Radioisotopes	Potency Max (W)		Electric (W)	Mass (Kg)	Shield (Kg)
NASA: Voyager 2	$^{238}Pu \rightarrow {}^{234}U + \alpha$	2400	----	160	4.5	39
ESA: Galileo	^{238}Pu	4400	----	300	7.8	55.5
Soviet	$^{90}Sr \rightarrow {}^{90}Y + \beta + \bar{\nu}$	230	----	10	0.26	560
Radioisotope Photo-electric or RLEG			Yield			
			Scintillation (W)	Photo-voltaic 30%		
	^{90}Sr	484.5	42.6	12.8	0.26	3
	$^{89}Sr \rightarrow {}^{89}Y + \beta + \bar{\nu}$	44695	2414	724	0.26	1
	$^{210}Po \rightarrow {}^{206}Pb + \alpha + \gamma$ (1%)	37382	6841	2052	0.26	4

The RLEG project could use the scintillator emission of light, to restrain the temperature increase and a thermo-coupling could absorb the excess heat. ^{89}Sr in amounts smaller than 1g do not require very active cooling, larger amounts could be ventilated, and the radio-luminescent cell could be manufactured as a fiber around a coolant tube, surrounded by mirrors pointing toward the photovoltaic cells [15].

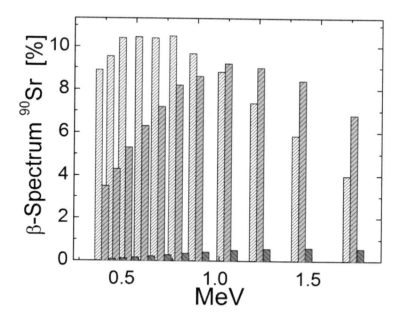

Figure 2. β-Energy distribution. Calculated as a percentege of the value obtained by suming-up the energy of β-particles in the range between 0.39MeV and 2.6MeV (▨). The percentage of β-particles with less than 0.6 MeV constitute 40% of the total, but sum up to less than 20% of total energy. The particles emitted at higher than 0.6 MeV, constitute 60% with 80% of total energy emitted at an average 1.4MeV (▨). The scintillator range efficiency for aproach 7% for $PbWO_4$ (▰).

Engineering of more than one scintillator in layers plus their geometrical arrangements around the ^{89}Sr-core adding to an adequate arrangement of mirrors could be investigated to improve system efficiency. The ^{89}Sr core of a battery can be contained in a metal box with external plugs. Only qualified personnel may be provided with an access key.

APPLICABILITY EVALUATION CONCLUSION

Battery ^{89}Sr-RLG vs. Li-ion

A battery of ^{89}Sr-photo-electric, with a core of 89ng of ^{89}Sr, has a specific power of 2.5×10^{-7} W/89ng, the Li-ion is 9 times smaller. 1nmol of ^{89}Sr-photo-crystal emits 5.1×10^{6} β-particles/s, each by collision with a molecule of the scintillator transfers 40eV [16] [17] [18]. Hence, with a scintillator of $\eta = 5.4\%$ could be obtained an emission of 1,350 photons per each β-particle. The light emission in u.v. region $\lambda = 320$nm to 400nm, could be absorbed by nano-crystals, which according to their increasing size, could re-emitted in different λ of the visible spectrum, corresponding by sizes to violet, blue, green, orange, etc.

An electric car consumes 14KWh/100Km with Li-ion battery of 16Kg has 2h of autonomy (with a charge-discharge cycle of 6h). Comparatively, it takes 5kg of ^{89}Sr and 5kg of scintillator, to reach similar potency but sustains it for about 50 days. As the decay is sustainable, the energy produced by a RLG device can be switched for to household electrical consumption, including recharging lithium-ion batteries.

REFERENCES

[1]   National Nuclear Data Center. "*NuDat 2.1 database*". Brookhaven National Laboratory (2005).

[2]   Mulligan, Joseph F., *Practical Physics: The Production and Conservation of Energy*, McGraw-Hill (1980).

[3]   Rohlf, James William, *Modern Physics from A to Z0*, Wiley (1994).

[4]   Turner S.L.,Gruenewald S., Spry N., Gebski V. & on behalf of the Metastron; "Less pain does equal better quality of life following strontium-89 therapy for metastatic prostate cancer", *Users Group Br. J. Cancer.*, 84(3), 297–302 (2001).

[5]   Lic Alberto Mancini, Coordinador Técnico del Centro Atómico Ezeiza de la Comisión Nacional de Energía Atómica, *Revista Argentina Nuclear*, No 59, oct/nov 96.

[6]   Halliday, Resnick and Walker, *Fundamentals of Physics*, 4th Edition, Extended, Wiley (1993).

[7]   N. F. Mott and H. S. W. Massey, *The Theory of Atomic Collisions*, Clarendon, Oxford (1933).

[8]   Krane, Kenneth, *Introductory Nuclear Physics*, Wiley (1987)

[9]   Krane, Kenneth, *Modern Physics*, 2nd Ed., Wiley (1996).

[10]   *http://physics.nist.gov/PhysRefData/Star/Text/ESTAR.html*

[11]   Eun-Kyoung Ryu, Young-Duk Huh; "Morphology-controlled synthesis of SrWO4 crystals", *Materials Letters* Volume 62, Issues 17–18, 3081–308330 (2008).

[12] Chunhua Zheng, Chenguo Hu, Xueyan Chen, Hong liu, Yufeng Xiong, Jing Xu, Buyong Wan and Linyong Huang, "Raspite PbWO4 nanobelts: synthesis and properties", *Cryst.Eng.Comm*, 12, 3277-3282 (2010)

[13] Xue Wang, Yong Ding, Zhong Lin Wang, and Chenguo Hu; "Temperature driven in-situ phase transformation of PbWO4 nanobelts", *J. Appl. Phys.* 109, 124309 (2011)

[14] Wan Youbao, Wu Rurong, Xiao Linrong Zhang Jianxin, Yang Peizhi, Yan Hui "*The Improved Scintillation Crystal Lead Tungstate Scintillation for PET*", (2009)

[15] G. Audi, A. H. Wapstra, C. Thibault, J. Blachot and O. Bersillon, "The NUBASE evaluation of nuclear and decay properties". *Nuclear Physics* A 729: 3–128 (2003)

[16] National Nuclear Data Center, "*NuDat 2.1 database*", Brookhaven National Laboratory (2005)

[17] Holden N.E., "Table of the Isotopes". In D. R. Lide. *CRC Handbook of Chemistry and Physics* (85th ed.). CRC Press. Section 11. ISBN 978-0849304859 (2004)

[18] Stoppani, A.O.M., Ramos, E.H., Widuczynski, I., Bennun, A. and De Pahn, E.M., The effect of 2,4-dinitrophenol on the oxidation of endogenous and exogenous substrates by the yeast Saccharomyces cerevisiae, Proceedings Conference, México City, 1961, in "*Use of Radioisotopes in Animal Biology and the Medical Sciences*" (C.M. Fried et al., eds.) Vol. 1, (1962), pp. 241-252, Academic Press, London.

In: Research and Applications for Energy …
Editor: Riad Benelmir

Chapter 11

AN ELECTRICITY DEMAND LONG TERM FORECASTING MODEL FOR SOUTH EUROPE BASED ON ECONOMIC PARAMETERS

Maria Samarakou and Emmanouil D. Fylladitakis[*]

Department of Energy Technology,
Technological Educational Institute (TEI) of Athens,
Aegaleo, Greece

ABSTRACT

Electricity demand forecasting is an imperative tool for the planning and operation of electric utilities. With today's uncertainty and turbulent economies, the development of long term forecasting models requires careful consideration. The mixed forecasting model proposed in this paper was developed for the long term electricity demand forecasting for the countries of south Europe andis capable of determining the per person annual electricity demand by using economic variables alone. The forecasting model displays excellent fit to historic data for all four of the countries under study, namely Greece, Spain, Portugal and Italy, the four of which were hit the hardest by the latest economic recession. Furthermore, the economic variable's coefficients need not to be recalculated for each country as the proposed model was developed in order to fit the electricity consumption profiles of all 4 countries. Finally, additional investigations revealed that the proposed model also fits the historic data of countries in central Europe, with the variable coefficients still unchanged.

Keywords: Long Term Forecasting, Electricity Markets, Electricity Demand, Electricity Consumption, MultipleRegression, Econometric Model

[*]Corresponding author: Tel.: +00302105385322; fax: +00302105385306. E-mail Addresses: marsam@teiath.gr (M. Samarakou), edf3@teiath.gr (E.D.Fylladitakis).

1. INTRODUCTION

Electricity demand forecasting is an imperative tool for the planning and operation of electric utilities. Several decades ago forecasting was limited to a simple linear extrapolation of the past; a technique which was proven to be extremely inefficient ever since the first oil crisis of 1973. As Ziauddin Sardar very accurately describes in his paper, we now live in postnormal times and can no longer expect the future to resemble the past (Sardar, 2010). As today uncertainty and turbulent economies are not the exception but the rule, it becomes clear that forecasting models need to present a good fit to turbulent historical data and be used alongside with a scenario analysis describing several sets of plausible future events (Goldfarb and Huss, 1988).

Depending on the planning horizon, forecasting models can be classified into short term, medium term and long term (Yalcinoz and Eminoglu, 2005). Short and medium term forecasting is critical for the assessment of both the magnitude of the demand and the location it will take place at. These parameters are necessary for the reliable and economic operation of the entire power system, as well as for the proper maintenance planning of distribution grids (González-Romera, Jaramillo-Morán, and Carmona-Fernández, 2008). Long term forecasting is being used by utility companies in order to make sound decisions on capital expenditure and future investments (Efendigil, Önüt, and Kahraman, 2009).

It is obvious that the continuously rising uncertainty of the economic environment nowadays makes accurate long term forecasting more critical than ever. The vast majority of the long term forecasting models developed to this date are econometric regression models. Econometric models, as the name suggests, make use of economic parameters to devise a model that can be used for long term forecasting. Although researchers believe that econometric models are not easy to apply in most cases because of the difficulty to accurately assess the input parameters, they concur that they can provide very robust results if the input data are carefully analyzed before a forecast (Kandil, El-Debeiky, and Hasanien, 2001). The oldest and still the most popular technique for developing long term econometric models is the regression method, which produces outputs based on a retroaction process in which the model uses as inputs the already treated results (Tripathi, Upadhyay, and Singh, 2008; Tsekouras, Dialynas, Hatziargyriou, and Kavatza, 2007). Perhaps the greatest advantage of regression models is that once they are developed and tested, they are relatively simple mathematical models which can be easily presented to and even used by non-experts.

A large number of long term regression models based on econometric parameters are linear or multiple linear regression models, a few of which are being used by national utility companies even today (Mohamed and Bodger, 2005). These models do present high accuracy once developed for a particular country but will not maintain their precision for other countries/regions unless all of the variable coefficients change. Furthermore, in turbulent economies with unsteady historical data, the fit of linear regression models with too few variables can be mediocre to very poor.

Logarithmic, Quadratic, Exponential and Mixed regression techniques have been used to construct econometric models with good end results (Pao, 2006; Piltan, Shiri, and Ghaderi, 2012; Pokharel, 2007). Multiple regressions in particular are proven to be a more successful method compared to the common regression methods, determining the relationships between dependent and independent variables by using the weighted least-squares estimation

(Feinberg and Genethliou, 2005). In this paper we will present a mixed long term electricity forecasting modeldeveloped forfour countries of south Europe (Greece, Italy, Spain and Portugal) based solely on economic parameters.

Historic data on all of the economic parameters used in this study, including the population and population projections, have been acquired from European Commission's Eurostat Statistics Database (Eurostat, 2012). The data used date from 1996 to 2010 and can be found in Appendix A.

2. DEMAND AND MULTIPLE LINEAR REGRESSION MODELS

Linear models offer the simplest form of quantitative forecasting available. One relatively simple model which offers an excellent fit to historic data has been proposed in 2005 by Zaid Mohamed (Mohamed and Bodger, 2005). The model Zaid Mohamed proposed is displayed in equation 1.

$$AED = X_1 * AGDP + X_2 * EP + X_3 * POP + u \tag{1}$$

where AED stands for the Annual Electricity Demand, AGDP stands for the annual national gross domestic product, EP stands for the electricity price, POP stands for the population and u is the error (disturbance term or white noise). As the electricity price varies depending on the level of demand and the nature of the consumer, the average annual domestic price including all taxes has been used in this model.

With the aid of the IBM's SPSS Version 19 software (Gougeon, 2012; Maceviciute, 2006; SPSS Inc., 2003), we were able to determine the optimum values for the coefficients X_1, X_2 and X_3 for the best possible fit to Greek historic data. The optimized model for Greece is shown in equation 2.

$$AED = 2.64 * 10^{-7} * AGDP + 17.1 * 10^3 * EP - 8.88 * 10^{-5} * POP \tag{2}$$

Figure 1 displays the fit of the model to historic data. R^2 is 0.9997, indicating a nearly perfect fit.

Despite the practically perfect fit of the model however, one immediate problem arises. The negative sign before the population indicates that the annual demand will drop as population increases, while the positive sign before the electricity price indicates that the annual demand will increase as prices rise; clearly, a paradox created because GDP and population are correlated figures, which may easily result to erroneous results in long term forecasts. A similar problem exists in a linear regression model recently proposed for Italy, where the coefficient of population is presented with a negative sign, designating that consumption should decrease as population increases (Bianco, Manca, and Nardini, 2009).

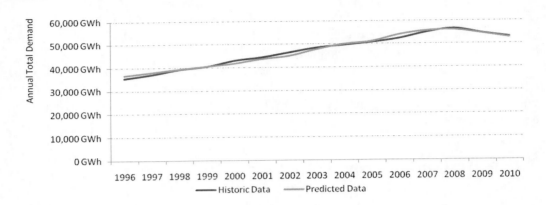

Figure 1. Multiple linear regression model fit for Greece.

Therefore, the calculation of linear model coefficients needs to be carefully constricted for the model to present realistic results. Furthermore, the model will not fit the historic data of any other country if the same coefficients are used. As seen in figure 2, the multiple linear regression model of equation 2 completely fails to fit the historic data of electricity demand in Italy, a country with advanced industry and entirely different consumption profiles than Greece, even after subtracting a massive constant (u value) of 175.000.

It is apparent that a multiple linear regression model derived from a certain set of economic data may be developed only for a single country or region and will not fit the data of other regions unless the calculated coefficients change entirely. Furthermore, the model's ideal coefficients as they are calculated with the aid of PC software may not represent actual consumer behaviours if no constrictions are carefully set, as we observed from the signs of equation 2.

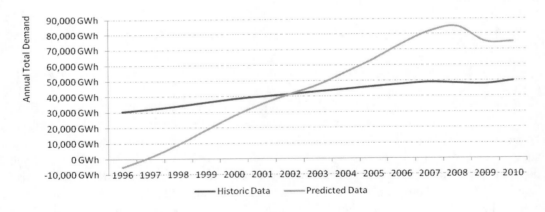

Figure 2. Multiple linear regression model with unchanged coefficients fit for Italy.

3. THE PROPOSED MODEL AND METHODS

For the purpose of assessing the per person annual electricity demand in the countries of south Europe, the mixed model displayed in equation 3 is being proposed, which exhibited exceptional fit with historical data dating back 15 years in 3 out of the 4 countries we focus this study on.Particularly for Italy, a correction constant needs to be subtracted in order for the model displayed in equation 3 to fit without changing any of the coefficients. Therefore, the model takes the form displayed in equation 4.

$$ADPP = 1.1 * PPS^{0.8346} + 4.34 * 10^{-5} * GDP^{1.77} - 2.454 * 10^{-6} * PPS * GDP - 0.0251 * PPS * DP - 0.1 * GDP * DP * IP (3)$$

where *ADPP* stands for the annual electricity demand per inhabitant (kWh), *GDP* stands for the real gross domestic product per capita (€), *PPS* stands for the purchasing power standard per inhabitant (€), *DP* stands for the average annual domestic price including all taxes (€/kWh) and *IP* stands for the average annual industrial price including all taxes (€/kWh).

$$ADPP = 1.1 * PPS^{0.8346} + 4.34 * 10^{-5} * GDP^{1.77} - 2.454 * 10^{-6} * PPS * GDP -$$
$$0.0251 * PPS * DP - 0.1 * GDP * DP * IP - 750 \tag{4}$$

In order to compare the model's fit to historic data we used the following fitness functions: mean absolute percentage error (MAPE), mean absolute deviation (MAD), tracking signal (TS) androot mean square error (RMSE).

The MAPE function, also known as mean absolute percentage deviation or MAPD, is used to assess the accuracy of the model and is given by equation 5:

$$MAPE = \frac{1}{n}\sum_{t=1}^{n}\left|\frac{H_t - F_t}{H_t}\right| * 100\% \tag{5}$$

where H_t is the historic value, F_t is the forecasted value and n is the number of periods (years).

The MAD function is used to measure statistical dispersion and is given by equation 6:

$$MAD = \frac{1}{n}\sum_{t=1}^{n}|H_t - F_t| \tag{6}$$

The tracking signal function, indicating the forecast bias of the model for each set of economic data, is given by equation 7:

$$TS = \frac{1}{MAD}\sum_{t=1}^{n}|F_t - H_t| \tag{7}$$

And finally, the root mean square error is given by equation 8:

$$RMSE = \frac{1}{n}\sum_{t=1}^{n}(H_t - F_t)^2 \tag{8}$$

4. HISTORIC DATA FITNESS RESULTS

In order to determine the accuracy and fitness of the model displayed in equations 3 and 4, we compared it over 15 years of historic data extracted from a single statistics foundation

(Eurostat, 2012). The data used to test the model date from 1996 to 2010. The fitness of the model proposed in this paper for the annual electricity consumption per inhabitant in Greece, Spain, Portugal and Italy can be graphically assessed from figure 3.

The coefficient of determination (R^2) of the non-linear forecasting model may also be seen in table 1, as it was extracted from the statistics software used to evaluate the data. In figure 3, the successful adjustment of the proposed model through the recession period of 2009-2010 in order to effectively fit the historic data of all four countries can also be discerned.

Table 1 displays the exact errors of the proposed forecasting model as they were derived with the use of several fitness functions.

Table 1. Forecasting errors of the proposed model with four fitness functions over four south Europe countries

Country	Fitness functions				
	MAPE	MAD	TS	RMSE	R^2
Greece	2.825%	134.05	13.21	164.23	0.864
Spain	1.617%	82.727	-10.97	101.01	0.988
Portugal	3.565%	147.34	-8.96	168.99	0.918
Italy	1.490%	72.68	-2.74	82.46	0.880

For every country the mean absolute percentage error is lower than 3.6%, while it falls as low as a mere 1.617% for the case of Spain. We can also determine that although the coefficient of determination for Italy was below 0.9, the model displayed a nearly perfect fit with a MAPE of 1.49% and the lowest RMSE and TS. Greece exhibited the lowest value of R^2, yet the MAPE and MAD errors were lower than those of Portugal. The above results clearly indicate that basing the accuracy of a model on the R^2function alone may easily lead to imprecise results. Through additional investigation, we also discovered that the model proposed in this paper provides very accurate fits for other European countries as well, with or without the need to add or subtract a constant.

For instance, as displayed in figure 4 the model proposed in equation 3 also presents very good fit to historic data for Germany and Hungary without the need of using a correction constant. If the correction constant of equation 4 is adjusted to +1450, the model also fits the historic data of Czech Republic very well. The corrected model for Czech Republic is displayed in equation 9 and the data are graphically presented in figure 5.

$$ADPP = 1.1 * PPS^{0.8346} + 4.34 * 10^{-5} * GDP^{1.77} - 2.454 * 10^{-6} * PPS * GDP - 0.0251 * PPS * DP - 0.1 * GDP * DP * IP + 1450 \tag{9}$$

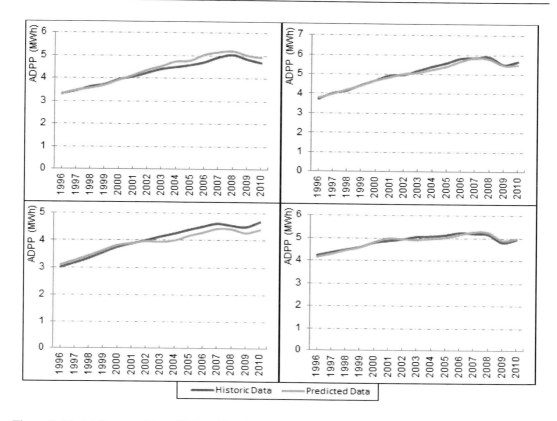

Figure 3. Model fitness of the ADPP to historic data for Greece (top left), Spain (top right), Portugal (bottom left) and Italy (bottom right).

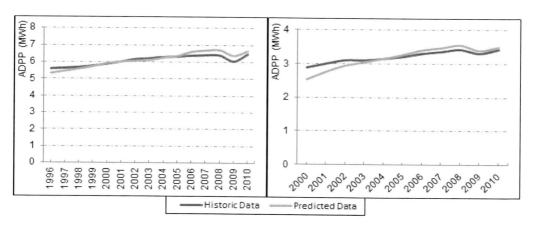

Figure 4. Model fitness of the ADPP to historic data for Germany (left) and Hungary (right).

Table 2 displays the errors of the proposed forecasting model as they were derived with four fitness functions for these new three countries under investigation. The MAPE is very low, ranging from 2.29% to 3.04%, while the TS isbelow |2.14| for two of the countries. The MAD and RMSE are reasonably low considering the magnitude of the data under investigation in all three of the cases. It is apparent that the model proposed in this paper may be used as-is or by simply adjusting the correction constant to determine the per inhabitant annual electricity consumption for more than the four countries that it was originally developed for.

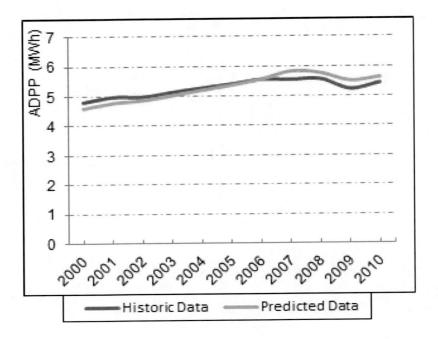

Figure 5. Eq. 9 model fitness of the ADPP to historic data for Czech Republic.

Table 2. Forecasting errors of the proposed model with four fitness functions over three central Europe countries

Country	Fitness functions				
	MAPE	MAD	TS	RMSE	R^2
Germany	2.989%	189.78	6.13	248.58	0.866
Hungary	3.042%	122.83	-2.13	153.95	0.968
Czech Republic	2.287%	165.42	1.75	195.14	0.880

5. FORECASTING SCENARIOS

In order to accurately forecast the electricity demand of a country or a region, utilities and energy regulation agencies employ the technique of scenario analysis in order to present feasible forecasts (Goldfarb and Huss, 1988). A scenario describes a set of plausible future events, their causes and consequences so can be used to highlight future possibilities. The scenario analysis technique can be adopted to appraise risk and examine the gap between expectation and reality. These methods apply quantification or qualification techniques through specific planning steps to help the experts take decisions (Chen, Yu, Hsu, Hsu, and Sung, 2009; Goldfarb and Huss, 1988; Yu, 2006).

The proper composing of scenarios is required for the use of any forecasting model, thus it must be done so carefully; otherwise any forecasting model is useless, despite how accurate it may be (Durance and Godet, 2010; Godet, 2000). Furthermore, those involved in strategic planning should always take qualitative parameters into account and prepare for them in order to be prepared for unforeseen events which are difficult to predict, such as a natural catastrophe (Godet, 1983).

In this study, we will attempt to develop three forecasting scenarios for Greece based on economic and regional factors. Finally, we will present forecasts up to 2050 using the linear model of equation 1 and compare the results to those attained by the model presented in this paper, studying any implications. Detailed figures on the data used to develop these three forecasts can be found in Appendix B.

5.1. Pessimistic Economic Growth Scenario

This scenario describes a highly pessimistic forecast of the Greek economy. Gross domestic product will decrease by 4% in 2012 and continue to decrease by 4%-0.25%·n, where n is the number of years after 2012. After the decline of GDP reaches 0% in 2028, growth will start taking place.

In this scenario, GDP is expected to grow by 0.5% each year for 12 years after 2028 by 1.2% each year between 2041 and 2050. Due to high taxation and austerity measures, PPS is expected to decline even faster, decreasing by 5% in 2012 and continue to decrease by 5%-0.5%·n After the decline stops in 2022, no growth will take place until 2028, after which year PPS will start increasing by 1% every year until 2035 and 2% every year after 2036 and up to 2050. Due to the severe recession, domestic and industrial electricity prices are expected to rise by 3% each year up to 2031 and 4% each year after 2031 and up to 2050.

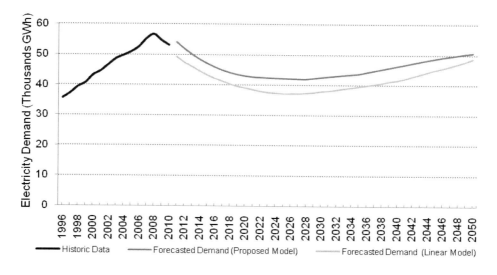

Figure 6. Pessimistic scenario forecasted electricity demand up to 2050.

Figure 6 displays the forecasted electricity demand as it was obtained by using both the model presented in this paper and the linear model proposed in (Mohamed and Bodger, 2005), using the pessimistic economic figures described in this subsection. The results of the proposed model are continuously 5-10% higher than that of the linear model, which could mislead long term planning into under sizing the power grid and/or the system's capacity.

5.2. Moderate Economic Growth Scenario

This scenario describes a moderate, balanced forecast of the Greek economy. Gross domestic product will decrease by 4% in 2012 and continue to decrease by 4%-1%·n, where n is the number of years after 2012. After the GDP rate of change reaches 0% in 2016, GDP is expected to stalemate until 2020, after which year it will start growing by 1%+0.2%·n each year for 10 years and then continue to grow by 3% every year until 2050. PPS is also expected to decline until 2016, decreasing by 4% in 2012 and continue to decrease by 4%-1%·$n$each year after that. After the decline stops in 2016, PPS will grow on equal grounds with GDP. In order to support competiveness, industrial electricity prices are expected to grow by only 0.5% each year up to 2030 and 1.5% each year every year between 2031 and 2050. As a result, domestic electricity prices will have to increase faster in order for the utility company to maintain workable annual budgets, with the prices growing by 4% each year up to 2031 and 3% each year for every year between 2030 and 2050.

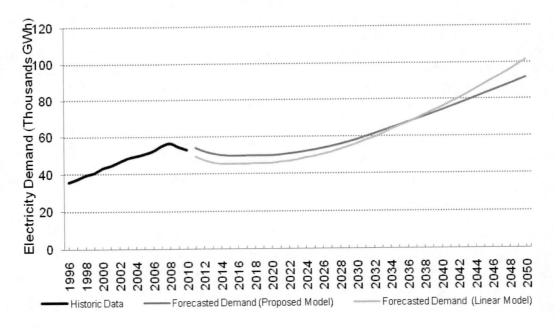

Figure 7. Moderate growth scenario forecasted electricity demand up to 2050.

Figure 7 displays the forecasted electricity demand as it was obtained by using both the model presented in this paper and the linear model proposed in (Mohamed and Bodger, 2005), using the moderate economic figures described in this subsection.

The linear model appears overly sensitive to the change of the GDP; additionally, the increasing energy prices lead to the further increase of the predicted demand due to the positive sign of the model's coefficient, as displayed in eq.2. For long term planning, this could lead to unnecessary expenses and an oversized power system.

5.3. Aggressive Energy Demand Scenario

This scenario describes forecast of the Greek economy where aggressive changes will take place, representing the most optimistic scenario for the country's industry and tourism. As with the previous scenario, the economy recession will stop in 2016 but growth will take place immediately. Gross domestic product will decrease by 4% in 2012 and continue to decrease by 4%-1%·n, where n is the number of years after 2012. After the GDP rate of change reaches 0% in 2016, GDP is expected to start growing by 1%+0.3%·n each year for 10 years after 2016 and then continue to grow by 4.0% every year until 2050. PPS is also expected to decline until 2016, decreasing by 4% in 2012 and continue to decrease by 4%-1%·n each year after that.

After the decline stops in 2016, PPS will grow on equal grounds with GDP. In order to support competiveness, industrial electricity prices are expected to grow by only 0.5% each year up to 2030 and 1.5% each year every year between 2031 and 2050. However, electricity generation in Greece will now either take place by using fossil fuels extracted from within the country rather than from expensive imports the country currently relies on, with a high demand percentage covered by renewable energy sources. Thus, electricity generation will be cheaper and domestic electricity prices will not be increasing as quickly as with the previous scenario. Domestic electricity prices will increase by 4% up to 2020, by 2.5% between 2021 and 2035 and by 2% between 2036 and 2050.

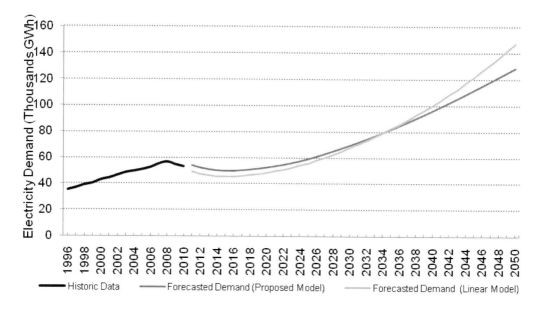

Figure 8. Aggressive growth scenario forecasted electricity demand up to 2050.

Figure 8 displays the forecasted electricity demand as it was obtained by using both the model presented in this paper and the linear model proposed in (Mohamed and Bodger, 2005), using the aggressive economic figures described in this subsection. For the same reasons as with the moderate economic growth scenario, the linear model would lead to an excessive and costly oversize of the country's power generation and distribution system.

CONCLUSION

A long term forecasting model capable of assessing the per person annual electricity demand by utilizing economic parameters for south European countries has been presented in this paper.

Unlike linear models, the model proposed in this paper displays acceptable fit to historic electricity consumption data without the need to change any of its coefficients, except from the subtraction of a correction constant for the case of Italy. At all times, the MAPE remained below 3.6% and it was as low as 1.49%, confirming the good fit of the model to historic data.

Furthermore, although the model proposed in this paper was initially developed for the countries of south Europe only, it also displayed excellent fit to countries of central Europe, with or without the use of a correction constant. Namely, the fit to the historic data of Germany and Hungary is excellent without the need to use a correctionconstant, with a MAPE of about 3% for both cases. The fit to the historic data of Czech Republic requires the addition of a correction constant, after which the MAPE is being reduced down to 2.3%.

This paper also demonstrates that it is possible to develop a long-term forecasting model capable of assessing the electricity demand per person for multiple countries and perhaps for entire continents.

Future work may develop a forecasting model usable for all European countries or even for all advanced economies without the need to recalculate the coefficients for each region.

We should not neglect however the necessity of the careful composing of possible scenarios. Proper development of scenarios and correct strategic planning is required for accurate forecasting.

Those involved in long term strategic planning should be capable of assessing future economic trends with relative accuracy and always take into account qualitative parameters, preparing for unforeseen events which numerical models are unable to foretell.

APPENDIX A

Table 3. Historic Economic and Population Data

Year	Greece						Spain					
	Population	GDP per Capita (€)	PPS per Capita (€)	DP (€/kWh)	IP (€/kWh)	Annual Demand (GWh)	Population	GDP per Capita (€)	PPS per Capita (€)	DP (€/kWh)	IP (€/kWh)	Annual Demand (GWh)
1996	10709200	12900	12900	0.0729	0.0683	35564	39479200	16400	14200	0.1258	0.0871	147182
1997	10776500	13300	13700	0.0725	0.0680	37213	39583400	17000	15100	0.1206	0.0807	159028
1998	10834900	13700	14100	0.0722	0.0676	39312	39722100	17700	16200	0.1154	0.0755	165173
1999	10882600	14100	14700	0.0671	0.0629	40617	39927200	18500	17100	0.1124	0.0760	177252
2000	10917500	14500	16000	0.0604	0.0611	43151	40264200	19200	18500	0.1091	0.0775	188459
2001	10950000	15100	17100	0.0620	0.0628	44542	40721400	19700	19400	0.1048	0.0671	200953
2002	10987600	15500	18500	0.0630	0.0640	46599	41314000	20000	20600	0.1047	0.0634	205510
2003	11023500	16400	19200	0.0654	0.0663	48625	42004600	20200	20900	0.1063	0.0644	217898
2004	11061700	17100	20300	0.0671	0.0680	49738	42691800	20600	21900	0.1079	0.0656	230669
2005	11103900	17400	20400	0.0691	0.0700	50904	43398200	21000	22900	0.1097	0.0836	242222
2006	11148500	18300	21800	0.0701	0.0728	52523	44068200	21500	24800	0.1152	0.0905	256466
2007	11192800	18700	22500	0.0852	0.0812	55190	44873600	21800	26200	0.1313	0.1047	262233
2008	11237100	18600	23100	0.1073	0.0974	56646	45593400	21700	25900	0.1462	0.1173	268731
2009	11282800	18000	22100	0.1093	0.1029	54713	45929500	20700	24200	0.1631	0.1319	252986
2010	11307600	17300	21900	0.1196	0.1088	53120	46072800	20600	24500	0.1790	0.1322	260578

Appendix A. Table 3. (Continued)

Year	Portugal						Italy					
	Population	GDP per Capita (€)	PPS per Capita (€)	DP (€/kWh)	IP (€/kWh)	Annual Demand (GWh)	Population	GDP per Capita (€)	PPS per Capita (€)	DP (€/kWh)	IP (€/kWh)	Annual Demand (GWh)
1996	56860300	12400	11900	0.1322	0.0793	30229	56860300	22100	18600	0.2074	0.0973	240694
1997	56890400	12900	12700	0.1327	0.0777	31940	56890400	22500	19400	0.2220	0.1051	248205
1998	56906700	13500	13500	0.1316	0.0749	33846	56906700	22900	20400	0.2234	0.1054	255160
1999	56916300	14000	14500	0.1263	0.0679	36120	56916300	23200	21100	0.2101	0.0991	261433
2000	56942100	14500	15500	0.1256	0.0675	38373	56942100	24000	22400	0.2048	0.1085	272975
2001	56977200	14700	15900	0.1262	0.0683	39937	56977200	24500	23400	0.1991	0.1174	277724
2002	57157400	14700	16400	0.1286	0.0698	41473	57157400	24500	23000	0.1928	0.1138	282751
2003	57604700	14400	16400	0.1322	0.0706	43164	57604700	24300	23000	0.1981	0.1176	291436
2004	58175300	14600	16700	0.1350	0.0719	44668	58175300	24500	23200	0.1939	0.1168	295531
2005	58607000	14600	17900	0.1381	0.0761	46322	58607000	24500	23700	0.1990	0.1219	300880
2006	58941500	14800	18700	0.1410	0.0851	47763	58941500	24900	24700	0.2108	0.1433	308777
2007	59375300	15100	19600	0.1531	0.0868	49024	59375300	25100	26000	0.2329	0.1526	309318
2008	59832200	15100	19500	0.1504	0.0943	48352	59832200	24700	26100	0.2129	0.1635	309317
2009	60192700	14600	18800	0.1551	0.0987	47855	60192700	23200	24300	0.2048	0.1677	290016
2010	60483400	14800	19600	0.1625	0.0973	49888	60483400	23500	24600	0.1943	0.1630	299313

Year	Germany						Hungary						Czech Republic					
	Population	GDP per Capita (€)	PPS per Capita (€)	DP (€/kWh)	IP (€/kWh)	Annual Demand (GWh)	Population	GDP per Capita (€)	PPS per Capita (€)	DP (€/kWh)	IP (€/kWh)	Annual Demand (GWh)	Population	GDP per Capita (€)	PPS per Capita (€)	DP (€/kWh)	IP (€/kWh)	Annual Demand (GWh)
1996	81896000	24200	19500	0.1509	0.1025	458358	N/A	N/A	N/A	N/A	N/A	N/A	N/A	N/A	N/A	N/A	N/A	N/A
1997	82052000	24600	20100	0.1461	0.0963	461727	N/A	N/A	N/A	N/A	N/A	N/A	N/A	N/A	N/A	N/A	N/A	N/A
1998	82029000	25100	20700	0.1462	0.0955	466127	N/A	N/A	N/A	N/A	N/A	N/A	N/A	N/A	N/A	N/A	N/A	N/A
1999	82087000	25500	21600	0.1562	0.0932	473481	N/A	N/A	N/A	N/A	N/A	N/A	N/A	N/A	N/A	N/A	N/A	N/A
2000	82188000	26300	22400	0.1534	0.0816	483453	10272500	7100	10300	0.0690	0.0566	49381	10272500	8300	13500	0.0581	0.0515	49381
2001	82340000	26600	22900	0.1603	0.0833	495267	10224200	7400	11500	0.0733	0.0602	50881	10224200	8600	14500	0.0664	0.0528	50881
2002	82482000	26600	23400	0.1664	0.0822	508508	10200800	7700	12500	0.0805	0.0663	50823	10200800	8800	15000	0.0814	0.0590	50823
2003	82520000	26500	24000	0.1700	0.0977	512885	10201700	8000	13000	0.0819	0.0676	52407	10201700	9200	15900	0.0793	0.0544	52407
2004	82501000	26800	25000	0.1709	0.0995	519701	10206900	8400	13600	0.1021	0.0850	53832	10206900	9600	16900	0.0806	0.0593	53832
2005	82464000	27000	26000	0.1793	0.1064	520954	10234100	8800	14200	0.1106	0.0919	55291	10234100	10200	17800	0.0870	0.0703	55291
2006	82366000	28000	27300	0.1853	0.1170	525804	10266600	9200	14900	0.1023	0.0851	57016	10266600	10900	18900	0.0990	0.0876	57016
2007	82263000	29000	28900	0.2027	0.1313	527352	10322700	9200	15400	0.1259	0.1169	57240	10322700	11500	20700	0.1065	0.1029	57240
2008	82120000	29300	29000	0.2172	0.1419	525549	10429700	9300	16000	0.1551	0.1416	58040	10429700	11700	20200	0.1287	0.1327	58040
2009	81875000	27900	27200	0.2288	0.1510	495573	10491500	8700	15200	0.1573	0.1553	54913	10491500	11100	19300	0.1359	0.1303	54913
2010	81757000	29000	28800	0.2407	0.1535	528958	10517200	8800	15800	0.1638	0.1316	57213	10517200	11400	19400	0.1369	0.1268	57213

APPENDIX B

Table 4. Economic parameters and forecasted demand using the proposed model for Greece

Year	Population[1]	Pessimistic Scenario					Moderate Scenario					Aggressive Scenario				
		GDP per Capita (€)	PPS per Capita (€)	DP (€/kWh)	IP (€/kWh)	Annual Demand (GWh)	GDP per Capita (€)	PPS per Capita (€)	DP (€/kWh)	IP (€/kWh)	Annual Demand (GWh)	GDP per Capita (€)	PPS per Capita (€)	DP (€/kWh)	IP (€/kWh)	Annual Demand (GWh)
2012	11362636	15456	20140	0.1281	0.1255	51985	15456	20352	0.1294	0.1224	52312	15456	20352	0.1294	0.1224	52312
2013	11390154	14876	19234	0.1320	0.1292	50133	14992	19741	0.1346	0.1230	51033	14992	19741	0.1346	0.1230	51033
2014	11417672	14356	18464	0.1359	0.1331	48527	14692	19347	0.1399	0.1236	50227	14692	19347	0.1399	0.1236	50227
2015	11445190	13889	17818	0.1400	0.1371	47150	14546	19153	0.1455	0.1243	49869	14546	19153	0.1455	0.1243	49869
2016	11461369	13472	17284	0.1442	0.1412	45942	14546	19153	0.1514	0.1249	49893	14546	19153	0.1514	0.1249	49893
2017	11477548	13102	16851	0.1485	0.1454	44936	14546	19153	0.1574	0.1255	49916	14691	19345	0.1574	0.1255	50348
2018	11493727	12774	16514	0.1530	0.1498	44122	14546	19153	0.1637	0.1261	49937	14882	19596	0.1637	0.1261	50934
2019	11509906	12487	16267	0.1576	0.1543	43491	14546	19153	0.1702	0.1268	49955	15120	19910	0.1702	0.1268	51657
2020	11526085	12237	16104	0.1623	0.1589	43036	14546	19153	0.1771	0.1274	49971	15407	20288	0.1771	0.1274	52521
2021	11533308	12023	16024	0.1672	0.1637	42717	14691	19345	0.1841	0.1280	50378	15746	20734	0.1815	0.1280	53512
2022	11540531	11843	16024	0.1722	0.1686	42565	14867	19577	0.1915	0.1287	50872	16140	21253	0.1860	0.1287	54659
2023	11547753	11695	16024	0.1774	0.1737	42437	15075	19851	0.1992	0.1293	51456	16592	21848	0.1907	0.1293	55968
2024	11554976	11578	16024	0.1827	0.1789	42331	15317	20169	0.2071	0.1300	52131	17106	22525	0.1954	0.1300	57451
2025	11562199	11491	16024	0.1882	0.1842	42244	15592	20532	0.2154	0.1306	52902	17688	23291	0.2003	0.1306	59118
2026	11565334	11434	16024	0.1938	0.1898	42162	15904	20942	0.2240	0.1313	53753	18342	24153	0.2053	0.1313	60960
2027	11568469	11405	16024	0.1996	0.1955	42097	16254	21403	0.2330	0.1319	54705	19076	25119	0.2105	0.1319	63011
2028	11571605	11405	16024	0.2056	0.2013	42049	16644	21917	0.2423	0.1326	55764	19839	26123	0.2157	0.1326	65125
2029	11574740	11462	16184	0.2118	0.2074	42318	17077	22486	0.2520	0.1332	56933	20633	27168	0.2211	0.1332	67305
2030	11577875	11519	16346	0.2181	0.2136	42586	17555	23116	0.2621	0.1339	58219	21458	28255	0.2267	0.1339	69550
2031	11583313	11577	16509	0.2247	0.2200	42860	18082	23809	0.2700	0.1359	59657	22316	29385	0.2323	0.1359	71869
2032	11588751	11635	16674	0.2337	0.2288	43108	18624	24524	0.2781	0.1380	61124	23209	30561	0.2381	0.1380	74256

Year	Population[1]	Pessimistic Scenario					Moderate Scenario					Aggressive Scenario				
		GDP per Capita (€)	PPS per Capita (€)	DP (€/kWh)	IP (€/kWh)	Annual Demand (GWh)	GDP per Capita (€)	PPS per Capita (€)	DP (€/kWh)	IP (€/kWh)	Annual Demand (GWh)	GDP per Capita (€)	PPS per Capita (€)	DP (€/kWh)	IP (€/kWh)	Annual Demand (GWh)
2033	11594189	11693	16841	0.2430	0.2379	43351	19183	25259	0.2864	0.1400	62622	24137	31783	0.2441	0.1400	76712
2034	11599627	11751	17009	0.2527	0.2475	43588	19758	26017	0.2950	0.1421	64150	25103	33055	0.2502	0.1421	79238
2035	11605065	11810	17179	0.2628	0.2574	43818	20351	26798	0.3038	0.1443	65708	26107	34377	0.2564	0.1443	81834
2036	11610072	11869	17523	0.2734	0.2676	44332	20962	27602	0.3130	0.1464	67293	27151	35752	0.2616	0.1464	84517
2037	11615078	11929	17873	0.2843	0.2784	44844	21591	28430	0.3223	0.1486	68908	28237	37182	0.2668	0.1486	87274
2038	11620085	11988	18231	0.2957	0.2895	45352	22238	29283	0.3320	0.1508	70553	29367	38669	0.2721	0.1508	90104
2039	11625091	12048	18596	0.3075	0.3011	45857	22905	30161	0.3420	0.1531	72227	30541	40216	0.2776	0.1531	93008
2040	11630098	12108	18967	0.3198	0.3131	46356	23593	31066	0.3522	0.1554	73930	31763	41825	0.2831	0.1554	95985
2041	11629775	12254	19347	0.3326	0.3256	46877	24300	31998	0.3628	0.1577	75628	33034	43498	0.2888	0.1577	98991
2042	11629452	12401	19734	0.3459	0.3387	47389	25029	32958	0.3737	0.1601	77351	34355	45237	0.2946	0.1601	102065
2043	11629130	12550	20128	0.3597	0.3522	47891	25780	33947	0.3849	0.1625	79100	35729	47047	0.3005	0.1625	105208
2044	11628807	12700	20531	0.3741	0.3663	48380	26554	34965	0.3964	0.1649	80874	37158	48929	0.3065	0.1649	108418
2045	11628484	12853	20942	0.3891	0.3809	48856	27350	36014	0.4083	0.1674	82672	38645	50886	0.3126	0.1674	111692
2046	11617946	13007	21360	0.4046	0.3962	49272	28171	37094	0.4206	0.1699	84419	40190	52921	0.3188	0.1699	114926
2047	11607408	13163	21788	0.4208	0.4120	49670	29016	38207	0.4332	0.1725	86183	41798	55038	0.3252	0.1725	118213
2048	11596869	13321	22223	0.4377	0.4285	50047	29886	39353	0.4462	0.1751	87965	43470	57240	0.3317	0.1751	121548
2049	11586331	13481	22668	0.4552	0.4456	50400	30783	40534	0.4596	0.1777	89761	45209	59529	0.3384	0.1777	124926
2050	11575793	13642	23121	0.4734	0.4635	50727	31706	41750	0.4734	0.1804	91571	47017	61911	0.3451	0.1804	128343

1 Population projection as provided by Eurostat (Eurostat, 2012).

REFERENCES

Bianco, V., Manca, O., and Nardini, S. (2009). Electricity consumption forecasting in Italy using linear regression models. *Energy, 34*(9), 1413-1421. doi: 10.1016/j.energy.2009.06.034.

Chen, T.-Y., Yu, O. S., Hsu, G. J.-y., Hsu, F.-M., and Sung, W.-N. (2009). Renewable energy technology portfolio planning with scenario analysis: A case study for Taiwan. *Energy Policy, 37*(8), 2900-2906. doi: 10.1016/j.enpol.2009.03.028.

Durance, P., and Godet, M. (2010). Scenario building: Uses and abuses. *Technological Forecasting and Social Change, 77*(9), 1488-1492. doi: 10.1016/j.techfore.2010.06.007.

Efendigil, T., Önüt, S., and Kahraman, C. (2009). A decision support system for demand forecasting with artificial neural networks and neuro-fuzzy models: A comparative analysis. *Expert Systems with Applications, 36*(3, Part 2), 6697-6707. doi: 10.1016/j.eswa.2008.08.058.

Eurostat. (2012). Statistics Database. Available from European Commission Statistics Database Retrieved 07 March 2012 http://epp.eurostat.ec.europa.eu/portal/page/portal/statistics/search_database

Feinberg, E. A., and Genethliou, D. (2005). *Load Forecasting: Applied Mathematics for Restructured Electric Power Systems*. In J. H. Chow, F. F. Wu and J. Momoh (Eds.), (pp. 269-285): Springer US.

Godet, M. (1983). Reducing the blunders in forecasting. *Futures, 15*(3), 181-192. doi: 10.1016/0016-3287(83)90164-7.

Godet, M. (2000). The Art of Scenarios and Strategic Planning: Tools and Pitfalls. *Technological Forecasting and Social Change, 65*(1), 3-22. doi: 10.1016/s0040-1625(99)00120-1.

Goldfarb, D. L., and Huss, W. R. (1988). Building scenarios for an electric utility. *Long Range Planning, 21*(2), 78-85. doi: 10.1016/0024-6301(88)90125-2.

González-Romera, E., Jaramillo-Morán, M. A., and Carmona-Fernández, D. (2008). Monthly electric energy demand forecasting with neural networks and Fourier series. *Energy Conversion and Management, 49*(11), 3135-3142. doi: 10.1016/j.enconman.2008.06.004.

Gougeon, D. J. (2012). Using SPSS: an interactive hands-on approach. [Book Review]. *Choice: Current Reviews for Academic Libraries, 49*(6), 1100-1101.

Kandil, M. S., El-Debeiky, S. M., and Hasanien, N. E. (2001). Overview and comparison of long-term forecasting techniques for a fast developing utility: part I. *Electric Power Systems Research, 58*(1), 11-17. doi: 10.1016/s0378-7796(01)00097-9.

Maceviciute, E. (2006). An Introductory Guide to SPSS(r) for Windows(r). [Book Review]. *Information Research, 11*(4), 19-19.

Mohamed, Z., and Bodger, P. (2005). Forecasting electricity consumption in New Zealand using economic and demographic variables. *Energy, 30*(10), 1833-1843. doi: 10.1016/j.energy.2004.08.012.

Pao, H.-T. (2006). Comparing linear and nonlinear forecasts for Taiwan's electricity consumption. *Energy, 31*(12), 2129-2141. doi: 10.1016/j.energy.2005.08.010.

Piltan, M., Shiri, H., and Ghaderi, S. F. (2012). Energy demand forecasting in Iranian metal industry using linear and nonlinear models based on evolutionary algorithms. *Energy Conversion and Management, 58*(0), 1-9. doi: 10.1016/j.enconman.2011.12.022.

Pokharel, S. (2007). An econometric analysis of energy consumption in Nepal. *Energy Policy, 35*(1), 350-361. doi: 10.1016/j.enpol.2005.11.004.

Sardar, Z. (2010). Welcome to postnormal times. *Futures, 42*(5), 435-444. doi: 10.1016/j.futures.2009.11.028.

SPSS Inc. (2003). *SPSS regression models 12.0*. Chicago, Ill.: SPSS.

Tripathi, M. M., Upadhyay, K. G., and Singh, S. N. (2008). Short-Term Load Forecasting Using Generalized Regression and Probabilistic Neural Networks in the Electricity Market. *The Electricity Journal, 21*(9), 24-34. doi: 10.1016/j.tej.2008.09.016.

Tsekouras, G. J., Dialynas, E. N., Hatziargyriou, N. D., and Kavatza, S. (2007). A non-linear multivariable regression model for midterm energy forecasting of power systems. *Electric Power Systems Research, 77*(12), 1560-1568. doi: 10.1016/j.epsr.2006.11.003.

Yalcinoz, T., and Eminoglu, U. (2005). Short term and medium term power distribution load forecasting by neural networks. *Energy Conversion and Management, 46*(9–10), 1393-1405. doi: 10.1016/j.enconman.2004.07.005.

Yu, O. (2006). *Technology Portfolio Planning and Management: Practical Concepts and Tools* (1st ed. Vol. 96). Berlin: Springer.

In: Research and Applications for Energy …
Editor: Riad Benelmir

ISBN: 978-1-62948-892-9
© 2014 Nova Science Publishers, Inc.

Chapter 12

INTEGRATIVE ANALYSIS OF NON-RENEWABLE AND RENEWABLE ENERGY SOURCES FOR ELECTRICITY GENERATION IN U.S.: DEMAND AND SUPPLY FACTORS, ENVIRONMENTAL RISKS AND POLICY EVALUATION

Ramesh Agarwal[1,*], Ping Wang[2], Lee Chusak[1],
and Zheming Zhang[1]
[1]Department of Mechanical Engineering and Materials Science,
Washington University, St. Louis, US
[2]Department of Economics, Washington University,
St. Louis, US

ABSTRACT

An equilibrium economic model for policy evaluation related to electricity generation was developed; the model takes into account non-renewable and renewable energy sources, demand and supply factors and environmental constraints. Non-renewable energy sources include three types of fossil fuels: coal, natural gas and petroleum, and renewable energy sources include nuclear, hydraulic, wind, etc. Energy demand sectors include households, industrial manufacturing and commercial enterprises. Energy supply takes into account the electricity delivered to the consumer by the utility companies at a certain price which maybe different for retail and wholesale customers. Environmental risks primarily take into account the CO_2 generation from fossil fuels. The model takes into account the employment in various sectors and labor supply and demand. Detailed data of electricity supply and demand, electricity cost, employment in various sectors and CO_2 generation were collected for a period from 1990 to 2006 in U.S

---

[*] Corresponding author: Tel: +1-(314)-935-6091; fax:+1-(314)-935-4014. E-mail addresses: rka@wustl.edu.

for model calibration. The calibrated model was employed for policy analysis experiments if a switch was made in sources of electricity generation, namely from fossil fuels to renewable energy sources. The consequences of this switch on supply and demand, employment, wages, and emissions were obtained from the economic model under three scenarios: (1) energy prices were fully regulated, (2) energy prices were fully adjusted with electricity supply fixed, and (3) energy prices and electricity supply both were fully adjusted. The model output suggested possible increase in employment with such switch, while government regulation was necessary to achieve any sort of carbon reduction through such switch.

Keywords: Electricity Generation, Renewable energy, Non-renewable energy, Energy Economics, Equilibrium Model, Policy Analysis

NOMENCLATURE

a household asset

c consumption

C aggregate household consumption demand

D CO_2 emissions

E total electricity demand

E^C commercial electricity demand

E^F industrial electricity demand

e^H household electricity demand

E^H aggregate household electricity demand

$E(s)$ electricity generated from sources s

K capital input

$M(s)$ material inputs for source s

N total labor demand

N^C commercial sector labor

N^E electricity sector labor

$N^E(s)$ electricity sector labor for sources s

N^F industrial labor

p price of electricity

q relative price of an investment in units of the consumption good

r real interest rate

s source of electricity, i.e., coal, nuclear, etc.

V^H household value function

F^F industrial value function

w wage

x consumption good

X aggregate household goods consumption demand

Y output

z investment

Z total investment

β^H household depreciation factor

β^F industrial depreciation factor

δ capital depreciation rate

$\gamma(s)$ unit pollution generation from source s

η Cobb-Douglass parameter

$\mu(s)$ unit cost of electricity from a given sources s

v unit cost of other inputs (energy sources)

θ source labor requirement parameter

σ constant growth rate for commercial electricity demand

ζ employee-energy mix parameter

1. INTRODUCTION

Modeling of CO_2 emissions and the economic factors related to the switch from fossil fuels to renewable sources for electricity generation has become very important with the recent trends of moving toward a more economically and environmentally sustainable society. The, "Brundland definition...of sustainable development...'development that meets the needs of the present without compromising the ability of future generations to meet their own needs' is considered key to sustainability" (Nakata, 2004). It is therefore necessary to create economic models that can be used by the policy makers to make informed decisions which can lead to a sustainable path to meet the energy requirements in an economically and environmentally acceptable manner. The effects of global warming and its impact on climate change of the planet are making it apparent that the path humanity has taken so far, that is burning excessive amounts of fossil fuels for meeting the energy needs, is not sustainable.

The United States generates most of the electricity from coal based power plants. The other power generation sources include: nuclear, hydroelectric, natural gas, biomass waste, biomass wood, geothermal, solar photovoltaic, solar thermal and wind. In 2006, coal (49.3%), nuclear (19.5%), hydroelectric (7.2%) and natural gas (20.0%) constituted the major sources for electric power generation compared to biomass waste (0.4%), biomass wood (1.0%), solar photovoltaic and solar thermal (0.01%), wind (0.6%) and geothermal (0.4%). During the past 15 years, wind power has become cheaper and competitive with fossil fuel based electricity generation, and therefore is increasingly deployed in the U.S. and around the world. Photovoltaic power generation is still very limited because at present it is not very efficient and is very expensive compared to other sources of electricity generation. Recently, there has been considerable emphasis by the Department of Energy (DOE) and electric utility companies on research in "Clean Coal Technologies." In particular, carbon capture and sequestration (CCS) is being considered as a viable technology that may make it possible the continued use of fossil fuels with CO_2 emissions being captured and then sequestered in geological formations. However, the CCS technology is yet to be tested for a medium to large-scale power generation facility. It is improbable that carbon capture and sequestration (CCS) will be wide spread among power generation facilities within the next 15 years. It is therefore necessary to explore other alternative renewable energy sources for power generation.

In this chapter, we consider the economics of electricity generation in the U.S. as the switch is made from non-renewable fossil fuel based energy sources to renewable energy sources. For this purpose we develop an energy economic model, which is an optimization based equilibrium model where the economy is modeled in a top-down manner and the electricity generation sector is modeled using the bottom-up approach. Other significant energy economic models discussed in the literature are the MRN-NEEM model and the National Energy Model. The MRN-NEEM model is a combination of the MRN (Multi-Region National) model which is a top-down general equilibrium model and the NEEM (North American Electricity and Environmental Model) model which is a bottom up model of the electricity generation sector. The MRN-NEEM model has been applied to the United States. The National Energy Model is a dynamic model that tracks the primary energy sources and how they are consumed by households and industry; this model has only been applied to Japan.

The motivation behind the development of an energy economic model for electricity generation in the U.S. has been to create a model that would forecast the effects on the United States economy of policy changes in the usage of energy sources from fossil fuels to renewables in order to achieve the target goals of greenhouse gas (GHG) emissions in the next 25 to 50 years. With a worldwide emphasis on sustainability, there is a great interest in switching electricity generation sources from predominantly coal based to more eco-friendly renewable sources. The goal then is to create a model that can determine the economically best mix of energy generation sources to achieve the environmental constraints on CO_2 emissions in 2025 and 2050. The model should also determine the impact of policy changes on electricity price, its supply and demand, and on employment. At present, there are very few models that address this goal in a comprehensive manner.

2. METHODOLOGY AND MODELING

2.1. Modeling Approach

There are mainly four types of approaches currently employed in the majority of energy-economic models: top-down, bottom-up, optimization and equilibrium, and dynamic. The top-down and bottom-up models can be used together to create a more detailed model. The household provides the firms with labor and investment, while the firms provide the households with goods, services and wages. The salient features of the models are briefly described below.

Top-Down/Bottom-Up Models

According to Nakata, "The top-down label comes from the way modelers apply macroeconomic theory and econometric techniques to historical data on consumption, prices, incomes, and factor costs to model the final demand for goods and services, and the supply from main sectors (energy sector, transportation, agriculture, and industry)" (Nakata, 2004). All of the agents in the model respond to changes in prices and allow for multiple regions to be linked by trade (CRA International, 2008). Bottom-Up models model a given sector in detail, in the present case – electricity generation. These models use detailed costs for current and future technologies to model the effects of policy on the electricity generation sector (CRA International, 2008). They, "capture technology in the engineering sense: a given technique related to energy consumption or supply, with a given technical performance and cost" (Nakata, 2004).

Optimization Based Models

Optimization based models are based on the concept of maximizing utility and minimizing the cost. The optimization takes place at a given point in time and is considered to be in steady state. The optimization based models employ either the top-down or bottom-up approach to modeling. The optimization equations used in this paper, for the most part, follow the format of the Bellman equation:

$$V(x_0) = \max_{a_0} \left[F(x_0, a_0) + \beta V(x_1) \right]$$
(1)

where V is the value function (Bellman, 1957). The value function is "the best possible value of the objective, written as a function of the state [variable]" (Bellman, 1957). The Bellman equation (1) gives the value function at a given time period as the maximum of some objective function (F) plus the value function of the next time period with a discounting factor β. This recursive format of the Bellman equation allows for the calculation of the value function at normalized time $t = 1$ if the value function and the objective function (F) are known at normalized time $t = 0$. The first-order conditions are the partial derivatives of the Bellman equation with respect to the variables over which the optimization is being preformed (not the state variables).

$$\frac{\partial}{\partial a_0} \left(V(x_0) = \max_{a_0} \left[F(x_0, a_0) + \beta V(x_1) \right] \right)$$
(2)

In this model, the states x_0 and x_1 are recursively defined as:

$$x_1 = G(x_0)$$
(3)

where G is a specified function. The Benveniste-Scheinkman condition, also known as the envelope condition, allows the calculation of the derivative of the value function with respect to the state variable (Bergin, 1998; Boileau, 2002):

$$\frac{\partial}{\partial x_0} \left(V(x_0) = \max_{a_0} \left[F(x_0, a_0) + \beta V(x_1) \right] \right)$$
(4)

Using the first-order necessary conditions and the Benveniste-Scheinkman condition, the value function can be calculated (Bellman, 1957).

The present model, developed in this paper, basically falls under this category; however it is only concerned with the steady state results. A bottom-up approach was applied to the electricity generation sector so that the effect of switching from one energy source to another could be analyzed; a top-down approach was also used to determine the economy wide effects of the policy changes.

Dynamic Models

Dynamic models are an extension of the optimization based models. They operate in a manner similar to the optimization models except that the optimization takes place on a time interval and does not assume the steady state. Dynamic models are based on the same mathematical background as described in the previous section. They "can also be termed partial equilibrium models. These technology-oriented models minimize the total costs of the [system], including all end-use sectors, over a 40-50 year horizon and thus compute a partial equilibrium for the [markets]" (Nakata, 2004). Unlike the present model developed in this paper, the dynamic model results into a time series that can provide information as to how the current decisions affect the future outcomes.

2.2. Present Model: Optimization Based General Equilibrium Model

2.2.1. Operative Sectors of the Economy

We consider a model economy with a continuum of households of mass N and three operative sectors: the industrial manufacturing sector, the commercial sector and the electricity generation sector. We omit the insignificant transportation sector because of relatively insignificant consumption of electricity compared to residential, manufacturing and commercial sectors. The government sector is also omitted because its behavior is different from the other sectors. The households pay the government taxes and the government grants the households subsidies. Firms can provide each other with goods and services. The optimum level of production by a firm is the point at which profit is maximized.

Household

Each household owns one unit of labor, whose consumption is produced by the consumption good (x) and electricity (e^H):

$$c = h(x, e^H) \tag{5}$$

Set the consumption good x as the numeraire and denote the unit price of electricity as p. The optimization problem is given by,

$$V^H(a_t) = \max_{c_t, e_t^H} \left(U(c_t) + \beta^H V^H(a_{t+1}) \right)$$

$$s.t. \quad a_{t+1} = (1 + r_t)a_t + w_t - x_t - p_t e_t^H \tag{6}$$

$$c_t = h(x_t, e_t^H)$$

where a denotes household asset, w the wage, r the real interest rate and β^H the subjective discount factor facing each household.

The total population of households (N) is assumed to be fully employed in the three (industrial manufacturing, commercial and electricity generation) sectors of the model economy. Aggregate household demands are then defined by,

$$C_t = N_t c_t \tag{7}$$

$$X_t = N_t x_t \tag{8}$$

$$E_t^H = N_t e_t^H \tag{9}$$

Industrial Sector

There is a mass of producers normalized to one. Each producer hires labor (N^F), in conjunction with capital input (K) and electricity (E^F), to manufacture goods Y:

$$Y = f(K, N^F, E^F) \tag{10}$$

The output Y is used for consumption and capital investment:

$$Y = X + qZ \tag{11}$$

where q denotes the relative price of investment in units of the consumption good.

Let capital depreciate at rate δ. The optimization problem is given by:

$$V^F(K_t) = \max_{N_t^F, E_t^F, Z_t} \left(Y_t - q_t Z_t - w_t N_t^F - p_t E_t^F + \beta^F V^F(K_{t+1}) \right)$$

$$s.t. \quad K_{t+1} = Z_t + (1-\delta)K_t \tag{12}$$

$$Y_t = f(K_t, N_t^F, E_t^F)$$

where β^F the subjective discount factor facing each producer.

The Commercial Sector

This is a sector with measuring difficulties. This sector includes not only commercial firms, but educational institutions and other nonprofit organizations. Its inputs and outputs are hard to measure. For simplicity, the commercial sector is modeled in a stylized manner with its demand for electricity given by,

$$E_{t+1}^C = (1+\sigma)E_t^C \tag{13}$$

where $\sigma > 0$ is assumed an exogenous constant. Under a Leontief production function specification, the demand for labor is given by,

$$N_t^C = \zeta E_t^C \tag{14}$$

where $\zeta > 0$ is the employee-energy mix parameter.

2.2.2. Aggregate Electricity Demand and Electricity Generation

Total electricity demand is therefore given by,

$$E = \sum_{i=H,F,C} E^i \tag{15}$$

Electricity can be generated via various sources $s = 1$ (coal), $s = 2$ (nuclear), $s = 3$ (hydro), $s = 4$ (petroleum), $s = 5$ (natural gas), $s = 6$ (biomass wood), $s = 7$ (biomass waste), $s = 8$(geothermal), $s = 9$ (solar thermal and photovoltaic) and $s = 10$ (wind). The generation function can be specified as follows:

$$E(s) = m(N^E(s), M(s), s) \tag{16}$$

depending on labor (N^E) and other inputs (M). Total electricity generated from all sources is:

$$E = \sum_s E(s) \tag{17}$$

while the labor demand by all sources of electricity generation is:

$$N^E = \sum_s N^E(s) \tag{18}$$

We assume fixed unit labor requirements θ across all sources:

$$N^E(s) = \theta E(s) \tag{19}$$

Thus, we have:

$$N^E(s) = \frac{E(s)}{E} N^E \tag{20}$$

and can rewrite (16) as:

$$E(s) = \min\left\{\frac{1}{\theta} N^E(s), g(M(s))\right\} \tag{21}$$

where $g(M(s)) = m(\theta E(s), M(s), s)$.

Denote the unit cost of other inputs as v. Utility firms using source s face the following optimization problem:

$$\min\left\{wN^E(s) + vM(s)\right\}$$

$$s.t. \quad E(s) = \min\left\{\frac{1}{\theta} N^E(s), g(M(s))\right\} \tag{22}$$

Total cost incurred in electricity generation is:

$$\sum_s \left[wN^E(s) + vM(s) \right]$$
(23)

Let $\mu(s)$ denote the unit cost of electricity generation under source s. We can compute:

$$vM(s) = \mu(s)E(s) - wN^E(s)$$
(24)

Since we can measure $M(1)$, v can be backed out as well as $M(2)$, $M(3)$, $M(4)$, $M(5)$, $M(6)$, $M(7)$, $M(8)$, $M(9)$ and $M(10)$.

Denote unit pollution generation of source s as $\gamma(s)$. Total pollution generation in electricity generation is:

$$\sum_s \gamma(s)E(s)$$
(25)

2.2.3. Aggregate Labor Market

Total labor demand is:

$$\sum_{i=F,C,E} N^i = N$$
(26)

In equilibrium, labor supply equals labor demand

2.2.4. Optimization and Equilibrium

Household's optimization can be rewritten as:

$$V^H(a_t) = \max_{x_t, e_t^H} \left(U(h(x_t, e_t^H)) + \beta^H V^H((r_t + 1)a_t + w_t - x_t - p_t e_t^H) \right)$$
(27)

The first-order necessary conditions are given by,

$$U_c h_x = \beta^H V^H_{a_{t+1}}$$
(28)

$$U_c h_{e^H} = \beta^H V^H_{a_{t+1}} \cdot p_t$$
(29)

implying,

$$\frac{h_{e^H}}{h_x} = p$$
(30)

where the time subscript is suppressed whenever it would not cause any confusion. The Benveniste-Scheinkman condition is:

$$V_{a_t}^H = \beta^H V_{a_{t+1}}^H \cdot (r_t + 1) \tag{31}$$

Manufacturer's optimization problem can be rewritten as:

$$V^F(K_t) = \max_{N_t^F, E_t^F, Z_t} \left(f(K_t, N_t^F, E_t^F) - q_t Z_t - w_t N_t^F - p_t E_t^F + \beta^F V^F(Z_t + (1-\delta)K_t) \right) \tag{32}$$

The first-order conditions are derived below:

$$f_{N_t^F} = w_t \tag{33}$$

$$f_{E_t^F} = p_t \tag{34}$$

$$\beta^F V_{K_{t+1}}^F = q_t \tag{35}$$

The Benveniste-Scheinkman condition is:

$$V_{K_t}^F = f_{K_t} + \beta^F V_{K_{t+1}}^F \cdot (1-\delta) \tag{36}$$

which can be combined with (35) to yield:

$$V_{K_t}^F = f_{K_t} + \beta^F V_{K_{t+1}}^F \cdot (1-\delta) \tag{37}$$

Under fixed labor requirements (19), utility firm's optimization leads to:

$$g_M(M(s)) = \frac{v}{w\theta} \tag{38}$$

$$E(s) = \frac{1}{\theta} N^E(s) = g(M(s)) \tag{39}$$

2.2.5. Steady-State Equilibrium

In steady-state equilibrium, all variables are constant. As a consequence, (31) implies:

$$1 + r = \frac{1}{\beta^H} \tag{40}$$

whereas (6), (12) and (37) yield the following steady-state relationship

$$x + pe^H = w + \left(\frac{1}{\beta^H} - 1 \right) a \tag{41}$$

$$Z = \delta K \tag{42}$$

$$f_K = \left(\frac{1}{\beta^F} - 1 + \delta \right) q \tag{43}$$

2.2.6. Model Calibration

For the purposes of calibration analysis, we impose the following functional forms:

$$U = \ln(c) \tag{44}$$

$$h(x, e^H) = x^\eta (e^H)^{1-\eta} \tag{45}$$

$$f(K, N^F, E^F) = A \left\{ \varphi \left[K^\alpha \left(N^F \right)^{1-\alpha} \right]^\rho + (1-\varphi)(E^F)^\rho \right\}^{1/\rho} \tag{46}$$

$$g(M(s)) = BM(s)^\psi \tag{47}$$

We can calibrate the model based on steady-state relationships. In particular, we use the 1990-2006 average values of X, Z, N^F, N^C, N^E, E^H, E^F, E^C, $E(s)$, $\mu(s)$, $M(1)$, w, and p as their steady-state values, where all values are in million dollars at 2000 constant prices. There are a few adjustments needed to fit with the model. First, the total employment in our model economy is computed using (26):

$$N = N^F + N^C + N^E = 22,424,294 + 76,203,146 + 62,139 = 99.249 \times 10^6 \tag{48}$$

Since total employment of the U.S. is 123.035×10^6, we must scale down all the aggregates by a factor of $99.249/123.035 = 0.8067$, yielding:

$$X = 5,019,207 \,,\, Z = 759,482 \,,\, E^H = 912,595 \,,\, E^F = 814,054 \,,\, E^C = 797,165 \tag{49}$$

So the employee-energy mix parameter in the commercial sector can be derived using (14): $\zeta = 95.5927$. Second, aggregate electricity demand and supply are not identical in the data. We thus adjust $E(s)$ so that the values in (15) and (17) are consistent. That is, call the raw data of electricity generation as $ES(s)$, define $ES = \sum_s ES(s)$ and set $E = E^H + E^F + E^C$. We must adjust electricity generation by the factor E to have: $E(s) = (E/ES) \cdot ES(s)$. Accordingly, we obtain:

$$E(1) = 1,298,463, \; E(2) = 496,095, \; E(3) = 204,693, \; E(4) = 75,993, \; E(5) = 393,439$$
$$E(6) = 26,208, \; E(7) = 12,878, \; E(8) = 10,581, \; E(9) = 354, \; E(10) = 5,181 \tag{50}$$

Third, material inputs of various forms of electricity generation are very different. To circumvent the problem, we choose to normalize the material inputs to generate $E(1)$ as unity, that is, $M(1) = 1$. We can then use the cost data (million dollars per million megawatt-hours):

$$\mu(1)=0.030509,\ \mu(2)=0.022675,\ \mu(3)=0.009513,\ \mu(4)=0.059974,\ \mu(5)=0.049816$$
$$\mu(6)=0.072496,\ \mu(7)=0.039934,\ \mu(8)=0.08,\ \mu(9)=0.348,\ \mu(10)=0.052359$$
$$(51)$$

in conjunction with (24) to compute:

$$v=29,270,\ M(2)=0.249303,\ M(3)=0.010817,\ M(4)=0.135025$$
$$M(5)=0.562525,\ M(6)=0.057777,\ M(7)=0.01065, M(8)=0.026039 \qquad (52)$$
$$M(9)=0.004115229,\ M(10)=0.007857166$$

The total electricity cost is then computed as follows:

$$TC = \sum_s \left[wN^E(s) + vM(s) \right] = \sum_s \mu(s)E(s) \qquad (53)$$

Next, we can use (8) and (9) to yield $x = 0.050572$ and $e^H = 0.009195031$. The average real interest rate is set at a commonly selected rate 5%, faced by all agents. Thus, (40) implies $\beta^H = \beta^F = 1/(1+r) = 1/1.05$. The capital depreciation rate usually falls in the range between 5% and 10%, which we set at 7.5%. The annual wage rate and the relative price of energy are given by $w = 0.03236$ and $p = 0.06936$, respectively. Then, from (41) and (42), we can compute:

$$a = \frac{x + pe^H - w}{r} = 0.37694 \qquad (54)$$

$$K = \frac{Z}{\delta} = 10,126,430 \qquad (55)$$

The Cobb-Douglass utility function simplifies (30) to:

$$\frac{1-\eta}{\eta} \frac{x}{e^H} = p \qquad (56)$$

which gives the calibrated parameter value,

$$\eta = \frac{x}{x + pe^H} = 0.98755$$

The nested CES production function implies that (33), (34) and (43) can be rewritten as:

$$f_{N^F} = (1-\alpha)\Gamma \frac{Y}{N^F} = w \tag{57}$$

$$f_{E^F} = (1-\Gamma)\frac{Y}{E^F} = p \tag{58}$$

$$f_K = \alpha\Gamma \frac{Y}{K} = (r+\delta)q \tag{59}$$

where $\Gamma = \dfrac{\varphi\left[K^\alpha (N^F)^{1-\alpha}\right]^\rho}{\varphi\left[K^\alpha (N^F)^{1-\alpha}\right]^\rho + (1-\varphi)(E^F)^\rho}$. The last equation above can be combined with

(11) to derive:

$$Y = \frac{X}{1 - \dfrac{\alpha\delta\Gamma}{r+\delta}K} \tag{60}$$

$$q = \frac{\alpha\delta\Gamma}{r+\delta}\frac{Y}{Z} \tag{61}$$

which can be further substituted into the marginal product of labor and marginal product of energy expressions to solve jointly α and ρ as functions of φ. From the household side, we learn that the energy demand share is $1 - \eta = 0.012454$. It is reasonable to set the energy demand share by manufacturers twice as much $1 - \varphi = 0.02491$, or $\varphi = 0.975092$. We can then calibrate $\alpha = 0.935881$ and $\rho = 0.635049$. Thus, manufactured output and the unit cost of capital investment are computed as: $Y = 11,374,760$ and $q = 8.36827$. These values together with the production function enables us to pin down the scaling parameter,

$$A = \frac{Y}{\left\{\varphi\left[K^\alpha (N^F)^{1-\alpha}\right]^\rho + (1-\varphi)(E^F)^\rho\right\}^{1/\rho}} = 1.102033 \tag{62}$$

Finally, we manipulate (20), (38) and (39), using the specific functional form, to calibrate:

$$\theta = \frac{N^E}{E} = 0.24615 \tag{63}$$

$$\psi = \frac{vM(s)}{wN^E}\frac{E}{E(s)} = 2.82979 \tag{64}$$

$$B = \frac{E(1)}{[M(1)]^\psi} = 1,298,463 \qquad (65)$$

Given the CO_2 production of 2,229.756 million metric tons essentially from sources 1, 4 and 5, we can obtain an emission conversion ratio (per million megawatts of electricity generated) at γ(fossil fuels) = 2,229.756/1,767,895 = 0.00126125, with $\gamma(2) = \gamma(3) = \gamma(6) = \gamma(7) = \gamma(8) = \gamma(9) = \gamma(10) = 0$, due to the fact that the majority of carbon emissions are coming from the combustion of fossil fuels. This completes the calibration procedure in steady- state equilibrium. Given calibrated parameter values η, α, φ, ρ, θ, ψ and constant real interest rates r, δ, we can set K_{1998} at its steady- state value and then plug the annual data of Z_t, $t = 1990,...,$ 2006 into (12) to obtain the time series of calibrated K over the entire sample period. Similarly, we can set a_{1998} at its steady-state value and then plug the annual data of w_t, x_t, p_t, and e_t, $t = 1990,...,$ 2006 into (6) to obtain the time series of calibrated a. Then, from $q_t = (\alpha\delta\Gamma_t/r+\delta)(Y_t/Z_t)$, the time series of q_t can be computed. We can also apply (24) to compute the time series of v_t, $M(2)_t$, $M(3)_t$, $M(4)_t$, $M(5)_t$, $M(6)_t$, $M(7)_t$, $M(8)_t$, $M(9)_t$ and $M(10)_t$. Finally we can use the functional forms, h, f, and g, to pin down the time series of c_t, A_t and B_t.

3. POLICY ANALYSIS

In this section, we perform the policy analysis. In order to do this, we need to derive a few more useful steady-state equilibrium relationships. From (41) and (56), we can write household's goods consumption demand and electricity demand as:

$$x = \eta(w + ra) \qquad (66)$$

$$e^H = \frac{1}{p}(1-\eta)(w + ra) \qquad (67)$$

From (14), (18), and (26), manufacturing firm's labor demand is given by,

$$N^F = N_\zeta E^C - \theta\, E \qquad (68)$$

Substituting this into the production function, (57) and (58) enable us to express Y, w and p all as functions of (K, E^F). Using (8), (10), (42) and (66), we can write household's asset as:

$$a = \frac{1}{r}\left(\frac{Y - \delta qK}{\eta N} - w\right) \qquad (69)$$

which is a function of (K, E^F) as well, as are x and e^H, based on the demand relationships derived above. Aggregating each household's electricity demand with use of (69) and equating it with electricity supply, we obtain:

$$E^H = \frac{1-\eta}{\eta} \frac{Y - \delta q K}{p} = E - E^C - E^F \tag{70}$$

This together with (59) enables us to solve jointly (K, E^F). The solution can then be substituted into other functions to derive Y, w, p, a, x, e^H, and E^H. We are now ready for policy experiments. The data inputs to policy analysis and the sources of the data are available in the Appendices of this chaper. We focus on switching 10% electricity generation from coal to 5% wind, 3% solar thermal and photovoltaics, 1% biomass waste and 1% biomass wood.

Scenario 1: Energy Price Fully Regulated

When energy prices are fully regulated, the source switch described above causes total electricity generation cost to go up by 17.93% and emissions would decrease by 7.345% without changing any other endogenous variables. This scenario is undesirable at this time because the government would have to pay for the increase in total cost of electricity generation. If at some future time fossil fuel based electricity became equal priced or more expensive than renewables then the government would either not lose money or make a profit.

Scenario 2: Energy Price Fully Adjusted with Electricity Supply Fixed

When energy prices are fully adjusted, the source switch described above will raise the energy price by 17.93% to par with the total electricity generation cost. Higher energy price lowers demand: household demand lowers by 16.38%, industrial demand lowers by 37.14% and total demand by 17.9%. In this scenario, electricity supply and the level of employment remains fixed. Both capital and market wages reduce by 1.11%, whereas the output is lowered by 1.23%.

As a consequence, household asset and goods consumption are lowered by 1.865% and 1.387% respectively. Additionally, fixed electricity supply implies emissions decrease by exactly 10% of the emissions from coal. This represents an overall reduction of 7.345% in CO_2 emissions.

Scenario 3: Energy Price and Electricity Supply Both Fully Adjusted

In this scenario, the source switch described above will raise the energy price and lower the electricity demand in the same manner as in scenario 2. In contrast with scenario 2, however, electricity supply is now fully adjusted to meet the demand, which causes a layoff of 111,207 workers. This means that, on average, a household may face a layoff rate of 0.112%. Therefore, the expected market wages reduce by 1.219% and goods consumption decreases by 1.457%. Because electricity supply is now fully adjusted downward, the total electricity generation cost goes down by 3.183% and emissions decrease 23.931%.

The above analysis has only been conducted on the average values for the time period considered (1990 − 2006, see "Data inputs to policy analysis", Section 1, Appendices for details). For a more in depth analysis of how the endogenous variables react to policy changes, the simulations must be run for each year in the time period.

The aggregate analysis shows the general trends for each statistic for different policy scenarios. They should not be interpreted as an accurate forecaster of future economic factors; however, the trends in the three policy scenarios should be accurate. The three policy scenarios represent what would have happened if the average input data for (1990 − 2006) had a different energy mix. The trends found from the three policy analysis could be used to determine future policy. Comparison between the three scenarios should be accurate because they are calculated on the same data set.

Scenario 3 yields the largest CO_2 reduction for the given energy generation mix. Allowing the free market to adjust price and supply will lead to the largest decreases in CO_2 emissions for a given energy generation mix for the near future (while fossil fuel based electricity generation is cheaper than renewable sources).

CONCLUSION

An economic model for electricity generation has been created that runs policy simulations on the aggregate data for 1990 − 2006.

1) The model predicts that without government subsidy there will be a decrease in the number of utility workers due to the decrease in demand of electricity with increasing prices. In reality this might not be the case. The model assumes that the utility workers are evenly distributed throughout the power generation sector based on the amount of energy produced. However, newer and less developed technologies are most likely to need more workers than older highly developed technologies used, for example, in coal fired power plants. It is therefore possible that a shift of 10% of coal generated electricity to 5% wind power, 3% geothermal, 1% biomass waste and 1% biomass wood based electricity may result in an increase in employment.
2) Because fossil fuel based electricity generation is cheaper than renewables based electricity generation, government regulation will be necessary to achieve any sort of CO_2 emissions reduction.

APPENDICES

1. Data Inputs to Policy Analysis

Total Consumption	6222.15 M$
Total Employment	123035470 people
Non-residential fixed investment	941.51 M$
Number of factory workers	22424294 people
Number of commercial workers	76203146 people

Number of utility workers	621239 people
Average wage	16.1813 $/hr
Price of electricity	0.06935 $/kWhr
Electricity cost $s = 1$	0.030509 $/kWhr
Electricity cost $s = 2$	0.022675 $/kWhr
Electricity cost $s = 3$	0.009513 $/kWhr
Electricity cost $s = 4$	0.059974 $/kWhr
Electricity cost $s = 5$	0.049816 $/kWhr
Electricity cost $s = 6$	0.072496 $/kWhr
Electricity cost $s = 7$	0.039934 $/kWhr
Electricity cost $s = 8$	0.08 $/kWhr
Electricity cost $s = 9$	0.348 $/kWhr
Electricity cost $s = 10$	0.052359 $/kWhr
Electricity from $s = 1$	1826291.5 MWhr*1000
Electricity from $s = 2$	697759.7 MWhr*1000
Electricity from s = 3	287800.1 MWhr*1000
Electricity from $s = 4$	106884.9 MWhr*1000
Electricity from $s = 5$	553372.6 MWhr*1000
Electricity from $s = 6$	36861.2 MWhr*1000
Electricity from $s = 7$	18113.2 MWhr*1000
Electricity from $s = 8$	14881.8 MWhr*1000
Electricity from $s = 9$	498.2 MWhr*1000
Electricity from $s = 10$	7287.6 MWhr*1000
Total CO_2 Emissions	2229.76 MMT CO_2

Sources of the above data are available at Section 2 "Data collection sources" in the Appendices.

2. Data Collection Sources

1. Employment for each state by sector for 2001-2006. Sectors: Agriculture, forestry, fishing and hunting, Mining; Utilities, Construction, Manufacturing, Transportation and Warehousing (excluding Postal Service), Government and Other as well as the total employment; Source: Bureau of Labor Statistics.

2. US electricity retail sales by sector in thousand megawatt hours for each state for 1990-2006. Sectors: Residential, Commercial, Industrial and Other, as well as total sales. Source: Energy Information Administration (EIA), 2008.

3. US energy generation data for 1980-2006 by source. Electricity generation sources: coal, petroleum, natural gas, other gases, total fossil fuels, nuclear, hydro (conventional), biomass wood, biomass waste, geothermal, solar/PV, wind, total renewables, other; as well as total for all sources. Source: EIA, Annual Energy Review, 2008

4. Total coal usage in power generation for 1990-2006 in thousands of tons of coal. Source: EIA, 2008.

5. US CO_2 emissions from the electric power industry for each state by source for 2003-2006. Sources: coal, petroleum, natural gas, geothermal and other renewables as well as the total. Source EIA, 2008.
6. US average electricity retail price in cents per kilowatt hour for 1998-2006. Source: EIA, 2007.
7. US electricity generation costs in cents per kilowatt hour.

A full data set is available for 2006. Additional years of data are available for some of the sources so that a curve fit could be made to fill in the gaps in the data for other years. Sources: coal, natural gas, nuclear, petroleum, wind, residential photovoltaics, commercial photovoltaics, industrial photovoltaics, solar thermal, geothermal, hydroelectric small and hydroelectric large.

Sources: Nuclear Energy Institute, *U. S. Electricity Production Costs and Components (1995-2008); Energy Information Administration, Annual Energy Review 2008; Table 8.2a Electricity Net Generation: Total (All Sectors), Selected Years, 1949-2008; World Energy Assessment; Overview: 2004 Update. Solarbuzz.com, Solar Electricity Price Index verses US Electricity tariff Price Index; Facts About Hydropower,* Wisconsin Valley Improvement Company.

8. US electricity generation for each state by source in megawatt hours for 1990-2006. Sources: coal, petroleum, natural gas, other gases, nuclear, hydroelectric, other renewables, pumped storage and other as well as the total. Source EIA, 2008.
9. US CO_2 emissions from energy consumption for each sector from 1980 to 2005. Sectors: residential, commercial, transportation, electric power. Source: EIA, 2008.
10. US electricity demand from 1980 to 2006 for each sector.
    Sectors: residential, commercial, industrial, transportation as well as total. Source: EIA, 2008.
11. State level CO_2 emissions from fossil fuel combustion for electricity generation from 1990 to 2004 in million metric tons of CO_2. Source: EIA, 2008.
12. Cost of living statistics (consumer price index) for the Northeast Urban, Midwest Urban, South Urban, West Urban, as well as US total for 1985-2006. Source: Bureau of Economic Analysis, 2008.
13. State level population data for 1970-2007. Source: US Census Bureau, 2008.
14. State level average number of people per household for 2007. Source: Bureau of Labor Statistics, 2008.
15. US Gross State Product (GSP) for each state for each industry in non-chained dollars for 1997-2006. Industries: agriculture, forestry, fishing and hunting, mining, utilities, construction, manufacturing, transportation and warehousing (excluding postal service), government and other; as well as the total. Source: Bureau of Economic Analysis, 2008.
16. State level motor vehicle registration for 2003-2005. Sectors: automobiles, motorcycles, busses and trucks. Source: Bureau of Transportation Statistics, 2008.

REFERENCES

Bellman, R.E. (1957). *Dynamic Programming*. Princeton NJ: Princeton University Press.

Bergin, P. (1998). Lecture Notes on Dynamic Programming: Economics 200E. Retrieved from University of California, Davis website: *http://www.econ.ucdavis.edu/faculty/ bergin/ECON200e/lec200e.pdf*. Accessed February 5, 2012.

Boileau, M. (2002). A Child's Guide to Dynamic Programming. Retrieved from the University of Colorado at Boulder website: *http://www.colorado.edu/Economics/courses/ boileau/7020/ Cgdynpro.PDF*. Accessed February 5, 2012.

CRA International. (2008). CRA *International Report: CRA International's MRN-NEEM Integrated Model for Analysis of US Greenhouse Gas Policies*. Retrieved from CRA International website *http://www.crai.com/uploadedFiles/RELATING_MATERIALS/ Publications/BC/Energy_and_Environment/files/MRN-NEEM%20Integrated% 20Model%20for%20Analysis%20of%20US%20Greenhouse%20Gas%20Policies.pdf*. Accessed February 5, 2012.

Nakata, T. (2004). Energy-economic models and the environment. *Progress in Energy and Combustion Science*, 30 (4): 417 − 475.

In: Research and Applications for Energy …
Editor: Riad Benelmir

ISBN: 978-1-62948-892-9
© 2014 Nova Science Publishers, Inc.

Chapter 13

PASSIVE METHODS FOR IMPROVING INDOOR ENVIRONMENTS AND ENERGY SAVING

*Naira Barkhudaryan and José A. Orosa**

University of A Coruña. Departament of Energy and M. P. Paseo de Ronda,
A Coruña, España, Spain

ABSTRACT

On the purpose to reduce the amount of energy used and to create environmental friendly indoor climate, heating and cooling systems can be substituted by passive climate control methods. Despite the fact that building thermal inertia is being analyzed in depth, there are other kinds of hygroscopic inertia that is reaching a special interest. Wall materials can serve as passive climate control methods. In particular, internal wall coverings materials have showed as the main barrier between indoor air and the construction walls which can act as reservoirs of humidity releasing it when the relative humidity level in the indoor ambience is reduced. In present paper main results obtained by the University of Coruña in different research works about this topic were summarized. These papers are based on real sampled data in 25 office buildings located in the northwest of Spain that showed the same construction characteristics except its internal wall coverings. By a statistical study it was concluded that real internal coverings can be classified in three different levels of permeability. Furthermore, these internal covering exert as control system of the indoor air condition defined by means of physical parameters, such as enthalpy, partial vapor pressure, temperature and etc. Finally, possible methods which contribute to providing comfortable indoor climate and, in consequence, to saving the amount of energy used inside the building were discussed and proposed.

---

*Corresponding author: Tel.: +34981167000; fax: +349811167107; E-mail address: jaorosa@udc.es.

1. INTRODUCTION

Recent research works have shown that one-third of energy of the commercial sector is consumed by office buildings. Therefore, minimizing the amount of energy is important issue which needs a solution. Since the last decade many research works have defined the more importance factors for designing sustainable buildings and reducing the amount of energy usage adoption of new technologies such as location, natural shade, shelter and building materials [1, 2].

In particular, after different international publications which validate the employed methodology and obtained results, we can say that wall internal coverings showed an interesting effect which has significant influence on the indoor thermal environment and the amount of consumed energy [1]. In this sense, there are several types of internal wall covering materials: permeable, semi-permeable and impermeable coverings in accordance with its different abilities for transferring humidity from indoor air to construction materials and vice versa [2]. Due to this property, these types of coverings exert different influence on indoor ambient [3]. For example, during the occupation period, comparably to impermeable coverings, permeable materials provide better indoor climate [2] as a consequence of the heat and mass transfer between the indoor air and walls during the unoccupied period. In other words, these materials serve as passive climate control methods controlling indoor air condition particularly in mild seasons [1].

On the other hand, nowadays there is an increasing interest to obtain an international calculation procedure that let us define the expected energy consumption of buildings improving its design. In this sense, European Committee for Standardization (CEN) and the International Organization for Standardization (ISO) developed ISO 13790:2008 standard as a tool for controlling and calculating the amount of energy used to heat and cool inside the building. This standard encompasses from monthly quasi-steady state calculation method to a simple hourly calculation method, and also, detailed simulation method.

Besides, ISO 13790:2008 represents calculation methods for the assessment of the annual energy usage during heating and cooling and provides standard rules for the boundary conditions and physical input data. To apply this standard to practical life, physical variables such as building inertia parameter and utilization factor, must be measured and evaluated. The utilization factor is a function of thermal inertia parameter and the ratio of energy gain and energy loss (Q_{gain}/Q_{loss}) [4]. In its turn, the inertia parameter shows the relation of indoor environment to the amount of energy employed to control it [1].

In consequence, higher the parameter of building inertia is, less the energy will be required for providing comfortable indoor climate [1]. For estimating thermal inertia within the building we can consider natural thermal processes which take place inside buildings and which can lead to reducing amount of energy usage. For example, solar heat which is cumulated inside the building construction materials during time when the weather is warm, can later be exempt to indoor environment which later will provide comfortable indoor climate, during the time when the weather changes to cold.

Another important parameter to be considered in these standards is water vapor concentration. Comparably to outdoor air, indoor air contains higher amount of water vapor concentration. The indoor air moisture level or vapor concentration can be normalized by using permeable coverings that let vapor to be adsorbed by the walls, which can lead to harmful consequences.

As a consequence of this, permeable coverings contribute to lowering the amount of indoor humidity and hence, to reducing the amount of peaks of energy consumption [5]. Besides, permeable coverings control fluctuations in moisture during humid as well as dry periods, provide comfortable thermal conditions and low energy consumption [4].

A last concept must be defined previous to show the methodology employed in ours papers. To determine the damping effect of vapor content and humidity level in the materials there are two constants, k and t, which should be considered [5, 6]. The constant k shows the proportionality between the amount of moisture migrated to wall and the difference in moisture content between air and materials. The constant t is time parameter, which defines the history of humidity in the indoor air [5, 6] by means of an exponentially weighted average time [5].

2. METHODOLOGY AND DISCUSSION

There are three types of methods employed for conducting each different research work; quantitative, qualitative and mixed [7, 8]. Quantitative research deals with measurable data whereas qualitative research with observations and descriptive data [8]. Finally, the mixed approach encompasses mixture of both qualitative and quantitative methods [7].

The choice of research method is made based on the particular research problem [9, 10]. Due to this paper considers qualitative approach since it intends to understand the research subject and to gather descriptive data based on experimental results.

In present paper main results obtained from different research works about permeable coverings developed in the department of Energy of the University of A Coruña will be summarized.

In particular, the experimental data were obtained from 25 Spanish office buildings with the same wall structure and different internal coverings. The sampled data were analyzed and groups of indoor ambiences were done in accordance with its instantaneous behavior by means of One Way ANOVA statistical tool. These groups of indoor ambiences could be related with the permeability level of internal coverings.

A simple and usual variable employed in nearly all the building energetic analysis is the dry air temperature [1]. In this sense, it is interesting to note that building design influence indoor temperature value. For example, comparably to old buildings, new buildings have higher temperature (more then 2 °C), thermal inertia and less partial vapor pressure [1].

Despite the fact that temperature is related with energy consumption, it is not good enough to analyze the whole building energy consumption due to it doe s not consider the relative humidity. To define a simple variable that considers simultaneous effect of materials and outdoor air over indoor temperature and relative humidity, partial vapor pressure was selected.

To define the hourly effect of permeable coverings over indoor ambience, it was necessary to develop an hourly One Way ANOVA analysis in summer and winter seasons. The impact level of covering materials is different during the day. Therefore, the day was split up to three periods. The first period is from 9:00 to 14:00, the second period is from 14:00 to 19:00 and the third-from 19:00 to 9:00. Results showed that internal coverings effects were especially valuable during the last hours of unoccupied period and the first hours of occupation period [3] and that the period from 12:00 to 19:00 is more influential during the winter. It is due to the real working period of internal covering on indoor climate was measured in unoccupied period since this period is free from the influence of ventilation rates [6]. Furthermore, its effects can be noted during all the day and, in particular, during the first hours of occupation.

In the case of impermeable coverings, in winter, in addition with low outdoor humidity, the renewed indoor air affects negatively the indoor climate. But when the doors in the building are closed, the indoor air conditions do not change for 4h [5].

According to experimental results, it could be seen that partial vapor pressure presents comparably higher value with permeable coverings [5]. Furthermore, permeable coverings provide the highest partial vapor pressure during winter time and the lowest during the summer, whereas impermeable allow the highest indoor partial vapor pressure in summer and the lowest during winter [3]. The value of partial vapor pressure took its maximum with the impermeable coverings and its minimum with permeable coverings during the interval between 9:00 to 14:00. The maximum value of partial vapor pressure with impermeable coverings was reached at 14:00 [6].

In winter, the maximum mean partial vapor pressure value of 1162 Pa was obtained with permeable coatings and the minimum mean value of 1136 Pa with impermeable coatings. In summer, the maximum mean value of 1658 Pa is obtained with the impermeable coatings, while the minimum mean partial vapor pressure value of 1474 Pa with permeable coatings [3]. In addition to permeability level, parameters, such as enthalpy, thermal inertia, temperature, moisture and partial vapor pressure influence the indoor ambient.

As it was commented before, partial vapor pressure parameter is used to express relative humidity level. In this sense, the indoor partial vapor pressure is comparably higher than the outdoor one. In summer, indoor vapor pressure is less than outdoor vapor pressure, whereas in winter indoor partial vapor pressure is higher then outdoor [11].

This paper also touches upon the partial vapor pressure difference and respective standard deviation. This standard deviation can be defined as the intensity of material activity. Comparable to impermeable coverings, permeable coverings have higher standard deviation during summer and winter time [6].

Once we have defined the effect of permeable coverings over indoor air relative humidity, it is time to define its effect over heating and cooling energy consumption due to its influence over moist air enthalpy. As it is well know, the moisture in the building materials adsorbed during occupation period is instrumental in saving the energy consumption. Hygroscopic materials adsorb moisture and, together with operating cooling systems, they can facilitate the reduction of indoor humidity and indoor enthalpy.

The less is the enthalpy the less energy will be required for cooling the indoor air [2]. During the summer time, the indoor enthalpy (h) is approximately 55 kJ/kg with impermeable coverings (during the day) and, with permeable coverings (from 9:00 to 14:00), enthalpy is about 44 kJ/kg and can have insignificant increase until 19:00. From 19:00 till 9:00 enthalpy have reached up to 48 kJ/kg [6].

Once it was defined the hourly effect of internal coverings over indoor partial vapor pressure and relative humidity, more interesting parameters were analyzed. In this sense, results showed a direct relationship between the amount of energy consumed and the permeability level. However, the amount of consumed energy to reach indoor thermal comfort conditions varies depending on the permeability level in each building [4]. In particular, it was concluded that buildings with internal coverings with higher permeability require less energy. For example, to heat indoor environments with permeable internal coverings has required amounts of energy near to zero, and with impermeable coverings certain amount of energy will be required to heat the indoor climate. On the other hand, cooling indoor ambient with impermeable coverings have required amount of energy within the interval from 0 kWh/m^2 to 3.5 kWh/m^2 [2]. To sum up, we can say that 35 % of energy consumption will be needed with permeable and semi-permeable coverings and 71.2 % with impermeable coverings [2].

Thermal inertia is the last level of analysis to define the conditions inside the building and the amount of consumed energy. As it is know, the amount of energy can be diminished since the building elements contain reserved heat remained from warm periods of the year [1]. For determining the efficiency of permeable coverings, utilization factor, expressed by the relation between the heat gains and heat losses in the building (Q_{gain}/Q_{loss}), was considered. The experimental results in [4] show that permeable coverings provide higher utilization factor, 0.6 in winter and 0.8 in summer seasons, while the lowest results belong to impermeable coverings, 0.5 in winter and 0.65 in summer seasons [4]. Thus, in winter the difference between coverings has less effect on indoor climate than in summer [5].

From this results we can conclude that, overall, it is possible to state that the walls from relatively heavier materials provide better indoor ambiences and passive covering methods can serve as an appropriate replacement to heating systems during mild weather [1]. In this sense, results showed that passive coverings affect indoor environment since they allow moisture circulate between indoor air and hygroscopic structures which in its turn moderates variations of indoor humidity and, hence, improves indoor thermal comfort.

From an energetic point of view, permeable materials, in reference to HVAC systems, enable energy saving up to 3 kWh/m^2 per year. They allow saving significant amount of energy during cold seasons and can serve as a substitute to heating and cooling systems in mild climates. As the permeable materials consider transient indoor and outdoor conditions, they may be considered as an adaptive comfort covering method [2]. According to experimental results permeable coverings are more beneficial during the first hours of occupation [3]. Permeable coverings are able not only to reduce amount of energy consumption but also, reduce noise and save from unnecessary harmful substances in the room, providing favorable indoor climate [11]. In consequence, future research works must be developed to define the optimal way to design buildings based on this new concepts of passive methods.

CONCLUSION

In present paper main results obtained by department of Energy of the University of A Coruña about the effect of internal coverings over indoor ambiences are showed. Real sampled data in 25 office buildings with the same wall structure and indoor activity were sampled during a year. Their only difference was its internal coverings.

Once sampled data was obtained, it was necessary to define the main analysis variable that considers indoor air temperature and relative humidity. In this sense, it was selected the partial vapor pressure difference between indoor air an outdoor air condition. In consequence, this variable was employed in different statistical analysis to show the next results:

1. Three types of passive coverings (permeable, semi-permeable and impermeable) affect the indoor environment differently.

2. If we consider the partial vapor pressure parameter influence indoor climate depending on permeability level, there can be seen that, the walls with permeable coverings show low value for partial vapor pressure in summer and higher value in winter. The results are particularly true during the occupied period and first few hours of unoccupied time. The rest of time the difference between covering level is becoming insignificant.

3. In summer, as consequences of refreshing indoor air condition the relative humidity is increasing, whereas in winter time humidity is decreasing and, since air renewal rate is slow.

4. Finally, the parameter, which is valuable to know, is enthalpy. Impermeable coverings provide higher enthalpy, comparatively to permeable coverings in summer. Thus, before implementing HVAC systems, it is reasonable to consider passive climate controlling method as the substitute to these systems. Passive climate controlling method will not only contribute to save the amount of energy usage, but also to create favorable indoor air climate.

5. In summer permeable coverings are more preferable due to the fact that these coverings provide optimal indoor air quality values. With permeable coverings in both summer and winter seasons, the amount of energy consumption decreases, which allows saving 3 kWh/m^2 of energy annually.

6. In winter indoor ambient can be improved with impermeable coverings, since partial vapor pressure lower and indoor enthalpy higher compared with permeable coverings. In winter, peak loads with impermeable coverings takes place during the first hours of occupation, because of the low ventilation rate preserved from inoccupation time.

From these results we can conclude that permeable coverings let us get buildings with a higher utilization factor than impermeable coverings. Furthermore, permeable coverings help to decrease air change rate and hence increase hygroscopic thermal inertia.

Finally, future research works must be developed to define the optimal way to design buildings based on this new concepts of passive methods. In particular, more researches must be done about passive methods to substitute the usually HVAC (Heat, Ventilation and Air Conditioning) systems.

REFERENCES

[1]   José A. Orosa, Armando C. Oliveira. A field study on building inertia and its effects on indoor thermal environment. *Renewable Energy* 37 (2012) 89-96.

[2]   José A. Orosa, Armando C. Oliveira. Energy saving with passive climate control methods in Spanish office buildings. *Energy and Buildings* 41 (2009) 823–828.

[3]   José A. Orosa, A. Baaliña. Improving PAQ and comfort conditions in Spanish office buildings with passive climate control. *Building and Environment* 44 (2009) 502– 508.

[4]   José A. Orosa, Armando C. Oliveira. Implementation of a method in EN ISO 13790 for calculating the utilisation factor taking into account different permeability levels of internal coverings. *Energy and Buildings* 42 (2010) 598–604.

[5]   José A. Orosa, Armando C. Oliveira. Hourly indoor thermal comfort and air quality acceptance with passive climate control methods. *Renewable Energy* 34 (2009) 2735–2742.

[6]   José A. Orosa, Armando C. Oliveira. Reducing energy peak consumption with passive climate control methods. *Energy and Buildings* 43 (2011) 2282–2288.

[7]   Creswell J. W. (2003). Research *Design: Qualitative, Quantitative, and Mixed Methods Approaches*. Sage Publications Inc. United States of America.

[8]   Bryman, A. (1992). *Quantity and Quality in Social Research*. Routledge, London.

[9]   Flyvbjerg, B. (2006). Five Misunderstandings About Case-Study Research. *Journal of Qualitative Inquiry*, vol. 12, no. 2, April, pp. 219-245.

[10]   Merriam Sh. B., (2009). *Qualitative Research: A Guide to Design and Implementation*. John WileyandSons, Inc., San Francisco.

[11]   José A. Orosa, A. Baaliña, Passive climate control in Spanish office buildings for long periods of time. *Building and Environment* 43 (2008) 2005–2012.

In: Research and Applications for Energy …
Editor: Riad Benelmir

ISBN: 978-1-62948-892-9
© 2014 Nova Science Publishers, Inc.

Chapter 14

PARAMETRIC PERFORMANCE ANALYSES OF GEOTHERMAL HEAT PUMP SYSTEMS

Stuart J. Self[*], Bale V. Reddy and Marc A. Rosen
Faculty of Engineering and Applied Science
University of Ontario Institute of Technology
Oshawa, Ontario, Canada

ABSTRACT

Heat pumps are primary candidates for providing space heating with reduced emissions and economic benefits. Geothermal heat pump (GHP) systems use the earth just below the surface to supply a heat pump cycle with the thermal energy it requires for heating a space. Assessments of new GHP systems with alternative designs are reported to improve designs and facilitate more extensive applications as well as to provide information on how various operating conditions for varying heat pump arrangements affect performance and ground loop requirements. Three heat pump arrangements including the traditional heat pump cycle and two advanced cycles are considered within parametric investigations. The analyses, comparisons and parametric investigations reported of advanced GHP arrangements and systems improve understanding and design. These assessments reveal the sensitivity of the performance of the overall system to variations in numerous operating conditions and component efficiencies.

NOMENCLATURE

A_c	Cross sectional area, m^2
c_p	Specific heat at constant pressure, kJ/kg·K
COP_{HP}	Coefficient of performance for heat pump cycle
COP_{System}	Coefficient of performance for entire system
D_i	Inner diameter of ground loop piping, m

[*] E-mails:stuart.self@uoit.ca.

$\dot{E}_{motor,comp}$	Electrical power consumed by compressor motor, kW
$\dot{E}_{motor,pump}$	Electrical power consumed by pump motor, kW
$\dot{E}_{motor,total}$	Electrical power consumed by compressor and pump motors, kW
$\dot{E}_{motor,waste}$	Waste energy rate from compressor motor, kW
f	Friction factor
h_{conv}	Convection heat transfer coefficient, W/m^2·°C
h_f	Specific enthalpy at saturated state, kJ/kg
h_{fg}	Specific enthalpy difference between saturated vapour and saturated liquid, kJ/kg
h_i	Specific enthalpy at state i, kJ/kg
h_{ia}	Actual specific enthalpy at state i, kJ/kg
h_{is}	Ideal specific enthalpy at state i, kJ/kg
h_l	Specific enthalpy of species l in brine mixture, kJ/kg
h_m	Specific enthalpy of brine mixture, kJ/kg
k_{brine}	Thermal conductivity of brine fluid, W/m·°C
k_{grout}	Thermal conductivity of grout material, W/m·°C
k_{pipe}	Thermal conductivity of pipe material, W/m·°C
$l_{parallel}$	Length of a single parallel loop, m
mf_l	Mass fraction of species l in brine mixture
$\dot{m}_{GL,Evaporator}$	Mass flow rate of brine through evaporator, kg/s
$\dot{m}_{GL,parallel}$	Mass flow rate of brine through a parallel loop, kg/s
$\dot{m}_{main}$	Mass flow rate through main circuit in system 3, kg/s
$\dot{m}_{ref}$	Mass flow rate of refrigerant through condenser, kg/s
$\dot{m}_{supp}$	Mass flow rate of refrigerant through supplementary circuit in system 3, kg/s
Nu	Nusselt number
η_{comp}	Compressor isentropic efficiency
η_{EM}	Electric motor efficiency
n_{pl}	Number of parallel loops in ground loop
η_{pump}	Pump isentropic efficiency
ρ	Density, kg/m^3
P_i	Pressure at state i, kPa
$\Delta P_{parallel}$	Pressure drop in parallel loop, kPa
Pr	Prandtl number
$\dot{Q}_{evap}$	Heat input rate of evaporator to refrigerant, kW
$\dot{Q}_{GL,actual}$	Actual heat transfer rate required from ground, kW
$\dot{Q}_{GL,parallel}$	Heat transfer rate to a single parallel loop, kW
$\dot{Q}_{ht}$	Heat transfer rate from ground to brine fluid, kW
$\dot{Q}_{load}$	Heating load of building, kW
$\dot{Q}_{waste\ heat}$	Heat transfer rate from compressor motor to refrigerant, kW
Re	Reynolds number
R_i	Thermal resistance of section i, °C/W

r_i	Radius from center of ground loop piping of section i, m
R_{total}	Total thermal resistance, °C/W
$T_{\infty 1}$	Temperature of outer grout wall, °C
$T_{\infty 2}$	Average fluid temperature between states 7 and 5, °C
T_i	Temperature at state i, °C
μ	Dynamic viscosity, kg/m·s
$V_{avg,parallel}$	Average fluid velocity through parallel ground loop, m/s
v_i	Specific volume at state i, m³/kg
$\dot{W}_{comp}$	Power consumption of compressor, kW
$\dot{W}_{comp,i}$	Power consumption of compressor i, kW
$\dot{W}_{pump}$	Power consumption of pump, kW
$w_{pump,actual}$	Actual pump work, kJ/kg
$w_{pump,ideal}$	Ideal pump work, kJ/kg
X	Ratio of mass flow rates in main and supplementary circuits for system 3
x	Quality

1. INTRODUCTION

Many people feel that fossil fuel depletion and environmental concerns (especially greenhouse gas emissions) are important factors to be considered for sustainable and environmentally benign energy systems [1, 2].

One approach to developing such systems involves exploiting the fact that the earth's crust is a large storage medium of thermal energy. The U.S. Department of Energy [3] has studied the availability of ground-based, or geothermal, energy and concluded that geothermal energy resources exceed fossil fuel resources in terms of the quantity potentially available. Geothermal energy systems are typically more environmentally benign than conventional systems utilizing fossil fuels. For both electrical and heating applications, for instance, greenhouse gas emissions from geothermal systems are much lower than those from conventional fossil fuel energy systems [3, 4].

Geothermal energy is currently utilized in three prime ways: electricity production, direct heating, and indirect heating via geothermal heat pumps. These uses involve high (>150°C), moderate (90-150°C) and low (<90°C) temperatures, respectively [4, 5]. High and medium temperature resources are usually derived from thermal streams within the molten core of the earth, which collect in water or rock. Low temperature resources, which are the focus of this research, are mostly created by solar energy incident on the ground and ambient air temperatures. Such energy can be extracted from the ground at reasonable depths and raised to useful temperatures with heat pumps [4].

Research has been performed on geothermal heat pump systems and applications, in part to provide an improved understanding of system performance. Nevertheless, additional information and insights on the technology are required. Lack of adequate information can also introduce inaccuracies into the system designs, causing them to perform differently than originally intended. For example, the product temperature could be below that needed by a building heat distribution system, or the ground loop length may be too long or short, leading to systems that have either insufficient area to allow for the necessary heat transfer between the system and the ground or unnecessarily high initial costs [6].

Many studies reported in the literature consider static conditions, where they examine a system arrangement, either theoretically or experimentally [7]. Limited effort has been devoted to studying how varying operating conditions affect system performance and other system characteristics. These observations suggest research is needed to develop more detailed models and analysis methods in order to provide a better understanding of heat pump design. Parametric analyses are also needed to help improve performance and efficiency, given the limited studies that consider variations in system parameters. Investigations into how variations in different system parameters affect heat pump system operation and performance would enhance knowledge. Since limited information is available for geothermal heat pumps employing advanced vapour compression cycles, models for these systems along with relevant parametric analyses would also be beneficial for improving understanding and contributing to better designs of ground source heat pump systems.

The objective of the work reported here is to help address these needs by performing parametric investigations of geothermal heat pump components and operating parameters, considering the basic vapour compression heat pump cycle as well as advanced arrangements. Comparisons of advanced and basic vapour compression arrangements are also presented for heating applications. The heat pump systems investigated include a basic vapour compression cycle, the vapour compression cycle including electric motor cooling presented by Wang et al. [8], and the vapour compression cycle with an economizer presented by Ma and Chai [9]. The two advanced systems are relatively new. All systems use R-134a as the refrigerant.

The approach taken in this article has several parts. Models, energy analyses and comparisons are presented for advanced and basic geothermal heat pump arrangements for heating purposes. The analysis includes investigations into how varying compressor, pump, and motor efficiency affect the system performance. Variations in operating conditions are investigated, with the inclusion of condenser and evaporator pressure, and the degree of subcooling and superheating at the condenser and evaporator exit respectively. The systems are analyzed assuming that there is one centralized heat pump system supplying a space with the required heat, which is described by Natural Resources Canada [6] as the most basic system arrangement for heating. We only consider heating purposes. The model for each system is composed of two different loops including the heat pump cycle and ground loop heat exchanger, commonly referred to as the ground loop. The arrangement and analysis process for the ground loop is identical for each of the three systems. A vertical borehole ground loop connection is utilized within the study. The brine in the ground loop is taken to be a water/propylene glycol mixture. A complete understanding of the practicality of a system arrangement requires consideration of other factors, including economics and environmental impact [10], but these factors are not explored here.

2. BACKGROUND

Vapour compression heat pumps move heat from one medium to another at a higher temperature with the input of energy, making them useful for space heating and/or cooling. The heat pump is much more efficient for heating than conventional space heating devices [11]. Heat pumps can use as heat sources air, water or ground. Geothermal heat pumps

(GHPs) are also known as ground source heat pumps (GSHPs), use the ground, at depths sometimes exceeding 200 m, as a heat source [12, 13, 14, 15, 16]. GHP systems are comprised of three main components: the geothermal heat pump unit, the Earth connection (ground loop) and the interior heat distribution system [17]. Two main ground loop configurations are commonly used: open and closed. GHPs exploit the relatively constant ground temperature, which is warmer than ambient air during winter and cooler during summer.

GHPs are presently considered one of the fastest growing applications of renewable energy globally. Since 1994 the annual growth rate for geothermal heat pumps has been about 10%, and today there are close to a 1.7 million applications globally [17]. Worldwide installed GHP thermal capacity as of 2004 was around 12 GW, which required an annual electricity use of 20 TWh. About 30 countries were using these heat pump systems in significant numbers in 2004. The leading countries include the U.S., Sweden, Germany, Switzerland, Canada and Austria, and the technology is gaining popularity in many other countries [18]. Research is being carried out on ground heat pump systems, focused mainly on vapour compression systems. Comparisons between ground- and air-source heat pumps have been performed, and energy and exergy analyses have been reported. Little work has been reported on the effects of varying GHP system operating conditions and components on conventional and advanced GHP systems. These topics focus of the work reported here.

Some research relevant to this article has been reported. Regarding thermodynamic assessments, Hepbasli and Balta [19] experimentally assess the performance of a heat pump system using low temperature geothermal resources, and use energy and exergy analyses to determine system COP and irreversibilities. Also, Hepbasli and Akdemir [20, 21] analyze with energy and exergy methods GHP systems for district heating purposes. Healy and Ugursal [22] computationally investigate the effect on GSHP performance with a horizontal ground loop (GL) of various system parameters (GL depth and size, GL pipe size and horizontal pipe spacing, heat pump capacity, heat transfer fluid type and flow rate, and ground type). On economics, Kulcar et al. [23] describe the economics of exploiting heat from low-temperature geothermal sources for high-temperature heating of buildings using a heat pump, and demonstrate for a specific system that district heating of buildings is viable economically. Also, a comparative economic evaluation is presented of a GHP, an air source heat pump and a conventional heating/cooling system [22].

Several studies have been reported that are used for validation of the research reported in this article. Kara [24] experimentally determines the performance of a GHP system, with a single U-tube ground heat exchanger made of polyethylene pipe, in heating mode in the city of Erzurum, Turkey.

Wang et al. [8] investigate the effects of compressor and motor cooling, where the heat is transferred to the refrigerant for preheating, in a heat pump system. Ma and Chai [9] propose an improved heat pump cycle that incorporates an economizer into the vapour compression cycle with two compression processes between the condenser and evaporator. Ma and Zhao [25] extend the work of Ma and Chai [9] by experimentally comparing the improved heat pump cycle with a similar cycle that employs a flash tank with vapour separation and includes two compression processes.

3. APPROACH, ASSUMPTIONS AND DATA

3.1. Approach

Analyses are performed for three ground source heat pump arrangements: a basic vapour compression cycle (system 1), a vapour compression cycle including electric motor cooling (system 2) and a vapour compression cycle with an economizer (system 3). The systems are analyzed assuming a single centralized heat pump system that supplies the entire space with the required heat. Other arrangements exist where multiple heat pump units cool and heat different building spaces, but are not considered here. A constant heating load is assumed. Mass and energy balances are developed for each system, and used to develop a simulation model with Engineering Equation Solver (EES) software. The simulation facilitates calculation of various parameters and the performance of parametric studies. The analyses consider static operating conditions. Each analysis is performed with a common set of assumptions for each system arrangement. When the effect of varying a particular operating condition is explored, all assumptions are applied, except those affecting the condition being varied. Conditions are varied only over practical ranges, based on data in the literature or system operation limitations. In the analyses, heat pump and system COPs are compared, as are ground loop characteristics such as length and other system characteristics. Trends are identified and the sensitivities to particular parametric changes are compared for all systems.

3.2. Assumptions and Data

Several general assumptions made in this investigation. That is, pressure drops are neglected within the heat pump unit, all processes are treated as adiabatic (except heat exchange processes), changes in elevation are negligible, and the system operates at steady state, with steady flow conditions.

Additional assumptions are made specific to the heat pump and ground loop:

- *Heat pump.* Natural Resources Canada reports an average heating load of 100 kW for commercial and small institutional buildings [26]. This heating load is used for all systems considered here. Other system parameter values (Table 1) are determined from a set of initial simulations performed to determine suitable ranges.
- *Ground loop.* The ground loop fluid considered is a mixture of water and propylene glycol, which is specified as suitable antifreeze by Ochsner [27]. Natural Resources Canada [6] and Ochsner [27] specify an appropriate concentration of propylene glycol of between 15-40% by mass; 30% is used for the present study. The average ground temperature is found using Canada's National Climate Data and Information Archive [28]. Here, a mean ground temperature of 9.3°C is utilized which is the mean ground temperature well below the surface for Ottawa. Standard piping is used for ground source heat pumps and includes high density polyethylene DN32 PN10, which has a nominal diameter of 32 mm with a pressure rating of 10 bar and an inner diameter of 26.2 mm [2, 6, 29]. The polyethylene pipe interior is taken to be smooth [30], since the equivalent roughness value for new commercial polyethylene pipe is reported as zero by Cengel [31]. This assumption slightly under-predicts the pressure

drop compared to real applications. The thermal conductivity of the pipe material, based on an average from various sources, and is fixed at 0.375 W/m·K [32, 33]. In order to allow for the constant ground temperature the pipe depth is set to 100 m [34]. The borehole diameter is set at 101.6 mm (4 inches) [12] and the grout thermal conductivity taken as 1.56 W/m·K [35]. Other system parameter values (Table 2) are determined from a set of initial simulations performed to determine suitable ranges.

Table 1. Assumed heat pump system parameter values

Parameter	Value
Refrigerant	R134a
Condenser pressure	1000 kPa
Evaporator pressure	200 kPa
Intermediate pressure*	400 kPa
Degree of subcooling	5°C
Degree of superheating	5°C
Extra degree of subcooling*	5°C
Compressor efficiency	75%
Pump efficiency	90%
Electric motor efficiency	80%

*Specific to System 3 only.

Table 2. Assumed ground loop parameter values

Parameter	Value
Evaporator inlet temperature (GL side)	7.3°C
Evaporator outlet temperature (GL side)	1.3°C
Flow rate through individual parallel GL*	0.3 kg/s

* Note the flow rate was determined to allow for the proper flow regime within the GL piping; transitional or turbulent flow is desired within these systems [6, 26].

4. SYSTEM CONFIGURATIONS

This section describes the three systems considered and their operation. There are two loops within the system: the heat pump cycle and the ground loop. The arrangement and analysis for the ground loop is identical for the three systems.

4.1. Heat Pump Systems

The heat pump for System 1 is a basic vapour compression cycle, which is widely utilized due to its simplicity and ease of design [12, 36]. The heat pump cycle (Figure 1) consists of an evaporator, compressor, condenser and expansion valve, coupled with an electric motor for the compressor and a ground loop with a pump.

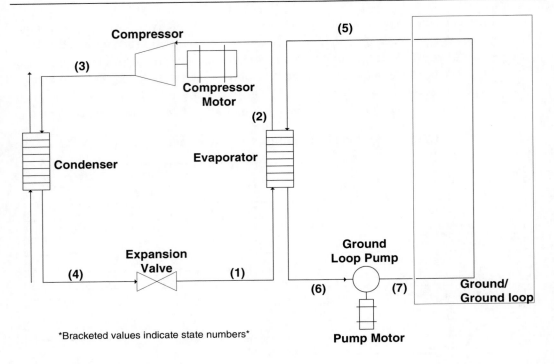

Figure 1. Heat pump system 1.

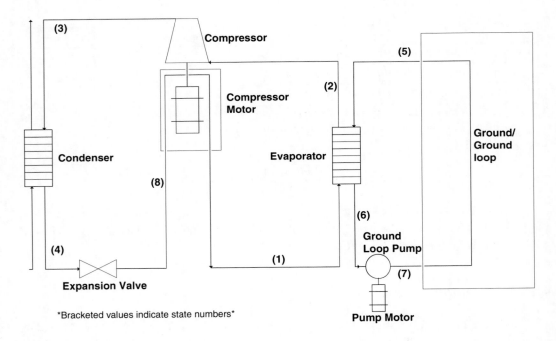

Figure 2. Heat pump system 2.

Refrigerant at state 1 enters the evaporator where thermal energy is transferred to it from the ground loop. At state 2, the refrigerant exits the evaporator as superheated vapour and enters the compressor, where the pressure increases and the refrigerant exits as a high pressure superheated vapour at state 3. The refrigerant enters the condenser where thermal energy is extracted from the refrigerant and supplied to the space. The subcooled liquid at the state 4 passes through an expansion valve that reduces its pressure to that of the evaporator.

Heat pump system 2 (Figure 2) is identical to system 1 except for a modified flow path used for motor cooling. The new path directs the refrigerant to the compressor electric motor assembly where wasted heat is recovered, increasing the energy content of the refrigerant at the evaporator inlet.

Heat pump system 3 (Figure 3) incorporates an economizer, following the work of Ma and Chai [9]. In the economizer heat exchanger, heat is transferred between two refrigerant flows.

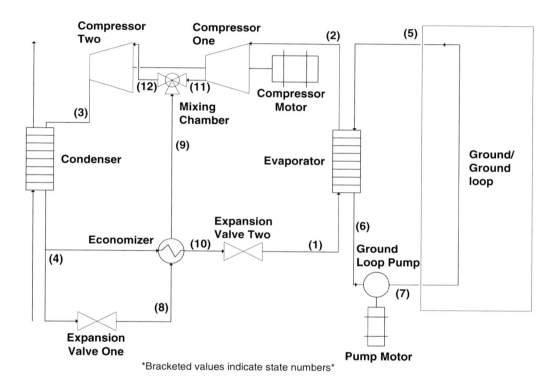

Figure 3. Heat pump system 3.

The new flow path, called the supplementary circuit, includes an expansion valve that allows the flow to exist at an intermediate pressure between the evaporator and condenser pressure. Heat is extracted from the main refrigerant circuit by the supplementary circuit, and the main flow passes through an expansion valve lowering its pressure to the evaporator pressure. The supplementary circuit flow passes from the economizer to the compressor through a supplementary inlet. For ease of analysis, Ma and Chai [9] as well as Ma and Zhao [25] suggest interpreting the compression process as quasi two-stage compression with an intermediate mixing chamber.

4.2. Ground Loop Heat Exchanger

All systems considered here utilize the same ground loop arrangement (Figure 4). The study considers commercial scale heat pumps. Natural Resources Canada [6] suggests a vertical borehole with a U-tube arrangement as best for heating and cooling applications, so this arrangement is adopted.

The borehole design consists of a main flow through the evaporator, a single pump, and multiple parallel loops. A cool water/glycol (brine) mixture flows from the evaporator to the pump, where the pressure is increased to the required level. The brine flow is then split into the parallel loops, and absorbs heat from the surrounding ground.

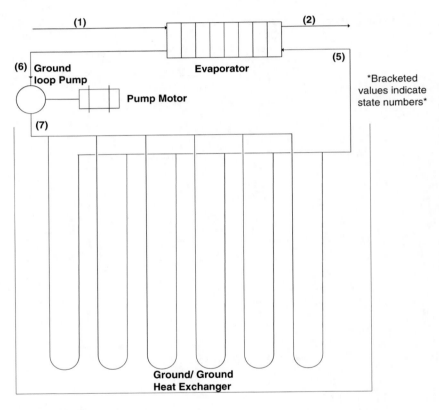

Figure 4. Basic layout of ground loop.

5. ANALYSIS

The analyses performed are explained in four sections: one for each heat pump in the three systems and one for the ground loop, which is common for each system.

5.1. Heat Pump System 1

Refrigerant enters the inlet of the compressor at state 2. The pressure at state 2 is assumed and the temperature is taken as the saturation temperature plus an assumed degree of superheating, as presented by Ma and Zhao [25] and Fu et al. [37]. The temperature at this state is restricted to be below that of state 5 (evaporator inlet for the GL). The refrigerant is compressed to a higher pressure at state 3.

The ideal enthalpy value at state 3 is determined assuming isentropic compression $(s_2 = s_{3s})$, and a preset pressure at the compressor exit. For an actual compression process, the specific enthalpy at state 3 is calculated using the compressor efficiency:

$$\eta_{comp} = \frac{h_{3s} - h_2}{h_3 - h_2} \tag{1}$$

where h_{3s} denotes the ideal specific enthalpy for an isentropic process, and h_2 and h_3 are the actual specific enthalpy at states 2 and 3 is the isentropic efficiency of the compressor.

The superheated refrigerant exiting the compressor is condensed at constant pressure. The amount of heat extracted from the refrigerant for space heating is set to meet the building load.

The temperature at state 4 is taken as the saturation temperature less an assumed degree of subcooling, as suggested by Ma and Zhao [25] and Fu et al. [37]. The mass flow rate of refrigerant can be found with a condenser energy rate balance:

$$\dot{Q}_{load} = \dot{m}_{ref}(h_3 - h_4) \tag{2}$$

where $\dot{Q}_{load}$ is the specified heating load, $\dot{m}_{ref}$ is the refrigerant mass flow rate, and h_3 and h_4 are the specific enthalpies for states 3 and 4, respectively.

Similar to the condenser, flow through the evaporator is assumed to incur no pressure drop and expansion is assumed isenthalpic $(h_4 = h_1)$. The quality of the refrigerant is evaluated as follows:

$$x = \frac{h_1 - h_f}{h_{fg}} \tag{3}$$

where h_1 is the specific enthalpy at state 1, h_f is the enthalpy of saturated liquid refrigerant and h_{fg} is the enthalpy difference between saturated liquid and saturated vapour refrigerant coinciding with the pressure at state 1.

The rate of heat transfer from the ground loop to the refrigerant ($\dot{Q}_{evap}$) through the evaporator is calculated as follows:

$$\dot{Q}_{evap} = \dot{m}_{ref}(h_2 - h_1) \tag{4}$$

The rate of heat transfer to the refrigerant is equal to the rate of heat removal from the GL brine through the evaporator (see section 5.4).

The rate of work required by the compressor is expressed as

$$\dot{W}_{comp} = \dot{m}_{ref}(h_3 - h_2) \tag{5}$$

The electric motor provides mechanical work to the compressor and its rate of electrical energy consumption can be evaluated as follows:

$$\dot{E}_{comp,motor} = \frac{\dot{W}_{comp}}{\eta_{EM}} \tag{6}$$

where η_{EM} is the efficiency of the electric motor.

The COP for the heat pump can be written as

$$COP_{HP} = \frac{\dot{Q}_{load}}{\dot{W}_{comp}} \tag{7}$$

where COP_{HP} is the coefficient of performance of the heat pump cycle with the exclusion of motor and pump work and $\dot{Q}_{load}$ is the building heating load. The COP can alternately be expressed as

$$COP_{HP} = \frac{\dot{Q}_{load}}{\dot{Q}_{load} - \dot{Q}_{Evap}} \tag{8}$$

where $\dot{Q}_{Evap}$ is the rate of heat transfer to the refrigerant through the evaporator.

The system coefficient of performance COP_{System} is similar to the heat pump COP, but employs the electrical energy supply rate in the denominator:

$$COP_{System} = \frac{\dot{Q}_{load}}{\dot{E}_{motor,total}} \tag{9}$$

where $\dot{E}_{motor,total}$ is the total rate of electrical energy consumed by the compressor and pump motors. The total rate of electrical consumption is

$$\dot{E}_{motor,total} = \dot{E}_{comp,motor} + \dot{E}_{motor,pump} \tag{10}$$

where $\dot{E}_{comp,motor}$ and $\dot{E}_{motor,pump}$ are the rates of electrical energy consumption of the compressor motor and pump motor, respectively.

5.2. Heat Pump System 2

The analysis of the heat pump system with motor cooling is similar to that of system 1. The differences are an additional state (state 8) and the conditions at state 1. No pressure drop is assumed between states 8 and 1. For isenthalpic pressure drop across the expansion valve ($h_4 = h_8$) the quality of the refrigerant is determined as

$$x = \frac{h_8 - h_f}{h_{fg}} \tag{11}$$

where h_8 is the specific enthalpy at state 8 and h_{fg} is the enthalpy difference between saturated liquid and saturated vapour refrigerant coinciding with the pressure at state 8.

The available waste energy from the compressor motor is the difference between the compressor work rate and the electrical energy consumption rate of the motor:

$$\dot{E}_{motor,waste} = \dot{E}_{comp,motor} - \dot{W}_{comp} \tag{12}$$

where $\dot{E}_{motor,waste}$ is the rate waste energy of the compressor motor, $\dot{E}_{comp,motor}$ is the rate of electrical energy consumption for the motor, and $\dot{W}_{comp}$ is the rate of work required by the compressor. It is assumed that all waste energy from the electric motor is converted to thermal energy which is transferred to the refrigerant. The transferred heat increases the specific enthalpy of the refrigerant from the inlet to outlet of the motor assembly:

$$\dot{Q}_{waste\ heat} = \dot{m}_{ref}(h_1 - h_8) \tag{13}$$

where

$$\dot{Q}_{waste\ heat} = \dot{E}_{motor,waste} \tag{14}$$

When motor cooling is incorporated, the heat pump COP is slightly modified so that the heat supply rate to the refrigerant from the motor is included:

$$COP_{HP} = \frac{\dot{Q}_{load}}{\dot{Q}_{load}-(\dot{Q}_{evap}+\dot{Q}_{waste\ heat})} \tag{15}$$

COP_{System} is defined the same as for system 1 (Equation 9).

5.3. Heat Pump System 3

System 3 is the same as previous systems, but the refrigerant enters the compressor at state 2 and is compressed to an intermediate pressure (state 11). The specific enthalpy at state 11 is calculated as follows:

$$\eta_{comp} = \frac{h_{11s}-h_2}{(h_{11}-h_2)} \tag{16}$$

where h_{11s} denotes the specific enthalpy for an isentropic process at state 11, and η_{comp} is the compressor isentropic efficiency.

The refrigerant at the exit of compressor 1 enters the mixing chamber with the refrigerant from the economizer in the supplementary circuit. An energy balance for the mixer yields:

$$\dot{m}_{ref}h_{12} = \dot{m}_{main}h_{11} + \dot{m}_{supp}h_9 \tag{17}$$

where $\dot{m}_{main}$ and $\dot{m}_{supp}$ are the refrigerant mass flow rates through the evaporator and the supplementary circuit, respectively.

For simplicity, the conditions at state 9 are set to those at state 11, following the approach of others [9, 25]. The sum of the mass flow rates at state 11 and state 9 is equal to the total refrigerant flow rate through the condenser. The ratio of the flow rate of the main circuit to the total refrigerant flow rate through the condenser can be written as

$$X = \frac{\dot{m}_{main}}{\dot{m}_{ref}} \tag{18}$$

Then, the flow rates through the regular and supplementary loops are expressible as

$$\dot{m}_{main} = X\dot{m}_{ref} \tag{19}$$

$$\dot{m}_{supp} = (1 - X)\dot{m}_{ref} \tag{20}$$

Combining Equations 17, 19 and 20 results in an expression for the specific enthalpy at state 12:

$$h_{12} = Xh_{11} + (1 - X)h_9 \tag{21}$$

The value of X can be calculated with an energy balance for the economizer, which involves the same flows as the mixing chamber:

$$\dot{m}_{main}h_4 + \dot{m}_{supp}h_8 = \dot{m}_{main}h_{10} + \dot{m}_{supp}h_9 \tag{22}$$

where $h_4, h_8, h_9,$ and h_{10} are the specific enthalpy at states 4, 8, 9 and 10, respectively. Rearranging and introducing Equations 19 and 20 yields an expression for X:

$$X = \frac{h_8 - h_9}{h_9 - h_8 - h_4 + h_{10}} \tag{23}$$

State 4 is determined assuming a degree of subcooling. At the condenser exit the refrigerant is split into two separate flows, one which feeds the main circuit and the other the supplementary circuit.

The main-circuit flow enters the economizer where heat is extracted from the refrigerant resulting in a higher degree of subcooling at state 10 [9, 25]. The extra degree of subcooling beyond state 4 is set as a degree of temperature difference between states 10 and 4 where

$$T_{10} = T_4 - \text{ degree of extra subcooling} \tag{24}$$

With an assumed intermediate pressure the properties at state 8 are determined assuming isenthalpic expansion through the expansion valve.

The temperature at state 9 is assumed, allowing the refrigerant at state 12 to exist as a saturated or superheated vapour after mixing with the flow at state 11. For the compression process,

$$\eta_{comp} = \frac{h_{3s} - h_{12}}{(h_3 - h_{12})} \tag{25}$$

where h_{3s} denotes the specific enthalpy at state 3 for isentropic compression, and h_3 and h_{12} are the actual specific enthalpies at states 3 and 12. The mass flow rate of refrigerant through the condenser is found using the enthalpies at states 3 and 4 and the load (Equation 2).

The heat transfer rate required from the GL for this arrangement is determined as

$$\dot{Q}_{evap} = \dot{m}_{main}(h_2 - h_1) \tag{26}$$

The overall compressor work rate is

$$\dot{W}_{comp} = \dot{W}_{comp,1} + \dot{W}_{comp,2} \tag{27}$$

where $\dot{W}_{comp,1}$ and $\dot{W}_{comp,2}$ are work rates for compressors 1 and 2, respectively, expressible as

$$\dot{W}_{comp,1} = \dot{m}_{main}(h_{11} - h_2) \tag{28}$$

$$\dot{W}_{comp,2} = \dot{m}_{ref}(h_3 - h_{12}) \tag{29}$$

The coefficients of performance for the heat pump and the entire system are as given in Equations 7-9.

5.4. Ground Loop Heat Exchanger

Initially the pressure at state 5 is set and the temperature at state 5 is determined as 2°C below the ground temperature. The ground loop consists of a mixture of water and glycol. Treating this as an ideal mixture, the enthalpy at state 5 is found as follows:

$$h_m = \sum_{i=1}^{k} mf_i \cdot h_i \tag{30}$$

where h_m is the specific enthalpy of the solution, mf_i is the mass fraction of species i, and h_i is the specific enthalpy of species i in the mixture at the given conditions. The mass fraction of glycol is fixed to provide the ground loop fluid with a reasonable freezing temperature, which is required to be below that of the coldest ground temperature and the temperature at the inlet of the evaporator on the HP side [30].

The pressure across the GL side of the evaporator is assumed constant. The temperature at state 6 is constrained to remain above the freezing temperature of the GL fluid. The mass flow rate of brine is calculated with an energy balance for the evaporator, and coincides with the calculated flow rate and enthalpies on the HP side of the heat exchanger.

The mass flow rate is then divided between a series of parallel loops. The mass flow rate through an individual loop is set to allow for a desired flow regime and also establishes the number of parallel loops required, as follows:

$$n_{pl} = \frac{\dot{m}_{GL,Evaporator}}{\dot{m}_{GL,parallel}} \tag{31}$$

where n_{pl} is number of parallel loops, $\dot{m}_{GL,Evaporator}$ is the flow rate across the evaporator between states 5 and 6, and $\dot{m}_{GL,parallel}$ is the flow rate though an individual parallel loop.

The pressure at state 7 is estimated from the pressure drop within the GL system and the specific enthalpy is found using the required pump work to counter the pressure loss. The pressure loss for an individual parallel loop is found as

$$\Delta P_{parallel} = f \frac{l_{parallel}}{D_i} \frac{\rho_{5,7} V_{avg}^{\;2}}{2} \tag{32}$$

where f is the friction factor, $l_{parallel}$ is the length of a single parallel loop, D_i is the inner diameter of the pipe, $\rho_{5,7}$ is the density of the fluid at the average temperature between states 5 and 7, and V_{avg} is the average fluid velocity in the piping. The temperature at state 7 is assumed to be that of state 6 in order to estimate the fluid properties between states 5 and 7.

A standard pipe size for the GL piping is selected and the velocity of the fluid inside a parallel loop is found using:

$$V_{avg,parallel} = \frac{\dot{m}_{GL,parallel}}{\rho_{5,7} A_c} \tag{33}$$

where $\dot{m}_{GL,parallel}$ is the fluid mass flow rate through a single parallel loop, A_c is the cross sectional area of the piping, and $\rho_{5,7}$ is the density of the fluid at the average temperature between states 5 and 7.

The Reynolds number of the flow through a parallel loop is found as

$$Re = \frac{\rho_{5,7} V_{avg,parallel} D_i}{\mu_{5,7}} \tag{34}$$

where Re is the Reynolds number, $\mu_{5,7}$ is the dynamic viscosity, D_i is the pipe inner diameter, and V_{avg} is the average fluid velocity in the piping.

Since the polyethylene pipe material is assumed smooth for internal flow [31], the friction factor of the pipe can be determined as follows:

$$f = \begin{cases} \dfrac{64}{Re} & \text{for } Re \leq 2300 \text{ (laminar)} \\[4mm] (0.790 \ln Re - 1.64)^{-2} & \text{for } Re > 2300 \text{ (turbulent)} \end{cases} \tag{35a}$$

$$\tag{35b}$$

The expression for laminar flow is a modified version of the Darcy-Wiesbach friction factor given by Cengel [31], while that for transitional and turbulent flow (Equation 35b) is the first Petukhov equation [31], which provides the friction factor for turbulent flow in smooth pipes.

To estimate the length of the GL heat exchanger, we assume that the outer surface of the grout is at the temperature of the ground and that the ground is an infinite heat source, yielding the cross sectional schematic and thermal resistance network in Figure 5. The thermal resistances of the layers in Figure 5, on a per unit length basis, are as follows:

$$R_1 = \frac{1}{h_{conv}(2\pi\, r_1 l)} \tag{36}$$

$$R_2 = \frac{\ln(r_2 - r_1)}{2\pi\, k_{pipe}\, l} \tag{37}$$

$$R_3 = \frac{\ln(r_3 - r_2)}{2\pi\, k_{grout}\, l} \tag{38}$$

where R_1 is the convection thermal resistance between the pipe wall and the GL fluid, R_2 is the conductive resistance through the pipe wall and R_3 is the conductive resistance through the grout encasing the pipe. The radii r_1, r_2, and r_3 are shown in Figure 5. The terms k_{pipe} and k_{grout} are the thermal conductivities of the pipe wall and grout, respectively. Also, h_{conv} is the convection coefficient between the GL fluid and the pipe inner wall, and is calculated assuming forced internal convection with constant surface temperature.

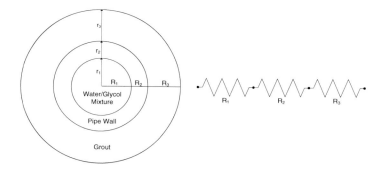

Figure 5. Cross-section of pipe configuration and thermal resistance network.

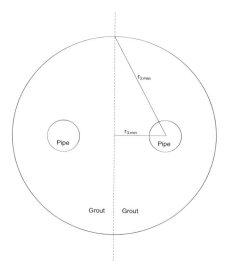

Figure 6. Cross-section of a single borehole.

Within vertical loop systems two pipes are contained in a single borehole and common borehole diameters exist in the industry. Figure 6 shows a diagram of a borehole cross-section, which has an axis of symmetry. The radius r_3 is estimated as the mean of the maximum and minimum grout radii.

To find h_{conv} the Nusselt number is evaluated as follows:

(39a)

$$Nu = \begin{cases} 3.66 & \text{for } Re \leq 2300 \\[2em] \dfrac{\left(\frac{f}{8}\right)(Re - 1000)Pr_{5,7}}{1 + 12.7\left(\frac{f}{8}\right)^{0.5}\left(Pr_{5,7}^{\frac{2}{3}} - 1\right)} & \text{for } 2300 < Re < 10{,}000 \qquad (39b) \\[2em] 0.023Re^{0.8}Pr_{5,7}{}^{n} & \text{for } Re \leq 10{,}000 \end{cases}$$

(39c)

where f is the friction factor and $Pr_{5,7}$ is the Prandtl number at the conditions between states 5 and 7. Equations 39b and 39c are known as the second Petukhov equation and the Dittus-Boelter equation, respectively. In Equation 39c, the coefficient n is set to 0.4 for heating [31]. The convection coefficient is then evaluated using

$$Nu = \frac{h_{conv} k_{brine}}{D_i} \qquad (40)$$

where k_{brine} is the thermal conductivity of the GL brine for the mean temperature between states 5 and 7.

The thermal resistances (Equations 36-38) sum to provide a total resistance per unit length of pipe:

$$R_{total} = R_1 + R_2 + R_3 \qquad (41)$$

The heat transfer to the ground loop fluid per unit length is

$$\dot{Q}_{ht} = \frac{T_{\infty 1} - T_{\infty 2}}{R_{total}} \qquad (42)$$

where $T_{\infty 1}$ denotes the temperature on the outer wall of the grout (ground temperature) and $T_{\infty 2}$ the mean fluid temperature between states 5 and 7. The length of a single parallel loop is related to its required heat transfer rate and the heat transfer rate per unit length as follows:

$$l_{parallel} = \frac{\dot{Q}_{GL,parallel}}{\dot{Q}_{ht}} \qquad (43)$$

The heat rate required from the overall ground loop can be determined as the product of the actual heat transfer rate required from the ground $\dot{Q}_{GL,actual}$ and the number of parallel loops:

$$\dot{Q}_{GL,parallel} = \frac{\dot{Q}_{GL,actual}}{n_{pl}} \tag{44}$$

When pump work is taken into account the heat rate required from the ground differs from the rate required by the HP through the evaporator. That is,

$$\dot{Q}_{GL,actual} = \dot{Q}_{evap} - \dot{W}_{pump} \tag{45}$$

The total pump work rate $\dot{W}_{pump}$ is dependent on the work required per unit mass to overcome the pressure drop within a parallel loop, the mass flow rate through a loop and the number of loops n_{pl} within the ground heat exchanger system:

$$\dot{W}_{pump} = n_{pl}\dot{m}_{GL,parallel}w_{pump,actual} \tag{46}$$

where $\dot{m}_{GL,parallel}$ is the mass flow rate through a single parallel loop and $w_{pump,actual}$ is the specific pump work. The pump isentropic efficiency can be written as

$$\eta_{pump} = \frac{w_{pump,ideal}}{h_{7a}-h_6} \tag{47}$$

where the ideal pump work is for isentropic pumping. The ideal specific pump work is related to the pressure difference across the pump:

$$w_{pump,ideal} = v_6(P_7 - P_6) \tag{48}$$

where P_7 is determined from the pressure drop in a parallel loop:

$$P_7 = P_5 + \Delta P_{parallel} \tag{49}$$

In solving the above equations, Equations 34 and 43 to 49 are solved concurrently. A new temperature for state 7 is calculated using the heat transfer rate required and the mass flow rate of a parallel loop, along with an estimated specific heat assuming the original man temperature between states 5 and 7, as follows:

$$\dot{Q}_{GL,parallel} = \dot{m}_{parallel}\,c_{p,5,7}(T_5 - T_{7,new}) \tag{50}$$

where $\dot{Q}_{GL,parallel}$ is the heat transfer rate in a parallel loop, $\dot{m}_{parallel}$ is the mass flow rate through a parallel loop, $c_{p,5,7}$ is the specific heat at the mean temperature between states 5 and 7, T_5 is the temperature at state 5, and $T_{7,new}$ is the new temperature at state 7. This iterative procedure is repeated to improve the estimate of T_7.

Finally, the electrical power required from the pump motor is found as

$$\dot{E}_{motor,pump} = \frac{\dot{W}_{pump}}{\eta_{EM}}$$ (51)

where $\dot{W}_{pump}$ is the pump work rate required for the GL and η_{EM} is the motor efficiency.

6. SIMULATION

To simulate the performance of the three systems and to assess their sensitivities to parameter variations, a computer code is developed using Engineering Equation Solver (EES) incorporating the assumptions and analyses in Sections 3-5. EES's thermodynamic property databases are utilized, and water/anti-freeze mixtures are assumed to be ideal. The simulation allows the overall system to adjust to variations in individual parameters.

The simulation program is verified in several ways. First, the system arrangements assuming process efficiencies of 100% are assessed manually and compared with the simulation. Then this verification is repeated for systems with losses. In all cases the simulation results were found to be in agreement.

To validate the simulations, the simulation code is applied to a system analyzed experimentally by Hepbasli [20]. That system consists of a basic vapour compression heat pump that uses a vertical borehole ground connection. The refrigerant is R-22 and the brine is a water/ethyl glycol mixture with 10% glycol by mass. The system parameters presented by Hepbasli [20] agree well with those determined by the developed simulation (Tables 3 and 4), with differences of about 1% for the HP and system COPs.

Table 3. Comparison of state conditions determined via simulation and experiment*

Location	Temperature (°C)		Pressure (kPa)		Specific enthalpy (kJ/kg)		Specific entropy (kJ/kg K)	
	Sim.	Expt.	Sim.	Expt.	Sim.	Expt.	Sim.	Expt.
Evaporator inlet	-11.12	-10.8	341	341	250.7	251.15	1.195	1.196
Evaporator exit	-6.0	-6.0	341	341	404.2	404.6	1.781	1.782
Condenser inlet	99.3	99.2	1911	1911	464.4	464.3	1.822	1.822
Condenser exit	40.77	40.8	1911	1911	250.7	251.15	1.169	1.170

*Sim. represents the simulation program used here, and Expt. represents the experimental study [20] utilized for validation.

Table 4. Comparison of performance characteristics determined via simulation and experimentally

Parameter	Simulation	Experiment
Compressor power (kW)	1.2	1.5
Refrigerant flow rate (kg/s)	0.199	0. 2
COP$_{HP}$	2.84	2.85

7. RESULTS AND DISCUSSION

The systems are compared under the original conditions and assumptions. Then, the effects of changing the efficiency of components that consume power and various operating conditions specific to the heat pump cycle are examined. The effects on performance and ground loop requirements of variations in condenser and evaporator pressure along with the degree of superheating and subcooling at the outlet of the evaporator and condenser, respectively, are explored. The ranges of parameter variations are selected so that the systems can theoretically operate, and encompass those described in the literature.

7.1. Basic Comparison

The systems considered are compared in terms of compressor and pump work rate, heat transfer rate from the ground loop system, overall ground loop length, and performance (for heat pump and system COPs). The state conditions for systems 1 to 3, respectively, are provided in Tables 5, 6 and 7. The main operation factors for the heat pumps are compared in Table 8.

Table 5. Conditions for system 1 for states in Figures 1 and 4

State	Fluid	Temperature (°C)	Pressure (kPa)	Quality	Specific enthalpy (kJ/kg)	Mass flow rate (kg/s)
1	Refrigerant	-10.09	200	0.2985	99.92	0.5136
2	Refrigerant	-5.093	200	1	248.7	0.5136
3	Refrigerant	61.16	1000	1	294.6	0.5136
4	Refrigerant	34.37	1000	0	99.92	0.5136
5	Brine	7.3	150	0	170.9	3.758
6	Brine	1.3	150	0	150.6	3.758
7	Brine	2.111	223.6	0	150.6	3.758

Table 6. Conditions for system 2 for states in Figures 2 and 4

State	Fluid	Temperature (°C)	Pressure (kPa)	Quality	Specific enthalpy (kJ/kg)	Mass flow rate (kg/s)
1	Refrigerant	-10.09	200	0.3542	111.4	0.5136
2	Refrigerant	-5.093	200	1	248.7	0.5136
3	Refrigerant	61.16	1000	1	294.6	0.5136
4	Refrigerant	34.37	1000	0	99.92	0.5136
5	Brine	7.3	150	0	170.9	3.468
6	Brine	1.3	150	0	150.6	3.468
7	Brine	2.111	223.6	0	150.6	3.468
8	Refrigerant	-10.09	200	0.2985	99.92	0.5136

Table 7. Conditions for system 3 for states in Figures 3 and 4

State	Fluid	Temperature (°C)	Pressure (kPa)	Quality	Specific enthalpy (kJ/kg)	Mass flow rate (kg/s)
1	Refrigerant	-10.09	200	0.2632	92.66	0.4905
2	Refrigerant	-5.093	200	1	248.7	0.4905
3	Refrigerant	61.86	1000	1	295.3	0.5117
4	Refrigerant	34.37	1000	0	99.92	0.5117
5	Brine	7.3	150	0	170.9	3.764
6	Brine	1.3	150	0	150.6	3.764
7	Brine	2.111	200	0	150.6	3.764
8	Refrigerant	8.91	400	0.1878	99.92	0.02119
9	Refrigerant	22.41	400	1	268.1	0.02119
10	Refrigerant	29.37	1000	0	92.66	0.4905
11	Refrigerant	22.41	400	1	268.1	0.4905
12	Refrigerant	22.41	400	1	268.1	0.5117

Table 8. Heat pump and ground loop characteristics for Systems

Characteristic	System 1	System 2	System 3
Pressure ratio	5	5	5
Compressor work rate (kW)	23.57	23.57	23.45
Compressor motor electricity rate (kW)	29.46	29.46	29.31
Pump work rate (kW)	0.2978	0.2749	0.2983
Pump motor electricity rate (kW)	0.3723	0.3436	0.3729
Heat rate supplied by GL system (kW)	76.43	70.54	76.55
Total GL length	3346	3088	3352
COP$_{HP}$	4.242	4.242	4.265
COP$_{System}$	3.352	3.355	3.369

System 3 is observed to have the highest COPs, with a HP COP of 4.265 and a system COP of 3.369, mostly due to its lower compressor work. System 3 also requires the most heat from the ground, leading to it having the longest round loop and consequently the greatest pump work. The increase in pump work reduces the system COP slightly. The HP COP and system COP for system 3 exceed those of system 1 by 0.54% and 0.54%, respectively. In system 3, only part of the refrigerant flowing through the condenser is compressed from the lowest to highest pressure, reducing the work required by the first compressor.

If system 3 yields the same compressor exit temperature as systems 1 and 2, a lower pressure ratio between the condenser and evaporator pressure would be required, which reduces the compressor work and increases the COP beyond the values in Table 8.

Systems 1 and 2 require the same compressor work and HP COP (4.242). But all the required heat in system 1 is extracted from the ground, whereas system 2 allows for some of the heat to be obtained from electric motor waste heat. Thermal energy is extracted from the ground for system 1 at a rate of 76.43 kW compared to only 70.54 kW for system 2. The reduction of the heat transfer rate from the ground reduces the required GL length by 260 meters (8%) for the same heating load, which reduces pump power and increases system COP (Equation 7).

The GL length per unit heat supply rate to the building space for systems 1, 2 and 3 is 33.46 m/kW, 30.88 m/kW and 33.52 m/kW, respectively. These values coincide with the vertical GL sizing guidelines of Natural Resources Canada [6], which suggests a range of 17 to 39 m of vertical loop length per kW heating load for GL layouts utilizing a nominal pipe size between 25.4 and 50.8 mm. Kara [24] calculates a length of 33.6 m/kW for the basic vapour compression cycle with similar operating conditions.

In Table 8 it can be seen that the differences, for systems 1 and 2, are about 8% for heat input rate, GL length and pump work rate. This energy saving is not directly evident in the system COP because pump work has little influence on it; the system with motor cooling exhibits has a system COP increase of only 0.09%.

Note that multiple parallel loops experience much lower pressure drops than a single loop, for a fixed heat supply rate.

7.2. System Component Analysis

This section investigates and compares the effects of varying several heat pump component parameters, including compressor, pump and electric motor efficiencies. The condenser and evaporator pressure for each system remain fixed at those for the basic systems.

7.2.1. Compressor Efficiency Analysis

The compressor efficiency is varied from 65% to 100% for each of the heat pump systems, following the range given by Cengel et al. [30] for low to high efficiency compressors. The results (Figure 7) show that HP COP increases nearly linearly with compressor efficiency. The curves for systems 1 and 2 are identical. The slopes of the curves differ for systems 1 and 3, with the COP of system 3 increasing more rapidly with compressor efficiency. The differences in heat pump COP range from 3.81 to 5.32 (or by 1.51) for systems 1 and 2 and from 3.80 to 5.42 (or by 1.62) for system 3. System 3 is more sensitive to variations in compressor efficiency than systems 1 and 2. This behaviour stems from the design and operation of system 3, which includes two stages of compression. For compressor 2, the conditions at the inlet (state 12) change with compressor efficiency, unlike compressor one which has static inlet conditions over the entire range of efficiencies. When the efficiency is low, the work required by system 3 exceeds that required by system 1 to achieve the same condenser pressure. As the efficiency is varied the mass flow rate of the refrigerant through the condenser varies as well, in relation to the specific enthalpy at state 3. Figure 8 shows that the specific enthalpy at state 3 for systems 1 and 2 are identical. Overall the specific enthalpy with regard to the same state within system 3 exceeds that of system 1 and progressively approaches the values observed for the basic system as efficiency increases.

The trend is inverted when the mass flow rate is considered (Figure 9). As the compressor efficiency increases the refrigerant flow rate increases. The flow rate for system 3 is always below that of the other two systems until the efficiency of the compressor is 100%, at which point the flow rates are equal. When the compressor efficiency is 100%, the compressor work in system 3 is lower than for the other two systems (Figure 10). The trend of decreasing compressor work and increasing mass flow rate through the evaporator seem to be contrdictive. The trend of reducing compressor work with increasing flow rate results from a slight change in refrigerant flow rate over the range of compressor efficiencies.

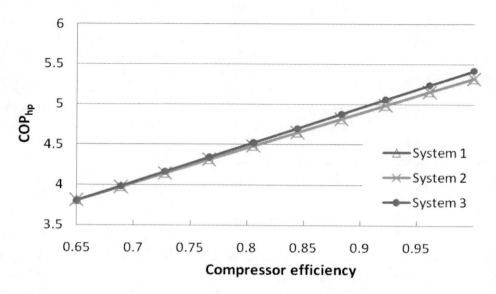

Figure 7. Effect of changing compressor efficiency on heat pump COP for each system.

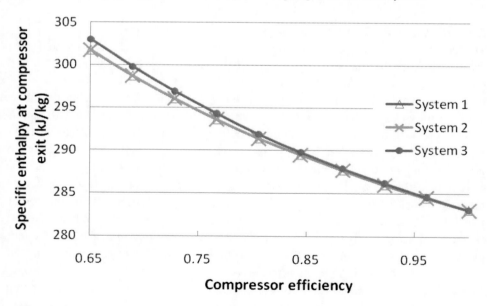

Figure 8. Effect of varying compressor efficiency on specific enthalpy at condenser inlet for each system.

It can also be observed in Figure 10 that system 3 is the most sentitive to changes in compressor efficiency as it covers the largest range of COP values. The economizer arrangement, within system 3, is best utilized when high efficiency compressors are available.

Similar trends are observed when system COP is considered (Figure 11). As the compressor efficiency increases, a larger difference is seen in system COP between system 3 and the other two systems, comparable to the HP COP trends. The system COP values for system 2 are slightly higher than for system 1. Despite the fact that different COP values are observed, the slopes of the two established trends are identical.

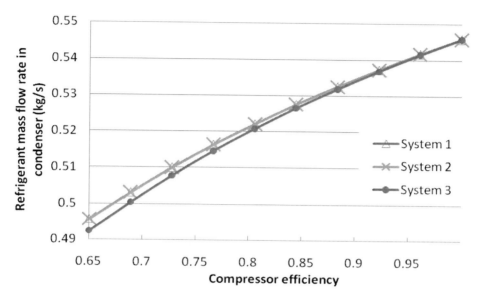

Figure 9. Effect of varying compressor efficiency on condenser flow rate for each system.

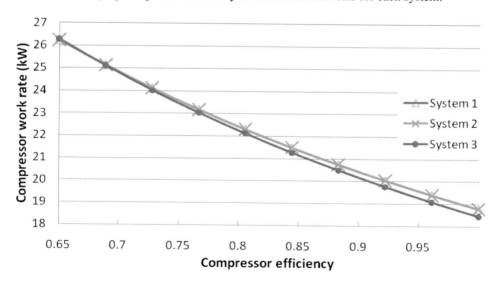

Figure 10. Effect of varying compressor efficiency on rate of compressor work required for each system.

The heat rate required from the GL varies with compressor efficiency. Figures 12 and 13 show that as the compressor efficiency increases so does the required heat transfer rate from the GL and in turn the GL length. As compressor efficiency increases less work is provided to the heat pump system; with a fixed heating load, an increased demand from the ground loop exists. It can be seen that system 3 has the largest range in heat transfer rate from the GL, attributable to the fact that system 3 exhibits the largest range in COP.

The results clearly indicate that as COP increases so does the amount of heat required from the GL and thus GL length. There are three main energy flows for the heat pump cycle: from the heat pump to the building, from the GL to the heat pump cycle, and from the compressor to the heat pump cycle.

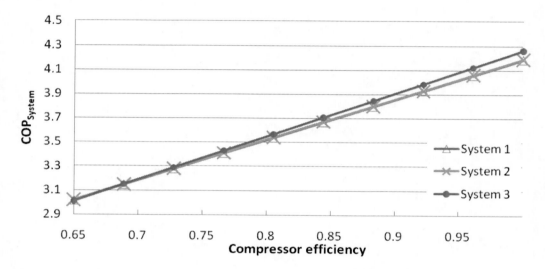

Figure 11. Effect of varying compressor efficiency on system COP for each system.

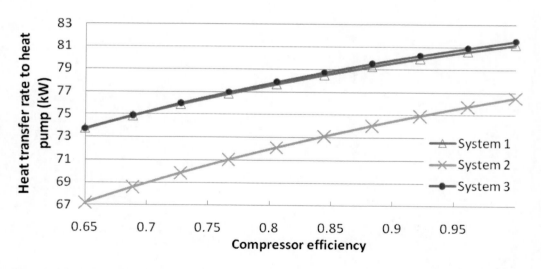

Figure 12. Effect of varying compressor efficiency on the rate of heat transfer to the heat pump from the ground loop.

When the heating load is static, reduction in the amount of energy being supplied to the heat pump cycle from the compressor creates an imbalance in energy flows into and out of the heat pump cycle.

To maintain a constant heating load, more energy is required from the GL. In an investigation of GL sizing for vertical closed loop arrangements, Cane et al. [38] illustrate that as the rate of heat required from the GL increases so does the GL length required.

RETScreen International [17] also provides information that suggests that there is a direct relationship between the COP of a heat pump system and the length required for the ground loop, when they describe ground source heat pump project analysis.

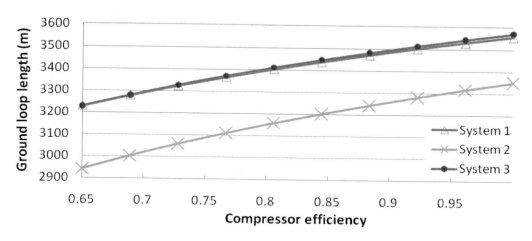

Figure 13. Effect of varying compressor efficiency on ground loop length for each system.

7.2.2. Pump Efficiency Analysis

The effect on the three different systems is investigated of varying pump efficiency, between 75% and 100%, based on values reported elsewhere [30]. When only the pump is considered, the operation of the HP systems, independent of the GL, remains constant. The rate of heat required by the refrigerant through the evaporator remains constant for each system, causing the HP COP for each system to remain unchanged throughout the investigation. System COP can only be considered for comparison of performance. The relationship between pump efficiency and system COP is illustrated in Figure 14.

The system COP for all HP arrangements increases with pump efficiency. Each system has an overall COP change of 0.013 for the range of efficiencies considered, which is relatively minor. The increase in system COP is due to a reduction in the pump work rate within all systems. Figure 15 illustrates the decrease in pump work rate as pump efficiency increases. Systems 1 and 3 have the same reduction in pump work rate (0.089 kW) and system 2 has a reduction of 0.082 kW.

The model equates the energy flows into and out of the GL. As pump power is reduced more energy must be drawn from the ground to supply the heat pumps with the energy they require. Each system experiences the same increase in the ground loop length of about 2 m, which is relatively insignificant when the entire HP system and total GL length is considered.

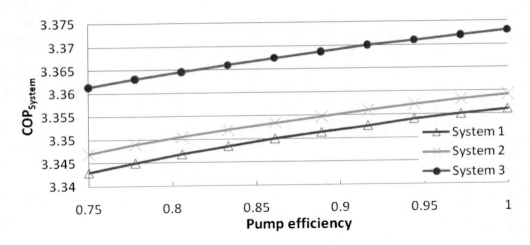

Figure 14. Effect of varying pump efficiency on system COP for each system.

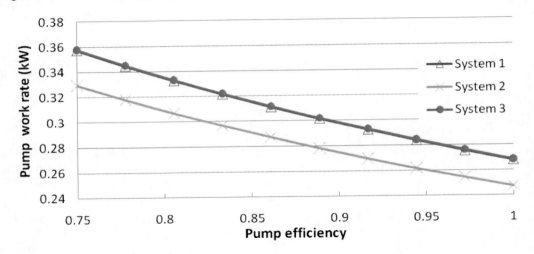

Figure 15. Effect of varying pump efficiency on rate of pump work required for each system.

7.2.3. Motor Efficiency Analysis

Electric motors are coupled to the compressors and pumps. The motor efficiency is varied from 35% to 100%, based on reported suitable ranges [30]. As in the pump analysis, varying motor efficiency affects the system COP (Figure 16). The systems behave similarly, showing a near-linear relationship between motor efficiency and system COP. The range of system COP values for all systems is seen in Figure 16 to be about 2.7 over the selected range of motor efficiencies. System 3 is slightly more sensitive to changes in motor efficiency.

The system COP range for system 2 is the smallest for the given range of motor efficiencies due to the fact that at the lowest motor efficiency the system has the highest COP which stems from lowered GL and pump requirements. When motor efficiency is low addtional thermal energy is available to the refrigerant through motor cooling, which reduces the energy transfer requirement of the GL as seen in Figure 17.

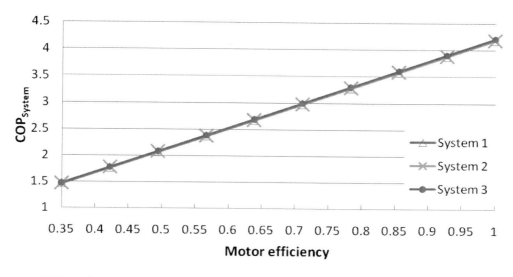

Figure 16. Effect of varying motor efficiency on system COP for each system.

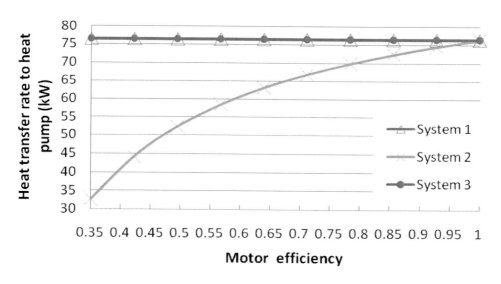

Figure 17. Effect of varying motor efficiency on rate of heat transfer to refrigerant through the evaporator for each system.

As the efficiency increases it is seen that the COP for system 2 approaches that of system 1. This trend is expected due to the fact that when the motor efficiency approaches 100% the amount of heat extracted from the motor assembly approaches zero.

The rates of heat transfer through the evaporators in systems 1 and 3 do not change with efficiency. The rate of heat transfer for system 2 is affected significantly by the motor efficiency, as motor waste heat contributes to the heat requirement of the HP system. Identical trends are found for the GL length and pump work rate requirement as those found for the heat requirement from the evaporator. When the GL load is reduced the length and pumping requirements associated also decrease (Figure 18), allowing for system 2 to have the highest system COP at low motor efficiencies.

Figure 19 illustrates the varyiation of the amount of energy consumed by the pump motor with motor efficiency. For systems 1 and 3 the trends are similar, with the amount of energy required by the pump motor decreasing with increasing motor efficiency. This trend is expected since the motor efficiency directly determines, for a given output, the amount of energy it requires, which for this model is rate of pump work. More energy is consumed by a motor with low efficiency compared to high (Equation 48). A strange trend arises for system 2 in the variation of the amount of energy required by the pump motor. Within a certain range of motor efficiencies, the amount of pump motor work increases and peaks before decreasing with an increasing efficiency.

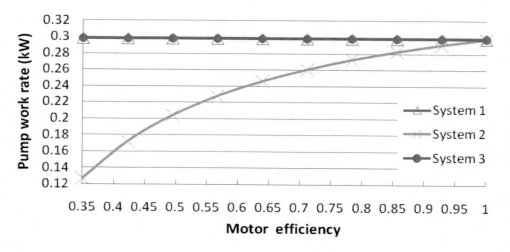

Figure 18. Effect of motor efficiency on pump work rate required within the ground loop for each system.

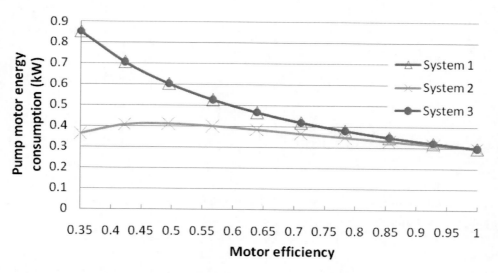

Figure 19. Effect of motor efficiency on pump motor work for each system.

The trend is attributable to the changing rate heat transfer from the GL for system 2 in this analysis. When the heat transfer requirement changes so does the GL length, with the variation in the GL length directly affecting the power required by the pump to move the brine around the loop. The pump work rate also decreases when the GL length is reduced; reducing the requirement of the pump motor to supply pump shaft work. This phenomenon coupled with variation in the pump motor efficiency leads to the trend seen in Figure 19 for system 2.

The range of pump motor energy consumption for system 2 remains relatively constant, exhibiting a variation of about 0.11 kW over the entire range of efficiencies compared to about 0.55 kW for the other 2 systems. A relatively constant, low, pump work requirement contributes to an increase in system COP.

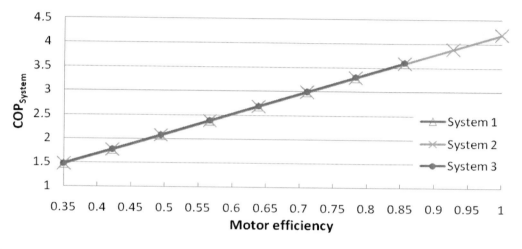

Figure 20. Effect of motor efficiency on system COP for each system, considering revised efficiency ranges.

The range of typical motor efficiencies considered in the analysis does not take into account motor design. But motors with efficiencies approaching 100% typically employ special methods to increase the efficiency, including motor or winding cooling. Thus, the motor efficiency ranges likely differ for systems with and without motor cooling. Figure 20 shows a more realistic representation of the COP trends with respect to a redefined range of motor efficiencies for systems 1 and 3.

Motor efficiency is varied from 35 to 85% for these systems, but the efficiency range is maintained at 35 to 100% for system 2. For these more realistic motor efficiency ranges, system 2 exhibits a larger potential for a high system COP, since the system COP values extend past those of systems 1 and 3.

Systems 1 and 3 are affected the most by varying motor efficiency since they exhibit the largest variations in system COPs. When realistic motor efficiencies are employed for systems 1 and 3, system 2 is found to have the largest range of system COPs. Motor cooling causes system COP not to be affected as drastically due to its reduced effect on the pump motor energy use. When the ground loop is considered only system 2 is affected.

7.3. Operating Conditions Analysis

The impact on the performance of the heat pump units is investigated by varying several operating conditions, including condenser and evaporator pressure as well as the degree of superheating and subcooling at the outlet of the evaporator and evaporator, respectively. System 3 utilizes an intermediate pressure between the evaporator and condenser pressure; the effect of varying this intermediate pressure is also investigated.

7.3.1. Condenser Pressure

A condenser pressure range of 400 to 3,000 kPa is utilized in the analysis, which spans the values reported in literature for similar systems. For working systems and in studies, the condenser pressure is usually below 2,500 kPa [19, 39]. An upper limit is set for this analysis at 3,000 kPa to provide a more comprehensive understanding.

The temperature at the condenser exit is dependent on the condenser pressure, where the temperature is set by assuming a degree of subcooling below the saturation temperature of refrigerant at the specified pressure. At low condenser pressures the temperatures at the condenser inlet and exit (states 3 and 4 for all system arrangements) become too low for use with the conventional heat distribution systems utilized in building design.

Figure 21 shows the condenser inlet and exit temperature for pressures between 400 and 3000 kPa. The inlet and outlet condenser temperatures are not useful at low condenser pressures, e.g., at 400 kPa the inlet and outlet temperatures for all the systems are about 22°C and 4°C, respectively.

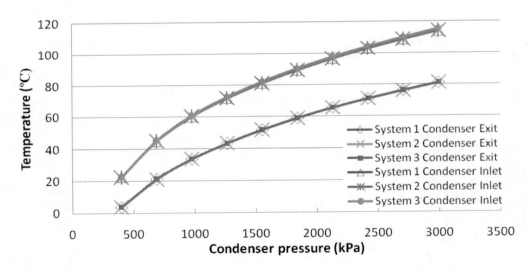

Figure 21. Effect of varying condenser pressure on condenser inlet and outlet temperatures for each system.

Of all the heat distribution arrangements, hydronic heat distribution systems typically have the lowest design temperature, usually 18-22°C. The inlet and outlet temperatures of the condenser on the building side should not be below this temperature range [9, 17, 18, 40]. Thus the lowest temperatures at the condenser inlet and exit for the heat pump cycle should be within or above the temperature range for hydronic systems to allow for proper heat transfer across the condenser. The analysis considers pressures between 650 and 3000 kPa. The HP and system COPs for all the systems decrease with increasing condenser pressure. All systems follow similar trends as pressure increases; with a rapid decrease in COP initially followed by a gradual decrease (Figures 22 and 23).

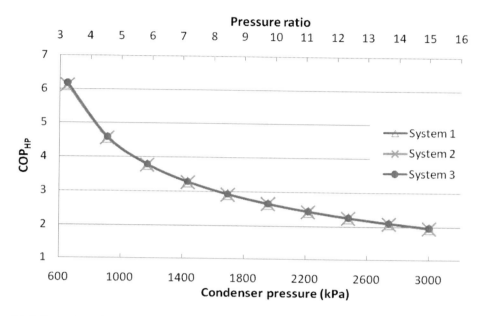

Figure 22. Effect of varying condenser pressure on heat pump COP for each system.

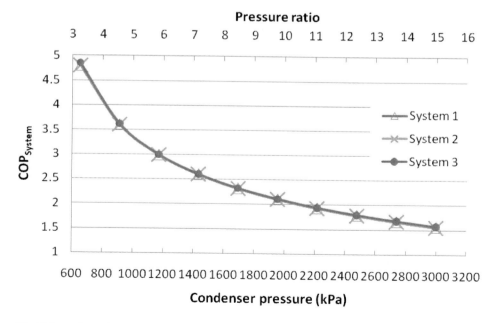

Figure 23. Effect of varying condenser pressure on system COP for each system.

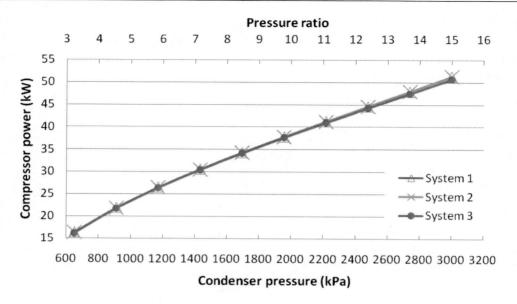

Figure 24. Effect of varying condenser pressure on compressor work for each system.

This trend is attributable to the change in compressor power over the range of condenser pressures. The increase in compressor power as pressure increases is notable at low condenser pressures and levels off at higher pressures (Figure 24). Also increasing condenser pressure raises the temperature at the inlet and exit of condenser. The condenser inlet and exit temperatures vary differently with condenser pressure (Figure 24).

The condenser inlet temperature increases more than the condenser exit temperature over the range of condenser pressures, which in turn reduces the refrigerant flow rate through the condenser. These two factors lead to the trends observed for compressor power as well as HP and system COP. It can be seen in Figures 22 and 23 that the COP decreases with increasing pressure ratio, and that system 3 exhibits a slightly higher sensitivity to variation in condenser pressure than the other two systems. As in previous analyses, the HP COPs for systems 1 and 2 are identical. It can be seen that systems 1 and 2 have a slightly smaller range of COP than system 3, mainly due to the difference in compressor power (Figure 24).

The GL length decreases with increasing condenser pressure (Figure 25), as a result of the decrease in HP COP values. When the HP COP decreases, more energy is supplied to the HP cycles through the compression process for the same heating load. For the energy flows in and out of the HP systems to match, the rate of heat transfer from the GL is reduced as condenser pressure is increased (Figure 26). System 2 is affected the most by changes in condenser pressure. An increase in compressor power creates an associated rise in the rate of compressor motor energy consumption, which is directly associated with an increase of available waste energy from the compressor motor for preheating the refrigerant in system 2. The motor waste heat is transferred to the refrigerant, reducing the heat transfer rate between the GL and the HP.

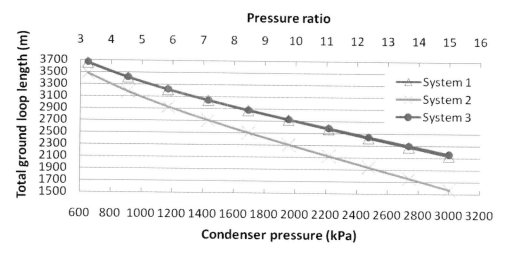

Figure 25. Effect of varying condenser pressure on ground loop length for each system.

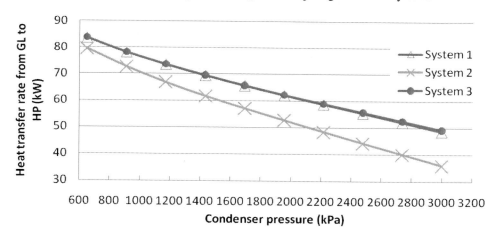

Figure 26. Effect of varying condenser pressure on the heat transfer rate from the GL for each system.

7.3.2. Evaporator Pressure

The effect of varying evaporator pressure on the systems is considered, with a minimum evaporator pressure fixed so that the refrigerant temperature at the evaporator inlet is above the freezing temperature of the brine solution in the ground loop (-13.08°C). The maximum pressure is set so that the refrigerant temperature at the evaporator exit does not exceed the brine temperature at the evaporator inlet and so that the refrigerant evaporator inlet temperature is below that of the brine evaporator exit temperature, to allow for proper heat transfer. An evaporator pressure range of 178 to 305 kPa satisfies theses conditions.

As evaporator pressure increases, HP and system COPs increase for all systems (Figures 27 and 28). The trends are similar to the ones observed in the condenser pressure analysis. As the pressure ratio between the condenser and evaporator increases, the HP and system COPs for the systems decrease.

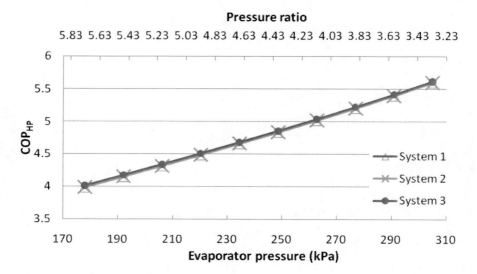

Figure 27. Effect of varying evaporator pressure on heat pump COP for each system.

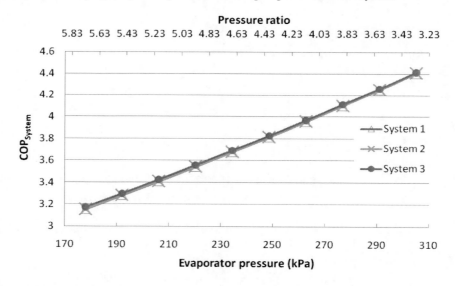

Figure 28. Effect of varying evaporator pressure on system COP for each system.

The difference in HP COP for systems 1 and 3 increases as the evaporator pressure is lowered (as pressure ratio increases); a direct result of the alteration in the fraction of total refrigerant that is fed through the main circuit of system 3. When the evaporator pressure is increased the specific enthalpy at the exit of compressor 1 (state 11) decreases. Equation 22 indicates that as the specific enthalpy at this point increases the proportion of the flow encountered by the main circuit decreases.

The specific enthalpy at the exit of compressor two is higher for system 3 than the other two systems, resulting in reduced refrigerant flow rate through the condenser. When the variation of the fraction of flow rate associated with the main circuit and the change in flow rate are combined, the trend observed in Figures 27 ad 28 are created.

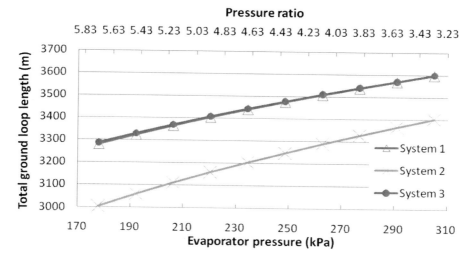

Figure 29. Effect of varying evaporator pressure on total GL length for each system.

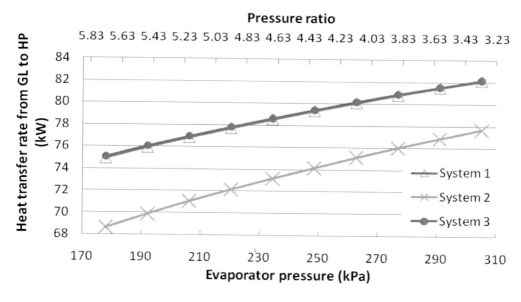

Figure 30. Effect of varying evaporator pressure on the heat transfer rate from the GL for each system.

Systems 1 and 2 are slightly more sensitive to variations in condenser pressure than system 3. System 1 and 2 have a larger change in HP COP than system 3, but the difference in HP COP ranges between systems 1 and 3 is small (0.01 or 0.62%). So in general systems 1, 2, and 3 have almost the same response to changes in evaporator pressure over the range of pressures considered.

The GL length increases with evaporator pressure (Figure 29). When the HP COP of a system increases, less energy is supplied to the HP cycles as compression work for the same heating load. For the energy flows in and out of the HP systems to be equal, the thermal energy extracted from the GL increases as evaporator pressure is increased (Figure 30).

7.3.3. Effect of Changing Condenser and Evaporator Pressures for Similar Pressure Ratios

To determine if the trends from the condenser and evaporator pressure analyses are the result of the pressures across the devices or a result of pressure ratio, the HP COPs from each analysis are compared for a common range of pressure ratios. Data utilized from the condenser pressure analysis (Section 7.3.1) match the pressure ratios specified in the evaporator analysis (Section 7.3.2). The pressure ratios coincide with varying evaporator pressure and a fixed condenser pressure of 1000 kPa and the pressure ratios corresponding to varying condenser pressure with a fixed evaporator pressure of 200 kPa. The trends with changing pressure ratios are compared in Figures 31 and 32.

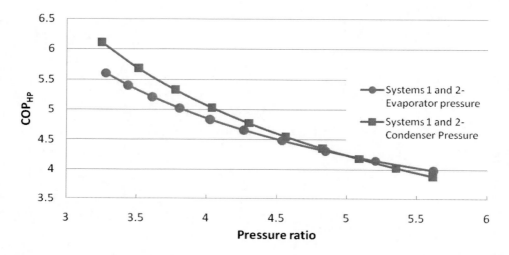

Figure 31. Variation of heat pump COPs with condenser and evaporator pressure ratio, for systems 1 and 2.

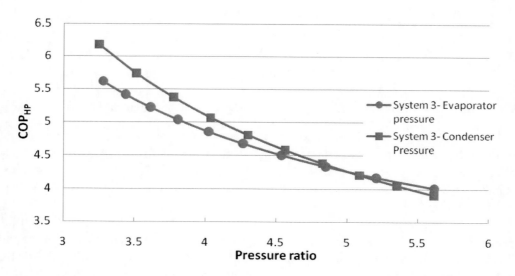

Figure 32. Variation of heat pump COPs with condenser and evaporator pressure ratio, for system 3.

As in the previous investigations, the HP COPs for systems 1 and 2 are identical. The HP COPs of these systems are independent of the pressure ratio between the condenser and evaporator, and are more dependent on the actual condenser and evaporator pressures for the systems. Hence, the pressure ratios can be the same for many combinations of condenser and evaporator pressures, but the COP values for each situation will not necessarily be identical.

For the pressure ratios considered, the HP COPs vary most with condenser pressure rather than evaporator pressure, which indicates that COP is more dependent on condenser than evaporator pressure.

7.3.4. Intermediate Pressure in System 3

The effect on performance and design parameters is examined of varying the intermediate pressure in system 3 between the condenser and evaporator pressure given in the basic analysis. To ensure proper heat transfer within the economizer, the temperature at state 9 must be below that of state 4. Similarly, the temperature at state 8 must be below that of state 10. The maximum pressure is 535.2 kPa to satisfy the conditions for states 8 and 10. The intermediate pressure is therefore varied from 200 kPa to 535.2 kPa.

The HP COP increases with the intermediate pressure (Figure 33). Over the range of intermediate pressures there is a difference of about 1.3% in COP. When the intermediate pressure is increased the flow rate through the main and supplementary circuit increase and decrease respectively. As the pressure changes, the specific enthalpy at the exit of compressor 1 increases, which causes the fraction of total flow rate in the main circuit to change.

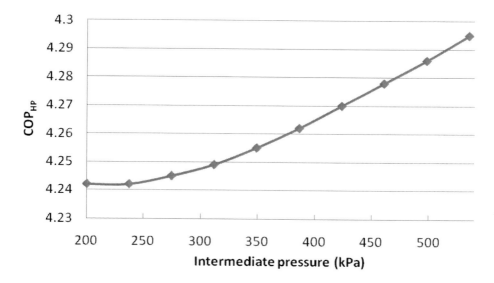

Figure 33. Effect of varying intermediate pressure on heat pump COP for system 3.

Simultaneously the specific enthalpy, at the exit of compressor two, decreases with increasing intermediate pressure. The combination of these effects leads to the reduction in the required compressor work rate with rising intermediate pressure, causing the HP COP to increase. The trend of increasing HP COP with intermediate pressure is consistent with the trends found by Ma and Chai [9] for this system arrangement.

If an increased intermediate pressure is used in the basic comparison of the systems (Section 7.1), the difference in COPs between system 3 and the other two systems would be greater. If all the analyses were repeated with a higher intermediate pressure, the results would likely exhibit a greater variation between the performance of system 3 and the other two systems.

7.3.5. Subcooling at Condenser Outlet

The effect of varying the degree of subcooling at the condenser on the performance and operation of the three systems is considered. The temperature at the condenser exit must be limited to a reasonable minimum to allow proper heat transfer to the heat distribution system. The degree of subcooling is considered varies from 0 to 20°C for a fixed condenser pressure of 1000 kPa.

The HP and system COPs increase almost linearly with increasing degree of subcooling (Figures 34 and 35). The trend is mainly caused by a reduction in mass flow rate through the condenser of all systems. When the temperature at the condenser exit is increased, the mass flow rate reduces according to Equation 2. The variation of the refrigerant flow rate through the condenser with degree of subcooling is nearly linear (Figure 36).

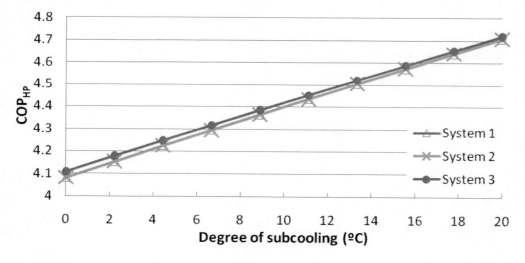

Figure 34. Effect of varying degree of subcooling at condenser exit on heat pump COP for each system.

Systems 1 and 2 are observed to be the most sensitive to subcooling. For a variation in subcooling of 20°C, the HP COP changes by 0.63 for systems 1 and 2 and by 0.61 for system 3. On a normalized basis, the HP COP changes by about 0.031 and 0.030 per degree of subcooling for systems 1 and 3, respectively. The system COP for system 2 exhibits the greatest sensitivity to variations in the amount of subcooling at the condenser exit, but the difference between systems 1 and 2 is miniscule.

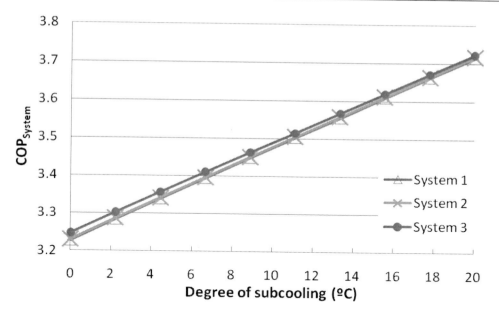

Figure 35. Effect of varying degree of subcooling at condenser exit on system COP for each system.

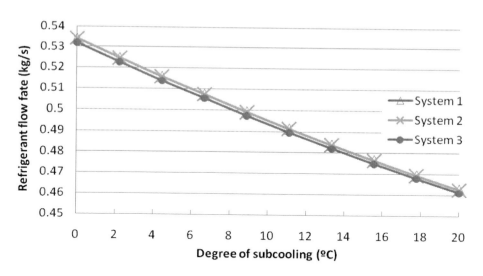

Figure 36. Effect of varying degree of subcooling at condenser exit on refrigerant flow rate for each system.

System 3 is the least effected by subcooling because of its supplementary circuit. In system 3 the degree of subcooling also affects the conditions at the economizer exit on the main circuit, which in turn changes the refrigerant flow rate through the supplementary loop.

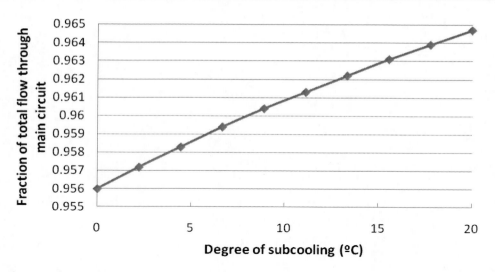

Figure 37. Effect of varying degree of subcooling at condenser exit on the amount of flow utilized in the main circuit of system 3.

From Figure 37 it is seen that as subcooling increases the fraction of the total refrigerant flow rate associated with the main circuit also increases. Therefore, if the degree of subcooling is increased sufficiently the COP of system 3 approaches that of system 1.

7.3.6. Superheating at Evaporator Outlet

The effect of varying the degree of superheating on the performance and operation of the three systems is investigated. The range of superheating is limited to between 0 and 17°C to ensure proper heat transfer across the evaporator. The HP and system COPs increase with increasing degree of superheating (Figures 38 and 39). For a variation of 17°C, the HP COP changes by 0.036 for systems 1 and 2 and by 0.033 for system 3. On a normalized basis, the HP COP changes by about 0.0021 and 0.0019 per degree of superheating for systems 1 and 3, respectively.

The ranges of HP and system COPs for systems 1 and 2 are greater than that for system 3, suggesting that systems 1 and 2 are affected most by the degree of superheating. The difference in trends between the systems is due to changes in the division of flow rate through the main and supplementary circuit within system 3. The temperature at the compressor exit increases as the temperature at the compressor inlet increases (Figure 40), which reduces the refrigerant flow rate across the condenser.

The result is a decrease in compressor work and an increase in COP. The effect of superheating on the supplementary flow rate for system 3 is shown in Figure 41. The flow rate through the supplementary circuit decreases with increasing evaporator temperature, confirming a similar finding by Ma and Zhao [25].

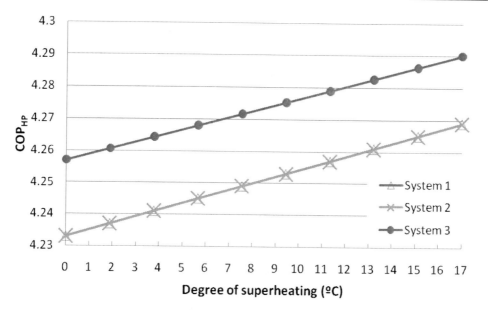

Figure 38. Effect of varying the degree of superheating at evaporator exit on heat pump COP for each system.

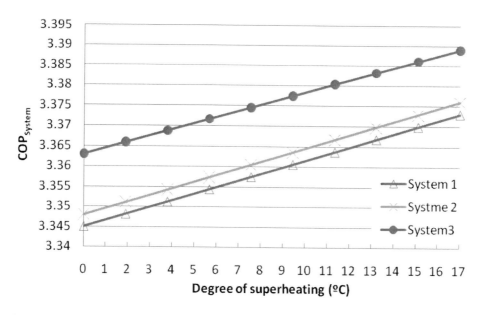

Figure 39. Effect of varying the degree of superheating at the evaporator exit on system COP for each system.

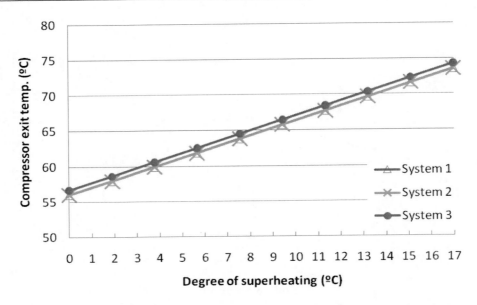

Figure 40. Effect of varying the degree of superheating at the evaporator exit on the compressor exit temperature.

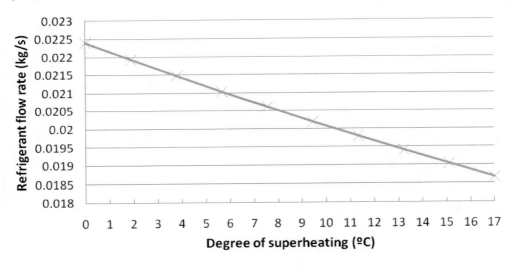

Figure 41. Effect of superheating on supplementary circuit flow rate.

CONCLUSION

The characteristics of three geothermal heat pump systems that provide space heat have been assessed, and parametric studies have been performed to determine the sensitivity to parameter variations. Several important conclusions have been identified. First, heat pump designs with an economizer have the potential for high efficiency, based on the observation that system 3 attains the highest COPs for the ranges of variables investigated. Second, a heat pump system that utilizes motor cooling/refrigerant preheating can reduce ground loop requirements without sacrificing performance relative to the basic vapour compression cycle. Third, systems with an economizer are the most resilient to parameter variations, where the COPs for heat pump designs that utilize an economizer are the least sensitive to variations in evaporator pressure, degree of subcooling and degree of superheating, relative to basic vapour compression cycles and compression cycles with motor cooling. Fourth, heat pump designs that utilize the basic vapour compression cycle or a compression cycle with motor cooling are the least sensitive to changes in compressor efficiency, motor efficiency and condenser pressure, compared to heat pump cycles with an economizer. Fifth, condenser pressure has the greatest effect on COPs for all systems considered, and the effect on system COP of the other parameters can be ranked from highest to lowest as motor efficiency, evaporator pressure, compressor efficiency, degree of subcooling, degree of superheating and pump efficiency.

Finally, heat pump COPs and ground loop lengths are directly related, with the required ground loop length increasing when the heat pump COP increases.

The findings and trends can assist design and optimization activities for ground heat pump systems, providing insights into possible improvements. Since the advanced systems covered in this article are not extensively investigated in literature, the present results and findings enhance the available information on the systems and their operation.

Extensions of the analyses in this article appear to be merited. For instance, 1) a wider range of operational data should be utilized to refine the ranges of realistic parameter values for components and operating conditions; 2) exergy analysis should be used as a complementary analysis to determine more meaningful efficiencies and which processes have the greatest irreversibilities; 3) other systems should be assessed, particularly where they are likely to be advantageous, e.g., a hybrid system containing a heat pump with motor cooling and an economizer unit could reduce ground loop length and increase HP performance; 4) supplementary heating and cooling should be considered to enhance the performance of the heat pump units, where supplementary heating utilizes provides external heat to the HP cycle beyond that from the GL and supplementary cooling uses a typical HP cycle with a cooling tower; 5) cooling aspects of the systems should be investigated; and 6) economics and environmental impact assessments should be carried out to complement the results reported in this article.

ACKNOWLEDGMENTS

The authors kindly acknowledge financial support provided by the Natural Sciences and Engineering Research Council of Canada.

REFERENCES

[1] Ediger, V. S.; E. Hosgor, E.; Surmeli, A. N.; Tatlidil, H. Fossil Fuel Sustainability Index: An Application of Resource Management. *Energy Policy* 2007, *35*, 2969–2977.

[2] Hammond G. P. Energy, Environment and Sustainable Developement: A UK Perspective. *Transactions of the Institution of Chemical Engineers, Part B: Process Safety and Environmental Protection* 2000, *78*, 304–323.

[3]   U.S. Department of Energy. Geothermal Today: 2003 Geothermal Technologies Program Highlights (Revised) [information pamphlet]. Washington, U.S.A., May 2004.

[4]   Geothermal Energy Basics [course notes]. Course C-1001, PDHengineer.com, Houston, TX, December 1997.

[5]   Geothermal Resources Council. What is Geothermal? [online]. (2005) [cited 2010.05.24]. Available from http://www.geothermal.org/what.html.

[6]   Natural Resources Canada. Commercial Earth Energy Systems: A Buyer's Guide. Canada, 2002.

[7]   Bloomquist R. G. Geothermal Heat Pumps Four Plus Decades of Experience. Washington State University Energy Program, GHC Bulletin, Dec. 2009.

[8]   Hwang, Y.; Radermacher, R.; Wang, X. Investigation of Potential Benefits of Compressor Cooling. *Applied Thermal Engineering* 2008, *28*, 1791–1797.

[9]   Ma, G.-Y.; Chai, Q.-H. Characteristics of an Improved Heat-Pump Cycle for Cold Regions. *Applied Energy* 2004,*77*, 235–247.

[10] World Bank Group. Economic Analysis of Environmental Externalities. *Pollution Prevention and Abatement Handbook*, July 1998.

[11] World Pumps. Heat Pump Technology for Energy Efficient Building. *Feature HVAC* 2007, 22–25.

[12] Omer A.M. Ground-Source Heat Pumps Systems and Applications. *Renewable and Sustainable Energy Reviews* 2008, *12*, 344–371.

[13] Natural Resources Canada. Heating and Cooling with a Heat Pump: Ground-Source Heat Pumps (Earth-Energy Systems) [online]. (2005) [cited 2010.05.24]. Available from   http://oee.nrcan.gc.ca/publications/infosource/pub/home/Heating_and_Cooling _with_a_Heat_Pump_Section4.cfm.

[14] Darling, D. Vertical Ground Loop [online]. *The Encyclopedia of Alternative Energy and   Sustainable   Living.*   [cited   2010.05.24].   Available   from http://www.daviddarling.info/encyclopedia/V/AE_ vertical_ground_loop.html.

[15] Chiasson, A. Geothermal Heat Pump Systems: Closed-Loop Design Considerations. Geo-Heat Centre, Oregon, U.S.A., 2007.

[16] U.S. Department of Energy: Office of Energy Efficiency and Renewable Energy. Types of Geothermal Heat Pump Systems [online]. [cited 2010.05.24]. Available from http://www.eere.energy.gov/consumer/your_home/space_heating_cooling/inde x.cfm/mytopic=12650.

[17] RETScreen International.Clean Energy Project Analysis: RETScreen Engineering and Cases Textbook, Natural Resources Canada, 2005.

[18] Curtis, R.; Lund, J.; Sanner, B.; Rybach, L.; Hellström, G. Ground Source Heat Pumps – Geothermal Energy for Anyone, Anywhere: Current Worldwide Activity. *Proceedings World Geothermal Congress* 2005, Antalya, Turkey, 24–29.

[19] Hepbasli, A.; Balta, M. T. A Study on Modeling and Performance Assessment of a Heat Pump System for Utilizing Low Temperature Geothermal Resources in Buildings. *Building and Environment* 2007, *42*, 3747–3756.

[20] Hepbasli, A. Thermodynamic Analysis of a Ground-Source Heat Pump System for District Heating. *International Journal of Energy Research* 2005, *29*, 671–687.

[21] Akdemir, O.; Hepbasli, A. Energy and Exergy Analysis of a Ground Source (Geothermal) Heat Pump System. *Energy Conversion and Management* 2004, *45*, 737–753.

[22] Healy, P. F.; Ugursal, V. I. Performance and Economic Feasibility of Ground Source Heat Pumps in Cold Climates. *International Journal of Energy Research* 1997, 21, 857–870.

[23] Kulcar, B.; Goricanec, D.; Krope, J. Economy of Exploiting Heat from Low-Temperature Geothermal Sources using a Heat Pump. *Energy and Buildings* 2008, 40, 323–329.

[24] Ali Kara, Y. Experimental Performance Evaluation of a Closed-Loop Vertical Ground Source Heat Pump in the Heating Mode using Energy Analysis Method. *International Journal of Energy Research* 2007, *31*, 1504–1516.

[25] Ma, G.-Y.; Zhao, H.-X. Experimental Study of a Heat Pump System with Flash-Tank Coupled with Scroll Compressor. *Energy and Buildings* 2008, *40*, 697–701.

[26] Natural Resources Canada. Survey 2000, Commercial and Institutional Building Energy Use: Summary Report. December 2003.

[27] Ochsner, K. Geothermal Heat Pumps: A Guide for Planning and Installing. London, UK: Earthscan; 2008.

[28] Environment Canada, National Climate Data and Information Archive. Canadian Climate Normals 1971-2000: Ottawa CDA [online]. [cited 2010.05.24]. Available from http://www.climate.weatheroffice.gc.ca/climate_normals/results_e.html?Provi nce=ONT%20andStationName=andSearchType=andLocateBy=ProvinceandProximity= 25andProximityFrom=CityandStationNumber=andIDType=MSCandCityName=andPar kName=andLatitudeDegrees=andLatitudeMinutes=andLongitudeDegrees=andLongitud eMinutes=andNormalsClass=AandSelNormals=andStnId=4333and.

[29] The Plastic Institute. HVAC Applications for PE Pipe. *PPI Handbook of Polyethylene Pipe* 2009, 463–472.

[30] Cengel, Y. A.; Boles, M.A. Thermodynamics: An Engineering Approach._5[th] ed. Boston, MA: McGraw Hill; 2006.

[31] Cengel, Y. A. Heat and Mass Transfer: A Practical Approach. 3rd ed. New York, NY: McGraw Hill; 2007.

[32] ISCO Industries. High Density Polyethylene: Typical Properties [online]. [cited 2010.05.24]. Available from http://www.isco-pipe.com/products_services/hdPE_ pipe_2typical.asp.

[33] Bulter, I. Understanding Polyethylene [online]. *Manufacturers' Monthly*. [cited 2010.05.24]. Available from http://www.manmonthly.com.au/article/understanding_ polyethylene/136748.aspx.

[34] Dowlatabadi, H.; Hanova, J. Strategic GHG Reduction through the Use of Ground Source Heat Pump Technology. *Environ. Res. Lett.* 2007, *2*, 1–8.

[35] CETCO Drilling Products. Geothermal Grout: Enhanced Thermally Conductive Grout. *Grouts and Sealants: Technical Data*, January 2009.

[36] Esen, H.; Esen, M.; Inalli, M. A. Techno-Economical Comparison of Ground-Coupled and Air Coupled Heat Pump System for Space Cooling. *Building and Environment* 2007, *42*, 1955–1965.

[37] Ding, G.; Fu, L.; Zhang, C. Dynamic Simulation of Air-to-Water Dual-Mode Heat Pump with Screw Compressor. *Applied Thermal Engineering* 2003, *23*, 1629–1645.

[38] Cane, R. L. D.; Clemes, S. B.; Hughes, P. J.; Morrison, A. Heat Exchanger Sizing for Vertical Closed-Loop Ground-Source Heat Pumps. *ASME/JSME/JSES International Solar Energy Conference* 1995: Maui, HI.

[39] Bergander, M. J. New Regenerative Cycle for Vapor Compression Refrigeration. *Final Scientific Report: Magnetic Development Inc*. 2005, Madison, WI.

[40] Climate Master. Water to Water System Design Guide [Information Pamphlet]. *Tranquility and Genesis Water-to-Water Systems,* Next Energy Geothermal, Canada.

In: Research and Applications for Energy …
Editor: Riad Benelmir

ISBN: 978-1-62948-892-9
© 2014 Nova Science Publishers, Inc.

Chapter 15

TRANSIENT STABILITY ANALYSIS OF SYNCHRONOUS GENERATOR

S. C. Tripathy[*]

Ghanashyam Hemalata Institute of Technology and Management,
Bhuan, PPuri, Orissa, India

I. INTRODUCTION

The Swing Equation: Consider the it generator unit of an n-unit system. The generator, Figure 1, receives via the shaft from the turbine the mechanical input, or turbine power, P_{Ti}.

It delivers the electrical output, or generator power, P_{Gi}, via the busbars to the network. If these two powers are equal (neglecting the relatively insignificant) the generator will run at its constant synchronous speed. If on the contrary, a difference exists between these two powers, this difference will be used:

1. To change the kinetic energy, or speed of the unit.
2. To overcome the damping torque that develops mainly in the damper windings.

The swing equation in per unit form for machine number i:

$$P_{T_i} - P_{G_i} = \frac{H_i}{\pi f^0} \frac{d^2\delta_i}{dt^2} + D_i \frac{d\delta_i}{dt} \tag{1}$$

The constant H_i is inertia constant, in second, and

$$P_{damper} = D_i \frac{d\delta_i}{dt}, \text{PUMW} \tag{2}$$

where D_i is damping constant

---

[*] E.mail : Sarattrtipathy1@gmail.com

δ_i = torque angle, radians

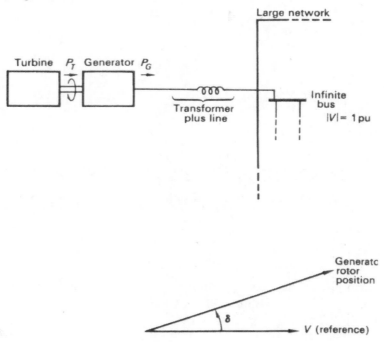

Figure 1. Single generator operating in to an infinite bus.

II. TRANSIENT TURBINE POWER

The rotor dynamics of the ith generator entirely depends upon the power difference $(P_{T_i} - P_{G_i})$, according to equation (2). When the difference power is positive, this difference is called accelerate, when negative, rotor will decelerate. The changes in the turbine power entirely depends upon the control action initiated by the load-frequency control (LFC) or so called automatic generation control (AGC). In the first secord (initial time), the turbine power will stay essentially constart, and for the initial transient period, we can therefore set the post-fault power equal to the constant prefault value, i.e.

$$P_T \approx P_T^0 = \text{constant} \tag{3}$$

III. TRANSIENT GENERATOR POWER

We next turn our attention to the generated electric power P_G .

It should be noted that we cannot use the following formula derived in prefult stata for transient real power (Figure 2)

$$P_G = \frac{|V^0||E'|}{x'_d} Sin\,\delta + \frac{|V^0|^2}{2}\left(\frac{1}{x_q} - \frac{1}{x_d}\right) \sin 2\delta \tag{4}$$

where $\delta = \underline{/E'} - \underline{/V}$
   V^0 = prefult voltage in per unit

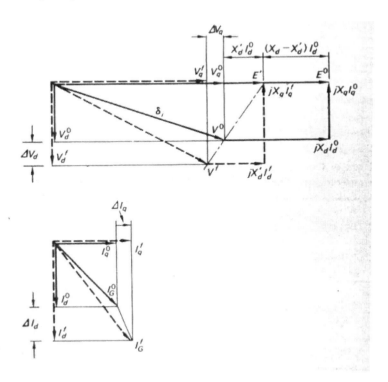

Figure 2. Phasor diagram showing the relationships between prefault and postfault voltages and currents.

The real part of the product $V^0(I_G^0)^*$ renders the prefault generator power P_G^0, and if we care to compute this product, we obtain the earlier Eq.(4).

where
   Synchromous generator for prefault
   case (steady state case) in per unit.
   $|V^0|$ = absolute value of terminal voltage of the Synchrous generator in prefault case (steady state case) in per unit.
   X_d = direct axis steady state synchronous reactance, p.u.
   X_q = quadrature axis steady state reactance, p.u.
   $|V^0|$ and excitation voltage $|E^0|$, X_d and X_q are constant , so P_G is function of δ and 2δ only. The second term is salient power term. If cylindrical rotor is used

$$X_d = X_q = X_d \qquad\qquad (5)$$
$$So P_G^0 = \frac{|V^0||E^0|}{X_d} \sin \delta \qquad\qquad (6)$$

Therefore, we must develop formulas that give us the electric generator output as a function of the angular position δ during the transient swings.

A special situation is as follows:

A generator is operating in nominal steady state into a large network.

A short circuit occurs somewhere out in the network, and as a result, the voltages on all its buses will experience sudden changes. The bus voltage at our particular generator will change from the prefault value V^0 to the post value V^f as shown in Figure 2. For our subsequent discussion we shall make the following assumptions about these voltages;

1. V^0 and V^f are both sinusoidal and possess three-phase symmetry. The post-fault voltage V^f may not necessarily be in phase with the prefault voltage V^0.
2. The change in voltage will be assumed instantaneous. Compared with the relatively slow mechanical transients, this is good assumption.

As a result of the sudden change in terminal voltage, there will be a corresponding charge in the armature currents, and thus in the real (and reactive) generator output, Let us investigate the nature of these changes.

The Prefault Current Picture

In Figure 2 we show in phasor diagram from the voltage and current situations before (solid lines) and immediately after the fault (dotted lines). We show the currents and voltage up the diagram. The prefault voltage has the d-axis and q-axis components V_d^0 and V_q^0, respectively.

The pre fault steady state generator current I_G^0 has the d, and q-axis components I_d^0 and I_q^0 respectively from Figure 2 we obtain directly the following expressions for these steady state current components.

$$\left| I_q^0 \right| = \frac{\left| V_d^0 \right|}{X_q} \tag{7}$$

$$\left| I_d^0 \right| = \frac{\left| E^0 \right| - \left| V_q^0 \right|}{X_d} \tag{8}$$

The real part of the product $V^0 (I_G^0)^*$ renders the pretautt generator power P_G.

The Post Fault Current Picture

As a result of the fault, the d, and q axis components of the bus voltage change instantaneously with the amounts ΔV_d and ΔV_q respectvely. These change and to bring about corresponding changes in the in the q and d components of the stator current. Let us study the nature of these changes.

Current Changes in D Direction

We analyzed the behavior of the synchronous machine under transient conditions. We are remained that any changes in the current component i_δ brings above proportional changes in the rotor current i_r [compare the last of Eqs.(10-18).

The effect of this magnetic coupling is a reduction of the effective reactance from the "steady-state" value X_d to the "transient" value X_d'.

A very gradual change in the voltage difference $|E|$ - $|V_q|$ would, be accord with Eq.(8), bring about a current change that would be determing by the reactance X_d. A very sudden change, which will be computed from

$$\Delta I_d = \frac{|\Delta V_q|}{X'_d} \qquad (9)$$

Current Changes in q Direction

Things are much simpler in q direction. The armature flux associated with the i_q current component is no linked with the rotor field winding and is thus free to change 'inertialess. Almost, that is. We must remember the damper winding. But this winding is very fast and its transients are over in a couple of cycles.

If we disregard the very short "subtransient bip" due to the dampet winding, we conclude that changes in I_q can be computed from the static relationship (7), i.e,

$$\Delta I_q = \frac{|\Delta V_d|}{X_q} \qquad (10)$$

Let us return for a moment to the prefault voltage and current state. Assume that we were to change, suddenly, the armature current to zero by disconnecting the generator from the network. Since the d and q current components would now change suddenly with the amounts I_d^0 and I_q^0, the corresponding change in the terminal voltage components in q and d direction would, in accordance with Eqs.(9) and (10), be $X'_d I_d^0$ and $X_q I_q^0$. The generator terminal voltage, would thus instantaneously change to the new value marked E' in Figure (3) (Note that the tips of the three phasors, V^2,) V', and E', must lie on a straight line. Why?)

We note from Figure 2 that the voltage E' has the magnitude

$$|E'| = |E^0| - (X_d - X_d') \, |I_d^0| \qquad (11)$$

If we substitute $|I_d^0|$ from Eq.(8), we can express $|E'|$ in terms of the Prefault voltages thus:

$$|E'| = \frac{X'_d |E^0| + (X_d - X'_d)|V_q^0|}{X_d} \qquad (12)$$

Transient Power Formula

The phasor diagram in Figure 2 clearly indicates that the transient postfault voltage phasors V', $jX_d'I_d'$ $jX_q' I_q'$, and E' are related to each other in a similar manner as are the static prefault voltage phasors V^0, $jX_dI_d^0$, $jX_qI_q^0$. and E^0. In fact, the static and transient phasor diagrams become of indentical form if we make the substitutions.

$$E^0 \longrightarrow E'$$
$$X_d \longrightarrow X_d'$$

This observation is important since it permits us to derive very simply an expression for the generator power valid under transient conditions. We remember that the static power equation was derived from the phasor diagram of Fig. Due to the above identity, the transient power must therefore be obtained from the same formula, with the above substitutions.

We therefore have for the transient power (perfault)

$$P_G = \frac{|V^f||E'|}{X_{d'}} \sin \delta + \frac{|V^f|^2}{2} \left(\frac{1}{X_q} - \frac{1}{X_{d'}} \right) \sin 2\delta \qquad (13)$$

where $\delta \triangleq /E' - /V^f$ and must not be confused with δ,

Example 1. Consider a synchronous turbo generator characterized by the following parameters:

$$X_d = X_q = 1.00 \text{ pu } X_{d'} = 0.20 \text{ pu}$$

Let us assume that the static dc excitation corresponds to an emf $|E^0| = 1.50$ pu.

Let us also assume that the generator operates onto a strong infinite bus having $|V^0| = |V^f| = 1.0$ pu.

The static power output of this generator follows

$$P_{G. \text{ stat}} = \frac{1.5 \times 1.0}{1.00} \sin \delta = 1.50 \sin \delta \text{ pu MW}$$

The static power is plotted versus δ in figure 3 (curve A).

For the transient power we must know the emf E', which can be determined only from a knowledge of the static prefault operating point. We shall assume that the generator delivers statically 0.75 pu MW to the network.

This corresponds to an initial power angle' δ^0 of 30^0. The static operating point is identified is Figure 4. From a knowledge of δ^0, we now get

$$|V_q^0| = |V^0| \cos \delta^0 = 1.00 \cos 30^0 = 0.866 \, pu$$

Equation (12) then renders

$$|E'| = \frac{0.20 \times 1.50 + (1.00 - 0.20)0.866}{1.00} = 0.993 \, pu$$

From Eq.(13) we get directly the transient generator power

$$P_{G. \text{ translent}} = 4.96 \sin \delta - 2.00 \sin 2\delta \text{ pu MW} \qquad (14)$$

This power is plotted versus δ (curve B) in Figure 3.

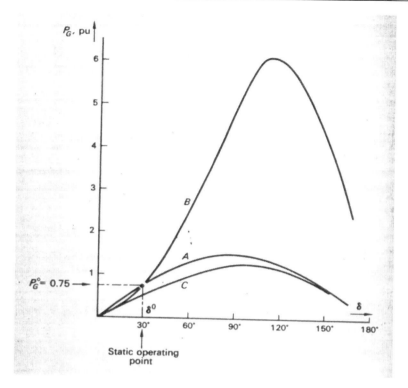

Figure 3. Static and transient generator powers for turbojenerator in text. (A), static power (B), transient power, if terminal voltage remains fixed at 1-00 p.u; (C) transient power of terminal voltage drops to 0.25 p.u.

Example 2. The transient power equation (14) was derived on the assumption that $|V^f| = 1$, i.e., the terminal voltage is fixed. Let us now obtain a formula based upon the assumption that the terminal voltage drops instantaneously to $|V'| = 0.25$.

By using Eq. (13), we get for $|Vf| = 0.25$ and $|E'| = 0.993$

$$P_{G.\ transient} = 1.24 \sin \delta - 0.13 \sin 2\delta \ pu\ MW \tag{15}$$

This is curve C in Figure 3.

We make the following observations in regard to the relationship between power output and rotor position.

1. For very slow (quasi-static) changes, curve A tells us the relationship between power output and rotor position.
2. For sudden changes (for example, loss of turbine torque) but constant terminal voltage, curve B applies.
3. For a sudden 75 percent drop in terminal voltage, curve C applies.
4. The static-torque curve does not have a "saliency" term because we assumed $X_d = X_q$.

5. The transient power contains a saliency term (i.e., the one proportional to sin 2δ), the magnitude of which is of second order.

6. The transient power may attain very large peaks compared with the static power.

Transient Power Formula, Neglecting Saliency

The preceding examples [compare Eq.(15)] indicate that the sin 2δ term is of comparably insignificant magnitude in many cases. We find it convenient on occasion to neglect it altogether. This means, in effect in Eq. (13) that we set

$$X_q = X_d' \tag{16}$$

The transient power equation (13) post fault simplifies now to

$$P_G \approx \frac{|V^f||E'|}{X_{d'}} \sin \delta \tag{17}$$

The sin 2δ term, in addition to being relatively small, also has the property of subtracting from the total power in the region

$$0^0 < \delta < 90^0$$

But adding to it in the region

$$90^0 < \delta < 180^0$$

When our angular swings range throughout these regions, the overall effect of this term therefore has a tendency to average out to zero.

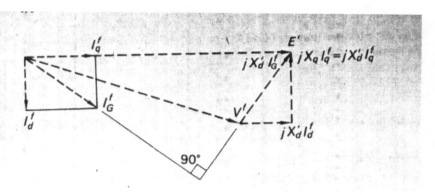

Figure 4. If saliency is neglected, i.e., if $X_q = X_d'$ the post-fault portion of Figure 2 looks like this.

If Eq. (16) applies, the postfault portion of the phasor diagram Fig.2 will look as depicted in Fig.4. The important feature is in the difference voltage E' − Vf is 90^0 ahead of the generator current I_G'. This is tantamount to saying that, from a postfault transient point of view the following relation applies:

$$^f = E' - jI_G{}^f X_d'$$ (18)

In this case the generator can be represented by an emf E' in series with the transient reactance X_d', as shown in Figure 5. For this reason the voltage or emf E', is often referred to as the "voltage behind the transient reactance".

Concluding our present discussion of transient modeling of the generator, we wish to stress that the emf E' in our preceding equations can be treated as a constant only if the field winding time constant is infinite.

As the rotor transient dies out, Eq. (18) gradually, over a period of several seconds, changes . Also we must remember that, superimposed upon this change, we have the effect caused by the voltage regulator. In sec.5 we discuss the latter. In most instances we will not introduce too much error in assuming that |E'| is a constant during the "initial" portion of our transient period.

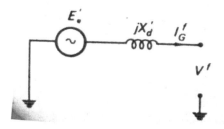

Figure 5. Equivalent network representation of Synchronous generator for the non-salient case.

III.1. Solution of Swing Equation

Having thus established the mathmetical models for the individual generators, we are now faced with the next problem, the solution of the swing equations. Having concluded that the transient generator power P_{Gi} is a nonlinear function of the dependent variable δ_i, we are faced with the prospect of solving a system of coupled nonlinear diffaerenital equations. In general, non analytical solution exist, and we must therefore resort to numerical computational techniques.

As a matter of fact, even the simplest conceivable case of a *single generator* operating onto an infinite network does not, in general, possess an elementary solution. Nevertheless, this simple case will afford us an opportunity to expose some important features of large-scale system dynamics.

The system is depicted in Figure 1. The generator is connected to the infinite bus via a line (or lines) and transformer. We shall study the dynamics of the generator rotor following certain disturbances. Throughout this section we shall base our analysis on the following assumptions:

1. The bus voltage V has a magnitude of 1.00 pu, which will remain constant during the transients.
2. The network frequency is assumed constant under all conditions. We will actually use V as our reference voltage.

3. The turbine power is constant = P_T^0 .
4. The emf E' behind the transient reactance retains constant magnitude.
5. We neglect damping torque.

In view of assumptions 3 and 5, the swing equation (12-5) will be of the form

$$P_T^0 - P_G = \frac{H}{\pi f^0} \frac{d^2\delta}{dt^2} \tag{19}$$

III.2. Small-Scale Oscillations

Let us first consider the case when the generator, running initially in a nominal steady state, is subject to relatively small disturbances. For example, a local load of 5 percent may suddenly be dropped from the generator bus (this bus is not shown in the figure). This permits us to linearize the nonlinear equation (19), and thus make it solvable.

Example 3

Let us assume the following generator and network data:

H = 2.00 s

$X_d = X_q = 0.90$ pu

$X_d' = 0.30$ pu

$X_{transformer + line} = 0.10$ pu

The initial nominal operating state is characterized by

$|E^0| = 1.50$ pu
$P_G^0 = P_T^0 = 0.75\ pu$

The static power formula is thus

$$P_{G.stat} = \frac{1.50 \times 1.00}{0.90 + 0.10} \sin \delta = 1.50 \sin \delta \tag{20}$$

We then compute the following initial variable values:

$$\delta^0 = sin^{-1} \frac{0.75}{1.50} = 30^0$$

$$V_G^0 = 1.00 \cos 30^0 = 0.866 \text{ pu}$$

$$|E'| = \frac{0.40 \times 1.50 + 0.60 \times 0.866}{1.00} = 1.12 \text{ pu}$$

From Eq. (13) we get

$$P_{G'\,transient} = \frac{1.00 \times 1.12}{0.40} \sin \delta + \frac{(1.00)^2}{2} \left(\frac{1}{1.00} - \frac{1}{0.40} \right) \sin 2\delta$$
$$= 2.80 \sin\delta - 0.75 \sin 2\delta \tag{21}$$

In Figure 6 we have plotted the static and transient generator powers versus δ. We show only a small region around the nominal operating point to bus the linear features in the neighborhood of this point.

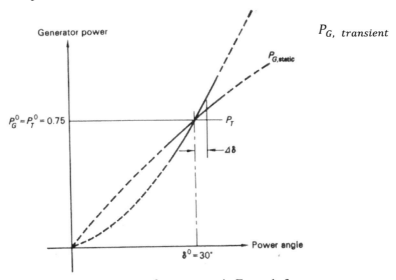

Figure 6. Static and transient generator powers for generator in Example 3.

For a small angular substation $\Delta\delta$, we have

$$P_G^0 + \left(\frac{\partial P_G}{\partial \delta} \right)^0 \Delta\delta \tag{22}$$

We compute from Eq. (21)

$$\left(\frac{\partial P_G}{\partial \delta} \right) = 2.80 \cos 30^0 - 1.50 \cos 60^0 = 1.67 \text{ pu MW / rad}$$

For the transient generator power we thus have

$$0.75 + 1.67 \, \Delta\delta$$

Upon substitution into Eq. (19), the swing equation therefore attend following linear form:

$$\frac{d^2}{dt^2} \Delta\delta + 157 \, \Delta\delta \approx 0 \tag{23}$$

We recognize this as the differential equation for an undamped harmonic oscillator swinging at the frequency.

$$f = \frac{1}{2\pi}\sqrt{157} = 2.1\ Hz$$

The amplitude depends, of course, upon the type and magnitude of disturbance. Assume, for example, that we drop a local load corresponding to 1^0 in the static power angle δ. The rotor will now assume the new static angle, 29^0, transient fashion indicated in Figure 7.

Example 4

The line between the generator and network in Figure 1 is suddenly subject to a solid three-phase short circuit. The protective relaying will cons the line to be disconnected. A fraction of a second later the line will be "reclosed" and assuming that the fault is now removed, we will back to "normal" operation. However, for the period of the fault, the generator output P_G will be zero and the turbine power, which is unchanged, will accelerate the rotor.

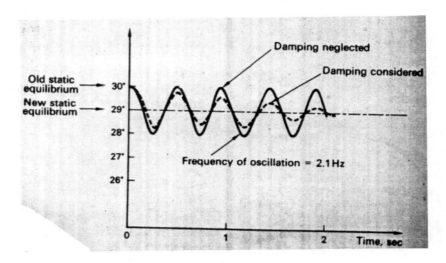

Figure 7. Static generator oscillations caused by small load drop.

Rotor swing angle δ

During this "acceleration" period the swing equation (19) will be of the form

$$P_{acc} = P_T^0 = \frac{H}{\pi f^0}\frac{d^2\delta}{dt^2} \tag{24}$$

Write our specific numerical values.

$$\frac{d_\delta^2}{d+2} = 40.6\ radian\ /s^2$$

We easily integrate this linear equation and obtain
$\Delta (t)= 30+2020t^2$ electrical degrees $\tag{25}$

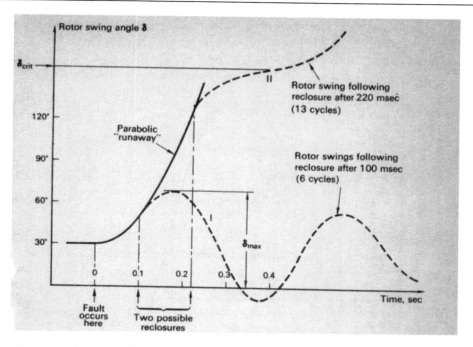

Figure 8. Rotor angular swings following the fault discussed in Example 4.

The rotor position increases as the square of t; that is, we experience a "runway" situation, as depicted in Figure 9.

In the Figure 10 the situation is further clarified by means of a Pδ graph. Note that during the acceleration period the accelerating power P_{acc} is independent of δ. [This explains why we could integrate Eq.24 so simply.]

At the moment of reclosure, the generator power instantaneously jumps to the value given by Eq.21. For the subsequent "deceleration" period the subtraction takes on the form

$$P_{dec} = 0.75 = (2.60 \sin \delta - 0.75 \sin 2\delta = \frac{H}{\pi f^0} \frac{d^2\delta}{dt^2} = 0.0106 \frac{d^2\delta}{dt^2}) \qquad (26)$$

As shown in Figure 9, positive accelerating power changes instantaneously to a negative decelerating power, which is dependent on δ.

This δ dependency has one immediate result: Eq.(26) does not, like Eq (24), integrate into any simple elementary function. We shall discuss numerical integration methods in the next section: at present we describe a qualitative picture of the rotor dynamics following the reclosing of the line.

The immediate effect of the torque reversal is a speed reduction. The dotted portions of the swing curves in Figure 9 indicate how the velocity δ begins to decrease at the moment of reclosure. If the reclosure does not occur too late, the speed of the "runway" rotor is halted, and then reversed.

This case is shown by the curve marked I. The rotor will settle down to the old steady state following an series of swings; i.e, the system is transient stable.

We can actually obtain a solution in terms of so-called elliptic integrals.

If the reclosure takes place too late, the rotor will have attained too high a speed, and the torque reversal will only slow down the rotor, although not enough to stop it before it reaches the critical angle δcrit identified in Figure 10.

If the rotor is permitted swing beyond this angle, the power difference, $P_T - P_G$, will again turn positive, the deceleration will change to acceleration, and now we lose the rotor for good. This case is exemplified by graph II in Figure 9.

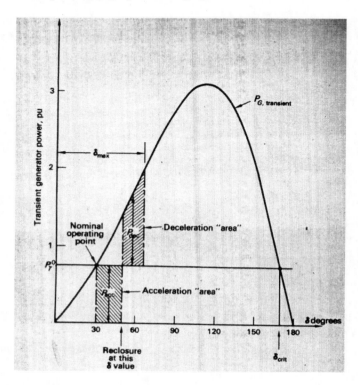

Figure 9. $P\delta$ graph of the transients in figure 8.

III.2. Direct Stability Analysis Methods

In the preceding example there is, obviously, a critical time limit beyond which the line must not remain open if stability is to be preserved. How do we find this limit?

The practice, two methods are used:

1. *The Indirect solution method* is presently by far the most useful approach, indeed the only practical one in the case of realistic-size systems. The swing equations are solved during and after the fault either by analog simulation or by some numerical, digital, computer-oriented, step-by-step integration method. Stability or the lack of it is determined from the a look of the resulting swing curves.
2. *By direct analysis method* the question of stability can be settled without actually solving the differential equations.

Direct analysis methods, as of this writing, have found little use speed beyond the single-generator case. The author believes strongly that view of the universal availability of digital computers, the indirect Solution methods will dominate over the direct for some time to come. Direct methods, particularly the popular (in other fields) Liapunov method, presently are of only academic interest in power system analysis. There is no reson why this situation could not rapidly change, however. Judged from the very few published reports, only seant interest has been shown in the application of the Liapunov method to power system stability. This area should prove very promising for research.

Of great historical interest is the fact a direct stability analysis hod, the so-called equal area method, proved to be very useful in the first attempts that were made to explain transient stability phenomena in power systems. It is true that it can be applied with real success in a single machine systems. It is true that it can be applied with real success in a single machine system. Since the method has great tutorial value, the author feels that it nevertheless has a place in a 1970 publication, consequently it will serve as our point of departure.

The Equal-Area method

Consider the swing equation (24) written in the following from:

$$P_{acc} \frac{H}{\pi f^0} \frac{d^2\delta}{dt^2} = \frac{H}{\pi f^0} \delta \frac{d\delta}{d\delta} \tag{27}$$

By separation of variables and integrating once, we get

$$\tfrac{1}{2} [\dot{\delta}^2(t) - \dot{\delta}^2(0)] = \frac{\pi f^0}{H} \int_{\delta(0)}^{\delta(t)} P_{acc} d\delta \tag{28}$$

The right-side integral obviously equals in magnitude the shaded "accretion area" depicted in Figure 11. Equation (28) therefore tells us the velocity increase attained during the acceleration interval is measured by area.

We can similarly conclude that the velocity decrease attained during deceleration period is measured by the "deceleration area" Since the swing will attain an amplitude (δ_{max}) characterized by zero total vide change, we conclude, therefore, immediately that the two areas must be. This equal-area criterion can be conveniently used to determine critical reclosure time that we earlier spoke of. Figure 12 shows. We concluded that the angular swing must not be permitted found to go beyond the value δ_{crit}. By trial and error we thus find the reclosure angle δ recel that corresponds to equal areas. Reclosure must take place before rotor reaches this position, and Eq. (25) gives us, then, directly minimum permissible reclosure time,

$$t_{max} = \sqrt{\frac{\delta_{recl} - 30^0}{2020}} \tag{28}$$

The reader should note that we thus have been able to find t_{max} without obtaining an explicit solution of the swing equations.

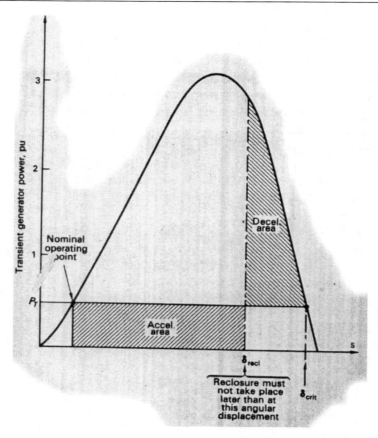

Figure 10. Application of the equal-area criterion to the pδ graph in the two shaded areas of equal size.

IV. COMPUTER SOLUTION OF SWING EQUATIONS ("INDIRECT" STABILITY ANALYSIS)

The most practical method for solution of the swing equation is integration by means of either analog or digital computer. We discuss both briefly.

Analog Simulation

In using the analog or digital computer it is convenient to write, first, the second-order swing equation (5) in a different form. For that purpose we introduce the two dynamic state rariables x_1 and x_2, defined as follows:

$x_1 \triangleq \delta$ rotor angular position in electrical radians
$x_2 \triangleq \dot{\delta}$ rotor angular velocity in electrical radians per second

These state variables constitute the components of the state vector

$$X = \begin{bmatrix} x_1 \\ x_2 \end{bmatrix} \triangleq \begin{bmatrix} \delta \\ \dot{\delta} \end{bmatrix} \text{ where } x_2 = \frac{dx}{dt}, = \frac{d\delta}{dt} \tag{29}$$

In terms of these state variables the second-order swing equation can be written as two coupled first-order state differential equations:

$$\dot{x}_1 = x_2$$
$$\dot{x}_2 = \frac{\pi f^0}{H}(P_T - P_G - Dx_2) \tag{30}$$

The generator power P_G is a function of δ ($= x_1$), and we can therefore write these equations in the following more general form:

$$\dot{x}_1 = f_1(x_1, x_2)$$
$$\dot{x}_2 = f_2(x_1, x_2) \tag{31}$$

In our specific case, the function $f_1(\ldots)$ is linear in x_2 and independent of x_1, whereas $f_2(\ldots)$ is linear in x_2 and nonlinear in x_1. Compare, also the nonlinear equations (31) with the linear equations. The latter contain control forces u, missing in Eqs. (31). The presence of control forces implies that the state can be controlled; and the absence, the state is controlled.

Or in vector form,

$$x = \dot{f}(x) \tag{32}$$

In terms of accepted analog computer symbolism these differential equations would be simulated by the programming setup depicted in Figure 11. Note that we need two integrators per generator. The nonlinear "function generator" must generate with sufficient accuracy nonlinear functions of the type of Eq. (21). Figure 13 shows the recordings the swing curves in Example 3. The various curves correspond to different line reclosing times.

Example 3

$$P_{G,transient} = 2.80 \sin\delta - 0.75 \sin 2\delta \tag{6}$$

The beauty of analog simulation lies in the fact that once the programming is done and "debugged" the solution of the swing equation is obtained by all integrators and function generators working simultaneously in "parallel". As a result, the solution time is the same for a single-generator as for a multigenerator system.

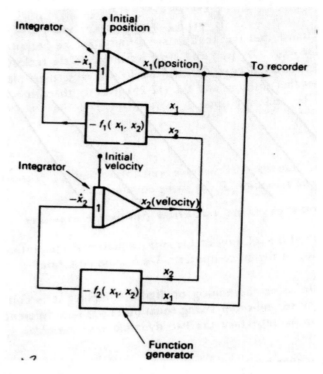

Figure 11. Analog setup for study of rotor transients.

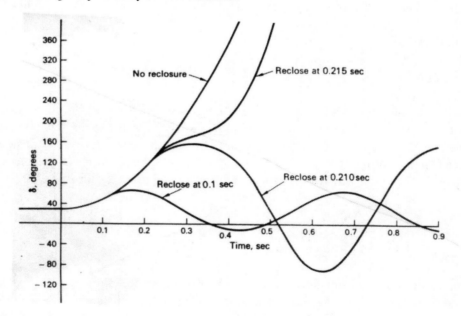

Figure 12. Swing curves of Example 3 obtained by analog computer.

Digital Simulation

The parallel-operation feature of the analog computer stands in sharp contrast with integration by means of the digital computer (digital simulation).

The general procedure of digital simulation is as follows: the independent variable t is discretized into time elements $t^{(0)}, t^{(1)}, \ldots, t^{(v)}, \ldots$, not necessarily equidistant. Starting with the known initial state $x^{(0)}$, we compute by means of some appropriate algorithm the new states $x^{(1)}, x^{(2)}, \ldots, x^{(v)} \ldots$.

As always in numerical analysis, the accuracy of the method depends upon the quality of the algorithm used. We shall discuss a couple of algorithms, and start appropriately, with the simplest of them all.

The Euler Numerical Integration Method

Preparatory to discussing the digital solution of the vector equations (32), let us consider the scalar case

$$\dot{x} = f(x) \tag{33}$$

For $t = t^{(v)}$, we can be set with some accuracy

$$\dot{x}^{(v)} \approx \frac{\Delta x^{(v)}}{\Delta t} = f(x^{(v)}) \tag{34}$$

Using this formula, we would perform the integration of Eq. (33) in the following steps (Figure 13):

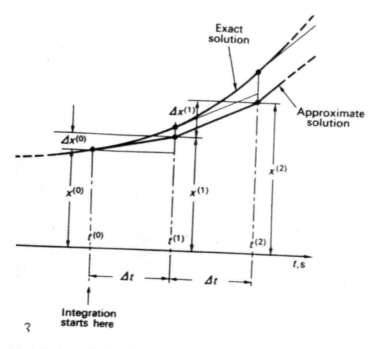

Figure. 13. Graphical display of Euler's integration method.

Step 0 For $t = t^{(0)}$ and $x = x^{(0)}$, compute the state increment $\Delta x^{(0)}$:

$$\Delta x^{(0)} = f(x^{(0)}) \, \Delta t$$

Step 1 For $t^{(1)} = t^{(0)} + \Delta t$, we therefore have the new state

$$x^{(1)} = x^{(0)} + f(x^{(0)}) \, \Delta t$$
Step 2 For $t^{(2)} = t^{(1)} + \Delta t$ we similarly obtain

$$x^{(2)} = x^{(1)} + f(x^{(1)}) \, \Delta t \text{ etc}$$

Clearly, the computational algorithm is

$$X^{(v+1)} = x^{(v)} + f(x^{(v)}) \, \Delta t \text{ for } v = 0, 1, \ldots . \tag{35}$$

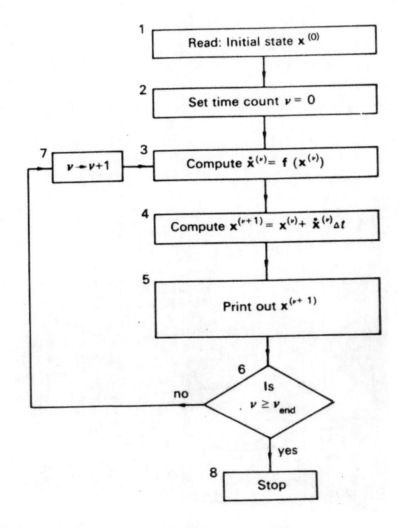

Figure 14. Computational flow graph for Euler's integration method.

We may readily extend this algorithm to the vector case. For the component of the x vector we have

$$x_i^{(v+1)} = x_i^{(v)} + f_i\left(x_1^{(v)}, x_2^{(v)}, \ldots, x_n^{(v)}\right)\Delta t \text{ for } i = 1, 2, \ldots, n \tag{36}$$

or in vector form,

$$\boldsymbol{x}^{(v+1)} = \boldsymbol{x}^{(v)} + \boldsymbol{f}(\boldsymbol{x}^{(v)})\Delta t \tag{37}$$

Figure 14 depicts a flow diagram for the computations involved Euler's method. The diagram should be self-explanatory. Euler's method is simple, but not particularly accurate. Figure 14 shows why. Since the state variables at the end of an interval are computed. On the basis of the derivative in the beginning of the interval, an error will be introduced which is the more pronounced the faster the derivative is changing within the interval Δt.

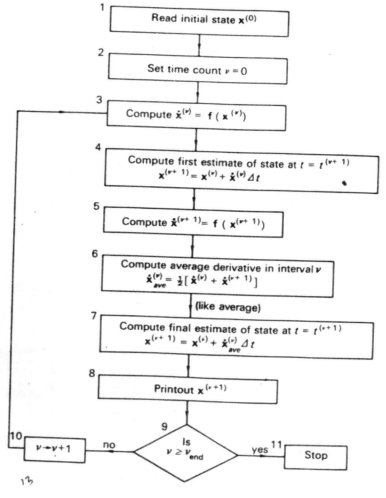

Figure 15. Computational flow graph for Euler's modified method.

The Modified Euler Method

The accuracy of the Euler method can be improved remarkably by the obvious modification of using an average value for the derivative throughout each time interval. The computational algorithm given in the preceding flow graph will now be modified in accordance with Figure 15. Let us discuss the changes introduced.

The computations proceed as before up to and including block-4. Based upon the tentative value of $x^{(v+1)}$ obtained in block-4, we compute in block 5 the derivative at the end of interval v.

In the next block 6, we then compute an average value derivative, we then proceed to recompute an upgraded value for $x^{(v+1)}$ in block7. This new value is better than the one previously computed in block 4. We may decide now that the improvement obtained in $x^{(v+1)}$ is sufficient and proceed to the next time interval. This is often done in stability analyses. We may, alternatively, decide to repeat the upgrading sequence of $x^{(v+1)}$ N times, or until no further. Improvement in $x^{(v+1)}$ can be detected. For this purpose we must introduce an iterative loop (not shown in Figure 16) around blocks 4 to 7.

Figure16 shows a digitally computed swing curve for our Example 4, using the modified Euler method. (The same curve, corresponding to a reclosure after 0.1 s, was earlier obtained by analog computer in Figure 11).

We used four widely different Δt values. Note that no discernible difference is obtained if Δt is chosen below the value. Other algorithms there is a large variety of integration algorithms in addition to those detailed above. None of them possess the inherent simplicity of the Euler method, and most of them require a vast amount of computation per time interval. (The reader may consult Ref.[4]).

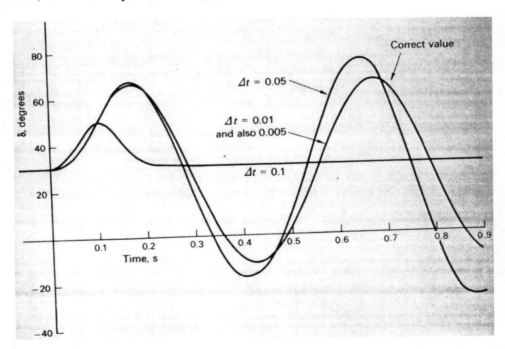

Figure 16. Euler modified approach used to find one swing curve in Example 4 Note that if $\Delta t \leq 0.01$,s no discernible improvement can be detected. For $\Delta t > 0.05$, we obtain totally unacceptable accuracy.

CONCLUSION

In this paper we introduced the reades to the basic theory of electromechanical transients in power systems. The electromechanical torques that exist within the synchronous machines tend, under normal operation, to hold the network together in a stable equailibrium state characterized by a perfect torque and power balance within each machine:

As a result of disturbances,(fault) which usually changes, the torque balance is upset within each machine. The individual machines, as a consequence, will be subject to accelerations or decelerations, causing angular rotor swings of such large magnitudes that certain machines may pull out of synchronism.

REFERENCES

[1]   S.B. Crary: "*Power System Stability*" vol. I and II, John Wiley and Sons, Inc, New York, 1945-1947.

[2]   E.W. Kimbark, "*Power System Stability*", John Wiley and Sons, Inc., New York, 1948.

[3]   V.A. Venikov (Ed), "Transient Phenomena in Electrical Power Systems," Pergamon Press, New York, 1965.

[4]   Collate; "*Numerical Treatment of Differential Equations*", Springer Verlag OHG, Berlin, 1966.

[5]   G.W. Stagg, and A.H.El-Abiad, "*Compmative Methods in Power System Analysis*", McGraw-Hill Book Co, New York, 1968.

[6]   O. Elgerd, "*Control System Theory*", McGraw-Hill Book Co., New York, 1967.

INDEX

F

I

S

X

Y